The Open University

M140
Introducing statistics

Book 5

Experiments and clinical trials

This publication forms part of an Open University module. Details of this and other Open University modules can be obtained from the Student Registration and Enquiry Service, The Open University, PO Box 197, Milton Keynes MK7 6BJ, United Kingdom (tel. +44 (0)845 300 6090; email general-enquiries@open.ac.uk).

Alternatively, you may visit the Open University website at www.open.ac.uk where you can learn more about the wide range of modules and packs offered at all levels by The Open University.

To purchase a selection of Open University materials visit www.ouw.co.uk, or contact Open University Worldwide, Walton Hall, Milton Keynes MK7 6AA, United Kingdom for a brochure (tel. +44 (0)1908 858779; fax +44 (0)1908 858787; email ouw-customer-services@open.ac.uk).

The Open University, Walton Hall, Milton Keynes, MK7 6AA.

First published 2014.

Edited, designed and typeset by The Open University, using the Open University TEX System.

Printed in the United Kingdom by Charlesworth Press, Wakefield.

ISBN 978 1 7800 7666 9

1.1

Contents

Contents

Contents

Unit 10

Experiments

Introduction

Experimentation plays a critical role in the advancement of knowledge and the development of our society. Technological development in numerous areas, such as agriculture, electronics, manufacturing and medicine, depends to a greater or lesser extent on knowledge that has been collected from scientific experiments. This unit discusses the nature of experiments, and you'll learn statistical methods that are suited to the analysis of small sets of data. You will also actually conduct an experiment, giving you hands-on experience of collecting **empirical data** – that is, data collected through observation or experimentation.

Section 1 says more about the role of experiments in the world and the diversity of questions that can be addressed through experiments. Different types of experiment are also identified, focusing on hypothesis-testing experiments because these make the greatest use of statistics.

In Section 2, you are asked to set up an experiment on the growth of plants, using mustard (or cress) seeds. This should give you an idea of some of the problems that are involved in even the simplest of experiments.

Important: planning your schedule

The timing of the experiment in Section 2 is important, and you therefore need to plan your schedule accordingly.

- It will probably take you about one-and-a-half hours to set up the experiment, assuming that you have already collected the items in the list – posted on the website some weeks ago, and repeated in Subsection 2.2.

- You will have to spend a few minutes on your experiment daily for four or five days after setting it up, and then about one-and-a-half hours taking measurements from your plants.

Not all experiments are like this one, performed in a laboratory.

The analysis of the data from this experiment uses a new form of test, called the t-test, which is the major topic of Sections 3 and 4. The t-test has many similarities to the z-test. Like the z-test, its purpose is to test hypotheses about population means. Also, as for the z-test, there is a two-sample test for comparing two populations, and a one-sample test for testing hypotheses about a single population. We can also form confidence intervals related to t-tests in the same way that we have with z-tests, as you will see in Section 5. The attraction of the t-test is that it can be used with samples of any size, including small sizes – unlike the z-test, which we use only with samples of size 25 or more.

With both z-tests and t-tests, the alternative hypothesis is usually 'two-sided' – the null hypothesis specifies the value of the population mean, and we reject this hypothesis in favour of the alternative hypothesis if the sample mean differs substantially from that hypothesised value. Occasionally, though, a 'one-sided' alternative hypothesis is appropriate, where we would only reject the hypothesised value if the difference were in a particular direction. (Perhaps we would not reject the null hypothesis if the sample mean turned out to be much bigger than the hypothesised value, but only if it were much smaller.) In Section 6 we look at one-sided alternative hypotheses.

Section 7 directs you to the Computer Book, where you will learn to use Minitab to perform t-tests and to calculate the associated confidence intervals.

1 Scientific experiments

In this section we first describe those forms of enquiry for which we use the term *experiment*. We then describe three different kinds of experiment that are common in scientific enquiry. One of these is looked at in more detail – the one which most commonly involves statistical analysis.

1.1 What are experiments?

Max Planck

'An experiment is a question which science poses to Nature, and a measurement is the recording of Nature's answer.'

Max Planck (1858–1947)

The term **experiment** means a variety of things to a variety of people. To many it conjures up a vision of a white-coated individual surrounded by dials, flashing lights and vaporous fluids bubbling sullenly in mysteriously coiled vessels. To others an experiment involves no more than adding a new ingredient to a tried and trusted pie recipe to see if the taste is improved, or planting the bulbs earlier than in previous years to see if they do better. These uses are all perfectly proper: it is not *what you do* that qualifies an activity as an experiment; it is *the way that you do it*.

In other words, the area in which you carry out an experiment might be nuclear physics or it might be cookery: neither lies outside the province of experimentation. But if other people are going to accept that you have carried out an experiment, then you must use certain methods and procedures.

One fundamental feature of any experiment is that it should *stand up to scrutiny*. Sometimes the only person interested in the result of an experiment is the person conducting it. For example, a golfer may have a set of lessons or experiment with his choice of golf clubs in order to improve his score. Quite possibly the outcome is only of interest to the golfer. However, for this to be an experiment, the golfer must gather information that is factual and would enable others to critically evaluate whether his golf has improved. To be of any value to others, though, the results must also generalise – we would want to know whether golf lessons are typically beneficial. To meet that aim, an experiment must be **repeatable**. If person A carries out an experiment, then he or she should be able to explain everything that took place during the experiment in such a way that another person (B) could, if necessary, go through exactly the same procedure. The results of this experiment should, again, be suitable for scrutiny so that B's results can be compared with A's.

The importance of recording the detail of an experiment is illustrated in procedures for developing a new drug, as you will learn in Unit 11. If a drug company carries out a clinical trial on a new drug, then they must be able to describe every part of their procedure to the outside world, including: how the experiment was designed; how many subjects were involved; how the drug was administered and in what quantities; how its effects were measured; etc. In fact, the European Commission *requires* such information before they grant a product licence. In just the same way, a cook who experiments by altering an ingredient in a recipe should be able to explain every part of the revised recipe so that other people could repeat the revised procedure exactly.

Another fundamental feature of an experiment is that *it sets out to answer a specific question or set of questions*. Does this drug alter blood pressure? Does this ingredient improve the taste of the pie? Does planting the bulbs earlier produce better flowers? Notice that each of these questions is framed in such a way as to demand that something be measured if the question is to be answered: namely, blood pressure, taste or flower quality. The questions may sometimes seem vaguer. For example: 'What happens in the long term from taking statins daily?' However, decisions must be made on which measurements are taken and what information is recorded, and these choices sharpen a vague question. Thus, blood pressure might be recorded in an experiment to examine the affects of statins. Then one question is: 'Do statins affect blood pressure?' Or weight might be monitored, or incidence of strokes or diabetes. In each case, examining this information in the context of the experiment implies a question.

Company or industrial confidentiality means that experiments and their results may not be in the public domain, but the company or industry will want that information.

Activity 1   *Pie-tasting*

A professional chef wants to discover if the addition of an extra ingredient improves the taste of a pie. Describe a suitable experiment to find this out.

This activity shows that it is possible to carry out scientific experiments on all sorts of things, not just on formally recognised scientific subjects. To illustrate the difference between the scientific approach to a question and other forms of inquiry, it is instructive to consider how a scientific experiment might be carried out on such an unlikely subject as poetry appreciation. Take a poem such as John Keats's ode *To Autumn*. (A copy of the poem is available on the M140 website.)

A literary critic might ask the question: 'Is *To Autumn* a great poem?'. Framed in this way the question is not amenable to scientific experiment. People might vary in their opinion of the poem, and they would probably produce more or less convincing evidence to support their viewpoint. One might point to the images that the poet uses and argue that they successfully convey the mood of autumn, another might complain that the overall effect is too languid for his taste, etc. Although people might agree as to what are good and bad criteria for judging the greatness of a poem, and although informed opinion might generally agree as to the greatness of this particular poem, there is no sense in which assessing the greatness of this poem is a scientific experiment. However, it is possible to ask questions about the poem which are open to experimental investigation.

Activity 2   *Two or three verses?*

The poem *To Autumn* has three verses. Someone might argue that the third verse is inferior to the others, and that without it the poem is greatly improved. How might you test this experimentally?

Of course nobody would imagine that this particular experiment is of any literary value. Our purpose is simply to show that experimental investigation need not be limited to the physical world.

1.2 Different kinds of experiment

Good experiments share two important features:

- They are recorded in detail so that they can be critically evaluated and repeated.
- They produce measurements or observations designed to answer specific questions.

random by cta

There are different kinds of experiment, addressing different kinds of question. This is not a case of, for example, some experiments being about physics and others about chemistry; it is a case of the questions being different in their purpose.

Some experiments answer questions of the form:

> *What happens if I do this?*

Some of the experiments that you will meet in Unit 11 answer questions of this sort. For example, the following question might arise in the early stages of drug testing:

> *What happens if I give this person this new drug?*

Such experiments are **exploratory** in nature, in the same way that toddlers' investigations of their surroundings are exploratory.

Francis Bacon, a sixteenth-century scientist and philosopher, urged his contemporaries to carry out experiments of this type, and for this reason you may find such exploratory experiments referred to as **Baconian**.

Sir Francis Bacon

Sir Francis Bacon (1561–1626) was a Renaissance thinker and an English statesman. He was a member of parliament at the age of 23, went on to be Attorney General and Lord Chancellor, was knighted, made a baron, and later made a viscount. However, his most enduring legacy is his contribution to scientific method. Bacon established and popularised *inductive* methodologies for scientific inquiry. By 'induction', Bacon meant the ability to gradually generalise a finding based on accumulating information. He argued that, to learn about nature, data should be gathered through organised experiments that provide tangible information and increase knowledge.

Francis Bacon (1561–1626)

A second kind of experiment has, as its primary purpose, not exploration but the **measurement** of a particular attribute. Such experiments are designed to answer questions such as:

- What is the velocity of light?
- How heavy is the Earth?
- How old is this rock?
- What is the population of the UK?

This kind of experiment is a very important part of scientific investigation, but we shall not discuss such experiments at length in this unit.

A third kind of experiment, however, is both important and relevant to this module. This is the kind that tests a specific *hypothesis*. Perhaps the best way to explain this kind of experiment is to give some examples.

Example 1 *Crying baby*

Hypothesis: The baby is crying because it is cold.

Prediction based on hypothesis: If the baby is made warmer, then its crying will stop.

Test: Make the baby warmer, but make sure that you do not change anything else in its environment.

Possible results and conclusions: The baby continues crying; therefore the hypothesis is wrong. The baby stops crying; therefore the hypothesis is supported. (Since you cannot discount the possibility that the baby would have stopped crying anyway, you cannot say that the hypothesis is correct.)

Example 2 *Broken TV*

Hypothesis: The television is not working because the fuse in the plug is broken.

Prediction based on hypothesis: If the fuse is replaced with one that does work, then the television will work again.

Test: Replace the fuse but do not alter anything else.

Possible results and conclusions: The television still does not work; therefore the hypothesis is wrong. The television works; therefore the hypothesis is supported.

Example 3 *Are microbes to blame?*

Hypothesis: Food putrefies if left for too long because of the action of microbes (small organisms) that are present in the air and that come into contact with it.

Prediction based on hypothesis: If the microbes are prevented from acting on the food, then it will not putrefy.

Test: Prevent the microbes from acting by killing them or otherwise preventing them from acting (for example, by deep-freezing).

Possible results and conclusions: The food putrefies; therefore the hypothesis is wrong. The food does not putrefy; therefore the hypothesis is supported.

Example 4   *Transmission of sound*

Hypothesis: Sound is transmitted through air because sound is a form of mechanical vibration and air contains particles (molecules) that can jostle each other and so pass the vibration from one particle to the next.

Prediction based on hypothesis: If all the air is removed from a container so that a vacuum remains, then it should not be possible to transmit sound through that vacuum. For example, it should not be possible to hear an electric bell ringing inside a container from which the air has been removed.

Test: Remove air from a container and discover whether an electric bell inside it becomes inaudible.

Possible results and conclusions: The bell can be heard through the vacuum; therefore the hypothesis is wrong. The bell cannot be heard; therefore the hypothesis is supported.

vacuum

Bell in a vacuum

The first two of these examples are homely examples of **hypothesis-testing experiments** of a kind that people routinely carry out in their daily lives. The latter two examples are well-known, formal, scientific experiments. The experiment in Example 3 was first carried out by Louis Pasteur (1822–1895), who successfully prevented microbes from attacking food by filtering the air in which the food was kept, and by taking food to the tops of mountains, where the combination of a low temperature and relatively microbe-free air prevented the food from decaying. Example 4 dates back to Athanasius Kircher (1601/1602–1680), who wrote in 1650 about experiments with bells in a vacuum – now a staple of physics lecture demonstrations.

All four of the examples have the following important features in common.

- *Hypothesis:*   In each, there is a specific hypothesis about the cause of a phenomenon. A hypothesis-testing experiment tries to explain how something works.

- *Prediction based on hypothesis:*   The experimenter makes predictions that flow directly from the hypothesis – if the hypothesis is true, then certain things must follow. For example, if it is true that microbes are the sole cause of food decay, then it automatically follows that food should not decay if microbes are absent.

- *Test:*   Each experiment consists of testing whether the things that the hypothesis predicts actually happen.

- *Possible results and conclusions:*   If the result of the experiment is not what the hypothesis predicted, then the experimenter has to accept that the hypothesis is wrong. For example, if food were to continue to decay, even when it was absolutely certain that no microbes were present, then the hypothesis that microbes are the only cause of food decay would have to be rejected.

It is important to note that even if the prediction that the hypothesis makes turns out to be correct, then it may still be wrong to assume that the hypothesis itself is perfectly correct.

Louis Pasteur (1822–1895)

Spraying against malaria in 1912

Consider, for example, the hypothesis that malaria is caused by a mosquito (more specifically, by a particular type of mosquito of the *Anopheles* genus). A prediction which follows from this hypothesis is that malaria should cease to occur in a district from which *Anopheles* mosquitoes have been eradicated. In fact, this is what normally happens in practice, so it would seem reasonable to conclude that the hypothesis is correct. However, although it is correct in one sense, it is not in another. In a district from which the *Anopheles* mosquito has been eradicated, some people may still continue to contract malaria, apparently spontaneously, long after the mosquitoes have gone. If you were ignorant of these cases of malaria, then it would be legitimate to believe in the original hypothesis that *Anopheles* mosquitoes cause malaria. As soon as these few instances come to light, the original hypothesis must be discarded and a new one sought.

In the case of malaria, the truth is that the mosquito is only a carrier for a parasite, called *Plasmodium*, which is the direct cause of malaria. *Plasmodium* can survive for long periods in the human body without giving rise to malaria. From time to time, however, it invades the blood, and malaria then develops.

To summarise, if the predictions that follow from a hypothesis turn out to be incorrect, then the hypothesis has to be abandoned or at least modified. If the predictions turn out to be correct, then the hypothesis is supported in the sense that it can be provisionally accepted that the hypothesis is correct. There is always the possibility that, one day, somebody may find that under certain conditions the predictions are incorrect. When that happens, the hypothesis has to be replaced by a new one.

1.3 Experiments and statistics

Before going any further, it is important to consider how this description of scientific hypothesis-testing experiments fits in with the ideas of statistical hypothesis-testing in Units 6 and 7. From the statistician's point of view, the examples of hypothesis-testing experiments in Examples 1 to 4 (Subsection 1.2) are framed in rather unconventional terms, because each concentrates on a hypothesis of the form *something affects something* and tests predictions flowing from that hypothesis. Nevertheless, it is perfectly possible to formulate each of the above experiments in statistical terms with null and alternative hypotheses, and it is essential to do so if you want to apply statistical hypothesis tests to data arising from such experiments. The null hypothesis, as its name implies, very often postulates the absence of a given effect or relationship.

When we carry out a statistical hypothesis test, we base our calculations on the assumption that the null hypothesis is correct. We ask:

> *What is the probability of obtaining a result at least as extreme as that which we have obtained, if we assume that the null hypothesis is true?*

If this probability is too low, then we reject the null hypothesis in favour of the alternative. (See Section 4 of Unit 6.)

This process is summarised by the flow chart given in Figure 1.

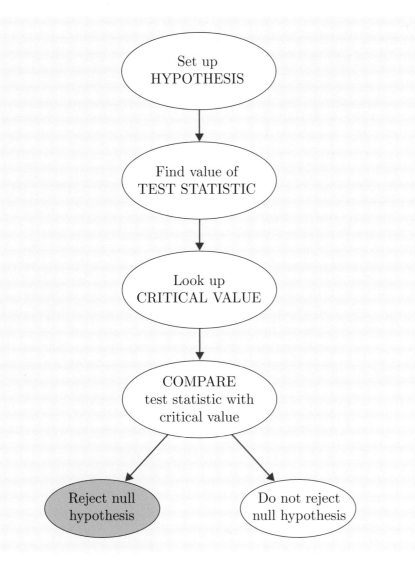

Figure 1   Steps in a hypothesis test

We shall now devise null and alternative hypotheses for the first two of the four experiments (Examples 1 and 2, Subsection 1.2). In each case, we shall assume that the tests are the same as those described earlier and we will state what conclusions we draw from the different results that could be obtained. In these examples, as often happens, the null hypothesis in the *statistical* hypothesis test is the converse (opposite) of the hypothesis in the scientific experiment. So then, in the test, the amount of evidence against the null hypothesis is assessed (see Subsection 1.3 of Unit 7). As a result, the reformulation is often not logically equivalent to the original experiment.

Example 5   *Example 1 revisited*

Null hypothesis: Cold has no effect on the baby's crying.

Alternative hypothesis: Cold makes the baby cry.

Test: Make the baby's surroundings warmer and set up suitable controls.

Possible results and conclusions: The baby's crying stops; therefore reject the null hypothesis. The baby's crying continues; therefore the null hypothesis is supported.

Example 6   *Example 2 revisited*

Null hypothesis: The present condition of the fuse is not responsible for the television's refusal to work.

Alternative hypothesis: The television is not working because the fuse is broken.

Test: Replace the fuse but do not alter anything else.

Possible results and conclusions: The television works; therefore reject the null hypothesis. The television still does not work; therefore the null hypothesis is supported.

Activity 3   *Forming null and alternative hypotheses*

Express the following experiments as statistical hypothesis tests.

(a) Example 3 experiment: Are microbes to blame?

(b) Example 4 experiment: Transmission of sound.

One final point needs to be made about the relationship between hypothesis-testing experiments and statistical hypothesis tests. A great deal of scientific experimentation consists of testing specific hypotheses of the sort just described. If the experiments require statistical analysis, then the experimenter should use statistical hypothesis tests. This will be the case if the experiments involve things that are intrinsically variable, such as people, plants or animals. Sometimes, however, a scientist may be interested not so much in testing whether or not a given treatment has an effect (perhaps somebody has already done an experiment which shows that it does) but rather in investigating how big that effect is. An agriculturalist might want to know, for example, by how much a new fertiliser increases the yield of a crop. In such instances the scientist conducting the research project would use statistical estimation procedures (for example, finding a confidence interval) rather than carrying out a hypothesis test.

Activity 4 *Identifying scientific experiments*

State whether each of the following is a scientific experiment.

(a) Measuring the distance between the Earth and the Sun.

(b) Leaving work an hour later to see if it makes much difference to your travel time to get home.

(c) Reading a tea-taster's report on a brand of tea in order to decide whether to buy it or not.

(d) Investigating whether obesity is caused by overeating.

Activity 5 *Types of experiment*

For each of the experiments in Activity 4 that you identified as scientific, state which of the three kinds it is: exploratory, measurement or hypothesis-testing.

Activity 6 *Forming statistical hypotheses*

For those scientific experiments in Activity 5 which you identified could be hypothesis-testing experiments, formulate them as statistical hypothesis tests.

Hypothesis-testing experiments involve testing deductions that can be made from a hypothesis. For this reason, scientific experimentation is sometimes said to proceed by the **hypothetico-deductive method**. This description of scientific method is frequently associated with the philosopher Karl Popper (1902–1994). There has been considerable debate about whether science does proceed by this method under all circumstances, but this debate lies outside the scope of this module. Many scientists feel that carrying out an experiment is rather like riding a bicycle: if you think too hard about what you are doing, you fall off! Accordingly, it is probably most profitable to leave such discussions of the nature of scientific experimentation and to get down to the practicalities of carrying out an experiment.

Karl Popper (1902–1994)

Kinds of experiment

In summary, there are at least three kinds of experiment that can be recognised: they are distinguished by the kind of questions they attempt to answer.

- Exploratory (Baconian) experiments
- Measurement experiments
- Hypothesis-testing (hypothetico-deductive) experiments

Exercises on Section 1

Exercise 1 *Scientific experiment?*

State whether each of the following is a scientific experiment.

(a) Driving a car with all the windows open to see whether petrol consumption is affected.

(b) Viewing a television advert for car insurance in order to decide whether to purchase the insurance or not.

Exercise 2 *What form of experiment?*

(a) For the scientific experiment identified in Exercise 1, state which of the three kinds it is: exploratory, measurement or hypothesis-testing.

(b) Formulate this scientific experiment as a statistical hypothesis test.

2 Carrying out your own experiment

Now that you have read about some of the basic principles of experimentation, it is worth trying to put these principles into practice by setting up and carrying out your own experiment – as detailed in this section.

You should read the whole of Section 2 before you start the experiment.

The experiment is concerned with the growth of mustard (or cress) seedlings. Mustard is better, because it grows faster, but cress will do perfectly well. You should set up the experiment and then leave the seedlings to grow for four or five days, checking them from time to time and pruning some of them after two or three days. Provided that you have already collected all the necessary items (as detailed in Subsection 2.2), it should not take you more than about one-and-a-half hours to set up the experiment. You will then need to take measurements as part of the experiment, which is likely to take another one-and-a-half hours. The details of these activities are in Subsections 2.3 to 2.6.

After you have taken the measurements and read about t-tests in Section 3, you will be ready to analyse your results statistically.

2.1 Purpose of the experiment

The purpose of the experiment is to discover whether light affects the growth of plant roots. Most people are familiar with the fact that light is important to plants, and realise that it affects the growth of the stems and leaves. If you keep a potted plant on a window sill, for example, and never turn it round, then it is likely to grow quite noticeably towards the light. But what effect, if any, does light have on the growth of the roots? Normally, of course, the roots are underground and so are not exposed to the light, but it is quite conceivable that the roots could become exposed as they grew – for example, if the plant was growing on an irregular surface or if rain washed some of the soil away. Under such circumstances the plant would probably not benefit from the root continuing to grow out into the open. Roots give plants mechanical support, and they absorb water and nutrients from the surrounding soil. They can do none of these things if they are growing in the open air. It seems a plausible hypothesis, therefore, that light suppresses root growth so that the roots will tend not to grow in the open air. (It is also possible to argue plausibly that the roots will tend to grow longer in the open air.)

1. Clarify

The experiment which you are asked to carry out is on mustard seedlings. Thus the precise question to be answered is:

> *Does light affect the root growth of mustard seedlings?*

The principle of the experiment is simple. You are asked to grow two groups of mustard seedlings, one entirely in the dark and the other entirely in the light, but otherwise in as near identical conditions as possible. After some time has elapsed you should measure the lengths of the roots of the seedlings and compare the two groups. As in any experiment, it is essential to control various factors.

2. Collect

Activity 7 *Controlling factors that might undermine the experiment*

List some factors which need to be controlled, and suggest how such control might in each case be achieved.

This experiment should provide a reasonable amount of data. Before going on to analyse the data from your experiment, you will need to consider the hypothesis being tested (as in Section 1).

3. Analyse

Activity 8   *Hypotheses and potential results*

State the null hypothesis that is being tested by this experiment. State the prediction that follows if the null hypothesis is correct. State the conclusions that you can draw from the different results which you might get.

4. Interpret

If you were to discover, however, that the difference appears only in seedlings whose stems have not been cut, then you should suspect that light does not directly affect root growth, but does so indirectly through its effect on the leaves and stem.

2.2   Items needed for the experiment

Figure 2   The items needed for the experiment

As shown in Figure 2, you will need the following:

- Two identical plastic containers such as small flower pots or empty cartons, e.g. of margarine or yoghurt. These need to be at least 6 cm (2.5 inches) in diameter at the open end or, if rectangular, need to have sides at least 5 cm (2 inches) long.

- Two large containers (ice cream tubs, sandwich boxes, small buckets or large bowls) that will hold at least half a litre (or 1 pint) of water without leaking, and which can each hold one of the plastic containers mentioned above (see Figure 4, Subsection 2.3). These larger containers will need to stand side by side in a well-illuminated position, e.g. on a window ledge.

- One small packet of mustard seeds (*Sinapis alba*, *Brassica alba* or *Brassica hirta*) – various companies supply these. (If these are difficult to obtain, then use cress seeds (*Lepidium sativum*).)

- One piece of aluminium kitchen foil about 30 cm × 30 cm (12 inches × 12 inches).

- One piece of clear plastic (e.g. from a plastic bag) about 30 cm × 30 cm (12 inches × 12 inches) or a clear plastic bag.

- Some pieces of (superior quality) toilet tissue, or kitchen roll.

- Two sheets of high quality (printer or writing) paper, preferably coloured so that the seedlings show up against the paper.

- Four elastic bands to go round the tops of the flower pots or margarine or yoghurt cartons.

- A jug or bottle for pouring about half a litre (or a pint) of water into the large containers.

- A pair of dividers or a piece of plasticine (or a similar material) plus two pins.

- A ruler measuring millimetres.

- Two teaspoons.

- A pair of fairly small, sharp-pointed scissors.

- A magnifying glass would be helpful but is not essential.

2.3   Setting up the experiment

Here are the instructions for setting up the experiment.

1. Empty all the seeds (i.e. at least 40) into a bowl containing cold tap water (see Figure 3), and leave them to soak for an hour. (Seeds remain dormant while they are dry; soaking them ensures that all the seeds start germinating at the same moment and that they all get off to a good start.)

Figure 3   Soaking the seeds

2. Make sure that the two large and the two small containers which you are going to use are thoroughly clean, and thoroughly rinsed free of detergent, soap or any other contaminant.

3. Put half a litre (or a pint) of tap water into each of the large containers.

4. Take the two small containers, and if they do not already have holes in the bottom, cut one or two so that the water can easily seep up through the holes (see Figure 4).

Half a litre of water in each large container

Holes in base of each small container

Figure 4   Flower pots and plastic containers

5. Crumple several lengths of toilet tissue or kitchen roll, and press them firmly into each small container. Continue until both containers are just overfull. The paper should be firm but not jammed solid.

6. Fold several lengths of tissue paper to make a smooth platform, then lay a sheet of high quality (printer or writing) paper on top. Ensure that this platform touches the crumpled tissue paper. Fix this platform of paper over the top of one of the small containers with an elastic band (see Figure 5). Repeat for the other small container.

7. Stand each small container in one of the large containers (see Figure 4).

8. By the time that the seeds have been soaked for one hour (see Instruction 1), the paper in each small container should be thoroughly damp. If it is not, then gently spoon over the paper surface some of the water from the big container in which the small container stands.

9. Reject any seeds that seem unusual – for example, those that are a different colour from the rest and those that float rather than sink in the water.

10. Mix the seeds well and then allocate them alternately to two groups until 20 have been allocated to each.

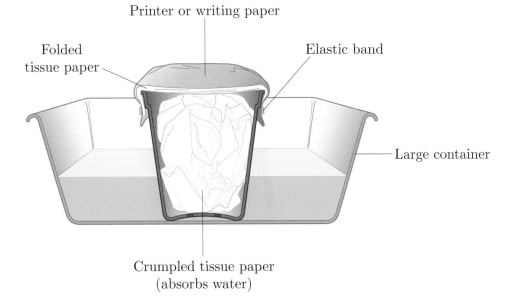

Folded
tissue paper

Printer or writing paper

Elastic band

Large container

Crumpled tissue paper
(absorbs water)

Figure 5   Setting up the platform

11. Arrange the two groups of 20 seeds as follows, one group on the
    writing paper surface over each small container. A teaspoon may help
    you to manoeuvre the seeds into position. Arrange each group of seeds
    in four rows of five, each row being at least 1 cm (half an inch) away
    from the next. The further apart you can put them, provided that
    they are spaced regularly, the better (see Figure 6).

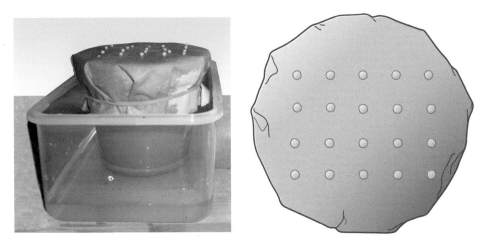

Figure 6   Spacing of seeds

12. Toss a coin to select, at random, the pot whose seeds will grow in the
    dark; then make a hood out of the aluminium foil and wrap it over the
    top of the chosen pot, leaving a space of at least 5 cm (2 inches)
    between the seeds and the top of the foil (see Figure 7). Secure the foil
    with an elastic band. Repeat the hood-making procedure, using the
    piece of clear plastic or plastic bag, for the second pot.

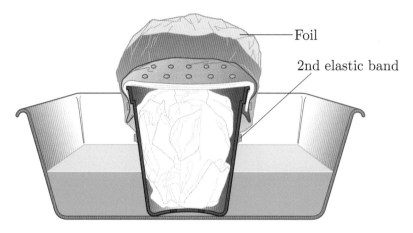

Figure 7   Putting a hood on the pots

13. Place the two sets of containers side by side in a well-lit spot safe from disturbance by children, pets or curious passers-by. Try to ensure that the temperatures of the two groups are the same.

This completes the setting-up procedure.

2.4   Maintaining the experiment

You also have to undertake a few tasks during the days that follow. Exactly how fast the seedlings develop will depend on the temperature, but you can expect to cut the stems off some of the seedlings (see Subsection 2.5) after about two to five days, and to measure the root lengths after three to seven days. The maintenance tasks are as follows.

1. To control for any difference in the temperature of the two groups of seedlings, swap the positions of the two large containers each day.

2. Make sure that there is still plenty of water in the large containers. If they begin to dry out, add another half a litre (or a pint) of water to each of the large containers.

3. Check the seeds which you can see (i.e. those growing in the light) once a day to see how rapidly the stems and roots are developing.

2.5   Cutting the stems

When most of the seedlings growing in the light have grown root hairs and have stems which are a little over 1 cm (about half an inch) long, cut the stems off 10 seedlings in each pot (i.e. 20 seedlings in all). Any seedling which has not grown sufficiently for its stem to be cut should be left uncut.

Figures 8 and 9 show you where to cut the seedlings.

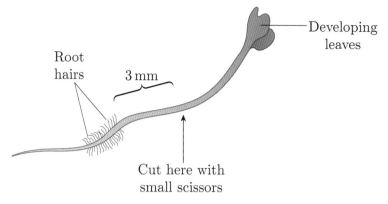

Root
hairs

3 mm

Developing
leaves

Cut here with
small scissors

Figure 8   Where to cut seedlings

You will see on most of the roots a white, fluffy area which is due to the presence of a multitude of very fine hairs, called root hairs. It is primarily through these hairs that the root absorbs water and nutrients. Use the top of the root, where the root hairs stop, as a reference point, and cut across the stem about 3 mm ($\frac{1}{8}$ inch) above this point. Cuts should be made without moving the seedlings, using small, sharp-pointed scissors. Any seedling which has not produced any root hairs should be left uncut.

Figure 9   Cutting a stem

When you have finished cutting the stems, replace the aluminium foil and clear plastic/plastic bag on the pots they were previously on, taking care not to squash the seedlings, and return them to their positions (in the large containers) by the window. If the cut stems start to grow rapidly, then repeat the cutting process a few days later.

2.6 Completing the experiment

Leave the pots until the roots of most of the seedlings in the light have grown to at least 1 cm (about half an inch) long. Some seeds may not germinate at all, and these should be ignored at this stage.

To measure the root lengths, you will need either a pair of dividers, a pair of compasses, or a piece of plasticine and two pins, or needles, assembled as shown in Figure 10. This is the trickiest part of the experiment. Start with one pot of seedlings and, working along each row in turn, carefully lift each seedling off the paper, taking great care to ensure that the tip of the root is not left behind. Lay the plant down on a flat, preferably dark-coloured, surface and straighten the root as far as possible. Measure from the tip of the root to the position near the top of the root where the root hairs stop (see Figure 10). You should do this by putting one point of the dividers etc. against the root tip and then moving the other until it lies opposite the position where the root hairs stop. Then measure the distance between the two points of the dividers etc. with the ruler (see Figure 11). Measure it in millimetres (to the nearest whole millimetre). You may find it difficult to measure the root lengths in this way; if you do, then try measuring the roots directly with the ruler instead.

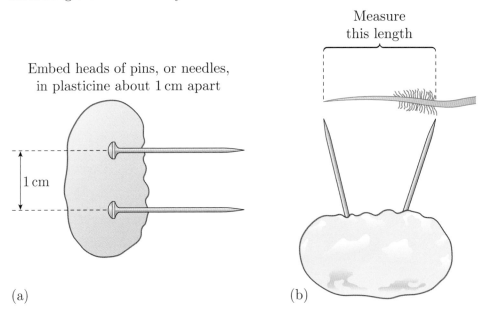

(a)   (b)

Figure 10 Measuring tool and measuring root lengths

Write the measurement down in the appropriate place in Figure 12. For each seedling, indicate very clearly whether or not you have previously cut its stem (e.g. underline the measurements of seedlings whose stems had been cut). You will also need to indicate any seeds that failed to germinate by putting a cross in the appropriate box. Measure all the seedlings in one pot in this way and then repeat the procedure for the second pot.

2. Collect

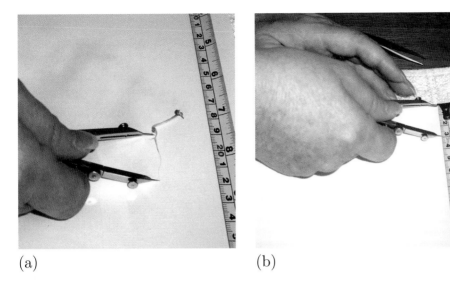

(a)   (b)

Figure 11   Measuring a root length

Seedlings grown in light   Seedlings grown in dark

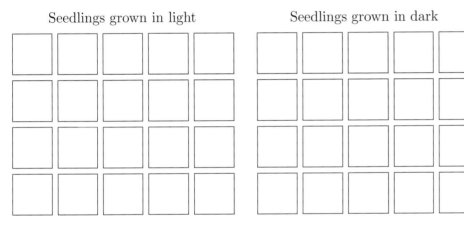

Figure 12   Grids for recording your results

2.7 Variability, error and clarifying the question

Whatever differences might exist between your two groups of seedlings, it
is likely that they will not be very large. If they are large, then there
would be no need to use a hypothesis test to analyse the data. One of the
reasons why any differences that might exist may not be obvious, despite
all the controls which you have used, is that the seedlings themselves are
variable. You may try very hard to ensure that all the seedlings grow in
the same conditions, but nevertheless there will be some small variations
that affect the plants. More importantly, even if they are grown under
identical conditions, different plants will still grow differently. We have also
explained that you might find some difficulty in measuring the lengths of
the roots accurately. In particular, because you may not be able to
straighten the roots perfectly, it is possible that you will consistently
underestimate their length. This kind of error, which is consistent in its
direction and approximately constant in its magnitude, is called
systematic error.

Most scientific experiments are subject to both variability and systematic errors. The task of the scientist (i.e. you) in carrying out an experiment is to discover, despite the presence of variability, bias and systematic errors, whether genuine differences exist between the two groups. One major source of variability, which you are very likely to experience, is that some of your seeds may not germinate at all. Later in this unit, when you calculate the means of the root lengths for your two groups of seedlings, should these non-starters be included?

There is no hard-and-fast rule as to how to deal with a problem like this, but it would seem sensible in this experiment to exclude them. Thus the aim of the experiment is to answer the following, even more precise, question.

1. Clarify

The question to be addressed

Does light affect the root growth of those mustard seedlings that germinate?

Now you should set up the experiment as described in Subsection 2.3. While you are maintaining it as described in Subsection 2.4, you should work through Section 3 to learn how to analyse the data that you will collect.

3 The *t*-test for two unrelated samples

The last section gave a procedure for setting up and running a scientific experiment to investigate the growth of mustard seedlings. The experiment yields data that are related to the question *Does light affect the root growth of those mustard seedlings which germinate?* You now need to decide how to analyse these data.

In this section we shall first consider how to do this in the context of the hypothesis tests that were introduced in Units 6 to 8. Then we shall introduce a further test which is particularly useful for the kind of data that we will have.

3.1 Which test?

In Units 6 to 8 we introduced some hypothesis tests: the sign test, the χ^2 test and the z-test. We shall now apply the principles of hypothesis testing developed there to the data that you will obtain from your mustard seedlings.

Activity 9   *Appropriate hypothesis test?*

Of the tests that you have already met in the module, is there one that would be appropriate for analysing your seedling data?

Is there a test that can be used on small samples of data?

The answer is a qualified yes: there is such a test, but it can be applied only to data from populations satisfying certain distributional conditions. These conditions will be described in Subsection 3.3. They include a requirement that the two populations must have the same variance. The other conditions are similar to ones you have met earlier in M140. (In Unit 12, you will meet a version of the test which does not require the population variances to be equal.)

Amongst the tests introduced in Units 6, 7 and 8, the one that comes closest to what is needed is the two-sample z-test. This test can be used to compare two unrelated samples of measurements, as with your seedlings data, but it can only be used for large samples of data, which rules it out. Nevertheless, it is worth looking again at the rationale behind the z-test to see why it requires large samples. We shall then give the test that you should use for your data. The test has close similarities to the z-test.

3.2   The z-test reconsidered

Suppose that you have unrelated samples of data from two populations, whose population means are μ_A and μ_B, and that you want to use the two-sample z-test to test the following null hypothesis H_0 against the alternative hypothesis H_1:

H_0: $\mu_A - \mu_B = 0$
H_1: $\mu_A - \mu_B \neq 0$.

Another type of z-test

The rationale of the z-test is as follows.

1. If the null hypothesis were true, then the means, μ_A and μ_B, of the two populations would be identical, so on average you would expect the means from two samples, one taken from each population, to be the same. In other words, on average you would expect the difference between the means of the two samples to be 0. If the means of the two samples are denoted by $\overline{x}_A$ and $\overline{x}_B$, respectively, then on average you would expect that $\overline{x}_A - \overline{x}_B = 0$.

2. If the null hypothesis were true and you took repeated pairs of samples from two populations like this, then you would find that sometimes $\overline{x}_A$ was a bit bigger than $\overline{x}_B$ and that sometimes $\overline{x}_B$ was a bit bigger than $\overline{x}_A$. Thus $\overline{x}_A - \overline{x}_B$ would sometimes be a bit bigger than 0 and sometimes be a bit smaller. In other words, $\overline{x}_A - \overline{x}_B$ has a sampling distribution. In Unit 7 we explained that, provided the samples are large enough, this sampling distribution of $\overline{x}_A - \overline{x}_B$ is approximately normal with a mean value of 0. The standard deviation of this sampling distribution is called the standard error (SE). The value of this standard error depends on the two population standard deviations and also on the two sample sizes.

3. The test statistic z is calculated as follows:
    $$z = \frac{\overline{x}_A - \overline{x}_B}{\text{SE}}.$$
    If the null hypothesis were true, then the sampling distribution of the test statistic z would be the standard normal distribution.

4. Unfortunately, the standard error is not usually known, because the population standard deviations are generally unknown – if we knew the population standard deviations, we would probably know the population means (μ_A and μ_B), and then there would be no need to test whether μ_A equals μ_B. We therefore have to estimate the standard error. In Unit 7 we calculated the following estimate of the standard error from the data being analysed:
    $$\text{ESE} = \sqrt{\frac{s_A^2}{n_A} + \frac{s_B^2}{n_B}},$$
    where s_A and s_B are the sample standard deviations of the two samples, and n_A and n_B are the sample sizes.

5. Then the test statistic, z, is calculated as
    $$z = \frac{\overline{x}_A - \overline{x}_B}{\text{ESE}}.$$

6. The null hypothesis is rejected whenever z is far enough away from zero. For example, using a 5% significance level, the null hypothesis is rejected if

    *   either $z \geq 1.96$

    *   or $z \leq -1.96$.

    The figure 1.96 is the critical value.

I CAN'T BELIEVE SCHOOLS ARE STILL TEACHING KIDS ABOUT THE NULL HYPOTHESIS.

I REMEMBER READING A BIG STUDY THAT CONCLUSIVELY DISPROVED IT YEARS AGO.

For large samples, the procedure in stages 5 and 6 above works perfectly well, but for small samples, particularly those involving fewer than 25 values, two problems arise.

- As we mentioned in Unit 7, the sampling distribution of $\overline{x}_A - \overline{x}_B$ is approximately normal only for reasonably large sample sizes (at least 25). Thus the z-test does not necessarily work for small samples because the sampling distribution of $\overline{x}_A - \overline{x}_B$ may not then be approximately normal. This problem does not arise if the two populations in question themselves have normal distributions: in this case, the sampling distribution of $\overline{x}_A - \overline{x}_B$ is normal for all sample sizes, however large or small. Thus, if it is reasonable to assume that the populations have normal distributions, then this difficulty is removed.

- The second problem is in the estimate of the standard error, which is

$$\text{ESE} = \sqrt{\frac{s_A^2}{n_A} + \frac{s_B^2}{n_B}}.$$

To be more precise, ESE is the sample estimate of the standard deviation of the sampling distribution of the difference between the sample means: $\overline{x}_A - \overline{x}_B$. It is used because the actual value of this standard deviation (i.e. the standard error) is not known. For large sample sizes, this estimate is likely to be very close to the true standard error, but, even for large samples, it is a number calculated from a sample, so it is not the same for all possible samples. Because of this variability between samples, the test statistic

$$\frac{\overline{x}_A - \overline{x}_B}{\text{ESE}}$$

has a distribution different from the standard normal distribution that you would get if you divided $\overline{x}_A - \overline{x}_B$ by its *actual* standard deviation (i.e. the *actual* standard error) rather than this sample estimate.

If the sample sizes, n_A and n_B, are large, then ESE will vary very little from one sample to another. Its distribution will have a very small spread, and so

$$\frac{\overline{x}_A - \overline{x}_B}{\text{ESE}}$$

will have a distribution which is very close to the standard normal distribution. If either n_A or n_B is small, then this distribution will not be close to the standard normal distribution: it will be more spread out than the standard normal distribution; i.e. it will tend to have fewer values close to zero and more values away from zero. We are still assuming that the null hypothesis $\mu_A - \mu_B = 0$ is true.

This has the following consequence: if you wish to compare small samples, then, even if you think that the populations have normal distributions, you cannot use the z-test.

W.S. Gosset (1876–1937)

However, under certain circumstances another test is available: it is called Student's *t*-test or, simply, the **t-test**. This test was developed by a famous statistician, W.S. Gosset (1876–1937), who published the results of his mathematical research in this area in 1908 under the pen-name *Student*.

W.S. Gosset worked for the brewing company Guinness and was required by conditions of his employment to remain anonymous.

Student investigated what distribution of values you would get for an expression like

$$\frac{\overline{x}_A - \overline{x}_B}{\sqrt{\dfrac{s_A^2}{n_A} + \dfrac{s_B^2}{n_B}}}$$

if you took repeated pairs of small samples from two populations whose distributions are normal with identical means and identical variances.

Since the distribution is not the standard normal distribution, the letter z can no longer be used to represent such a test statistic when it is calculated from small samples – instead, the letter t is used. The results of Student's work give a hypothesis test that has similarities to the z-test but does not require sample sizes to be large.

3.3   The two-sample *t*-test

If you go on to study further statistics modules, you will probably meet many statistical techniques that have not been described in this module. Therefore, we want to show you how a hypothesis test (which you might well find in a textbook from elsewhere) can be related to the principles of hypothesis testing that you have met in the module, and also to illustrate how to do this.

If you were to look in a statistics reference book to find a hypothesis test to compare two small unrelated (i.e. unpaired) samples of numerical measurements, then you might well find something like the following summary.

Two-sample *t*-test: summary

The data must be numerical measurements (such as length, weight, time) that form two unrelated samples. It is assumed that each sample is selected from a population whose distribution is normal. Also, it is assumed that the standard deviations of the two populations are equal or, equivalently, that the population variances are equal. Denoting the population means by μ_A and μ_B, the null and alternative hypotheses are:

$$H_0: \mu_A = \mu_B \quad \text{and} \quad H_1: \mu_A \neq \mu_B.$$

The test is carried out as follows.

1. Calculate the sample means, $\bar{x}_A$ and $\bar{x}_B$, of the two samples and the sample variances, s_A^2 and s_B^2. (s_A and s_B are the sample standard deviations.)

2. Check that the assumption of equal population variances is reasonable, or that the assumption is not seriously violated.

3. Calculate a pooled estimate s_p^2 of the **common population variance**:
    $$s_p^2 = \frac{(n_A - 1)s_A^2 + (n_B - 1)s_B^2}{n_A + n_B - 2},$$
    where n_A and n_B are the two sample sizes.

4. Calculate the test statistic:
    $$t = \frac{\bar{x}_A - \bar{x}_B}{s_p\sqrt{\dfrac{1}{n_A} + \dfrac{1}{n_B}}}.$$

5. The test statistic follows a ***t* distribution** with $n_A + n_B - 2$ degrees of freedom. Look up the critical value t_c of a t distribution with this number of degrees of freedom.

6. Reject H_0 in favour of H_1 if $t \geq t_c$ or $t \leq -t_c$. Otherwise the conclusion is that there is insufficient evidence to reject H_0.

Tea tasting: another *t*-test?

This test is very widely used in all kinds of applications of statistics. The procedure is fairly similar to that for the two-sample *z*-test, but there are several important differences.

1. There is a family of t distributions. Like the family of χ^2 distributions, each member of the family has its own number of degrees of freedom. For a two-sample *t*-test of unrelated samples of sizes n_A and n_B, the t distribution to use has $n_A + n_B - 2$ degrees of freedom. Hence the test statistic is compared with a critical value for that particular t distribution. (The critical values for this test, at the 5% significance level for $1, 2, \ldots, 40$ degrees of freedom, are listed in Table 2 later in this subsection.)

2.   The *t*-test can be applied only if it is reasonable to assume that the populations involved have normal distributions.

3.   The *t*-test can be applied only if it is reasonable to assume that the populations have variances that are equal.

Point 3 above gives the assumption that the population variances are equal. The validity of this assumption is readily examined as we have estimates s_A^2 and s_B^2 of the two population variances. One commonly used rule of thumb is to assume that the population variances are equal if neither one of s_A^2 and s_B^2 is greater than three times the size of the other. This is the rule we shall use in M140. If the rule is satisfied, the population variances might not be equal, but any difference between them is unlikely to be very large, and a moderate difference would seldom affect the outcome of the *t*-test.

Is there a common population variance?

Rule of thumb: if the sample variances (s_A^2 and s_B^2) differ by a factor of less than three, assume that there is a common population variance, or that, if the population variances differ, the difference is not large enough to invalidate the *t*-test.

This is not the only 'rule of thumb' of this form. Another quite common choice is to assume that the population variances are equal if neither one of s_A^2 and s_B^2 is more than *twice* the size of the other. A third choice replaces 'twice the size' with 'four times the size'. There is also a statistical hypothesis test (called the *F*-test) for testing the hypothesis that the population variances are equal. That test is outside the scope of M140, however you will learn in Unit 12 how to use Minitab to compare two population means without making assumptions about the population variances.

In the following example, we calculate sample variances for each of two separate samples, check that it is reasonable to assume the samples come from populations with a common population variance, and then pool the sample variances to estimate that common variance.

Example 7   *Pooling sample variances*

In an agricultural experiment to investigate the effect of different diets on the weights of calves, eight calves were allocated to two groups that were fed different diets, A and B. Both diets consisted of milk, hay and manufactured concentrates; the difference between them was that the concentrates in diet A were different from those in diet B. Unfortunately, one of the calves (on diet B) suffered from a disease which prevented proper digestion, so did not eat very much. That calf was therefore excluded when assessing the effects of the two diets.

The calves were kept in similar conditions, and the food intake and weight of each calf was monitored from birth. The allocation of the calves to the two groups was designed to control for birth-weight but was otherwise random. Table 1 contains some of the data collected in this experiment.

Table 1   Average daily weight gain over five weeks from birth-date (kg per day)

Calves on diet A	Calves on diet B
0.56	0.67
0.42	0.72
0.53	0.64
0.54	–

In Examples 8 and 9 we shall use the two-sample t-test to investigate whether there is a difference between the population means, μ_A and μ_B, of the daily weight gains of calves fed on the two diets. As preliminary steps towards that, we calculate the sample means and sample variances for each sample.

For Sample A,
$$\sum x_A = 0.56 + 0.42 + 0.53 + 0.54 = 2.05$$
and
$$\sum x_A^2 = 0.56^2 + 0.42^2 + 0.53^2 + 0.54^2 = 1.0625.$$
As $n_A = 4$,
$$\bar{x}_A = 2.05/4 = 0.5125$$
and
$$\sum x_A^2 - \frac{(\sum x_A)^2}{n_A} = 1.0625 - \frac{2.05^2}{4} = 0.011\,875,$$
so
$$s_A^2 = \frac{0.011\,875}{n_A - 1} = \frac{0.011\,875}{3} \simeq 0.003\,958\,3.$$

For Sample B,

$$\sum x_B = 0.67 + 0.72 + 0.64 = 2.03$$

and

$$\sum x_B^2 = 0.67^2 + 0.72^2 + 0.64^2 = 1.3769.$$

As $n_B = 3$,

$$\overline{x}_B = 2.03/3 \simeq 0.676\,666\,7$$

and

$$\sum x_B^2 - \frac{(\sum x_B)^2}{n_B} = 1.3769 - \frac{2.03^2}{3} \simeq 0.003\,266\,7,$$

so

$$s_B^2 \simeq \frac{0.003\,266\,7}{n_B - 1} = \frac{0.003\,266\,7}{2} = 0.001\,633\,35.$$

To examine whether it is reasonable to assume a common population variance, we divide the larger sample variance (in this case, s_A^2) by the smaller population variance (s_B^2):

$$\frac{s_A^2}{s_B^2} \simeq \frac{0.003\,958\,3}{0.001\,633\,35} \simeq 2.42.$$

As this ratio is less than 3, our rule of thumb says that we can pool the variances:

$$\begin{aligned}
s_p^2 &= \frac{(n_A - 1)s_A^2 + (n_B - 1)s_B^2}{n_A + n_B - 2} \\
&\simeq \frac{(4-1) \times 0.003\,958\,3 + (3-1) \times 0.001\,633\,35}{4 + 3 - 2} \\
&= \frac{0.015\,141\,6}{5} \simeq 0.003\,028\,3.
\end{aligned}$$

Thus s_p, our estimate of the common population standard deviation, is $\sqrt{0.003\,028\,3} \simeq 0.055\,030$. It is important to record this standard deviation to at least four significant figures, as it will be used in further calculations. (You should always check that s_p^2 lies between the two sample variances, here $0.003\,958\,3$ and $0.001\,633\,35$ – you have made a calculation error if it does not.)

Example 7 is the subject of Screencast 1 for Unit 10 (see the M140 website).

Activity 10 *Ball manoeuvres*

Two groups of children were asked to solve a simple puzzle in which they had to manoeuvre a ball around an obstacle course and into a hole. One group, A, of children saw the obstacle course before but were not told how to negotiate it. The other group, B, of children did not see the obstacle course before but were told in advance how to negotiate it.

The length of time (in seconds) taken by each child to manoeuvre the ball round the course is shown in the table below.

Group A	Group B
2	8
7	11
8	3
3	5
5	8

(a) Calculate the sample mean and the sample variance for each group.

(b) Check whether it is reasonable to assume that the groups come from populations whose distributions have a common variance.

(c) Calculate s_{p}^2, the pooled estimate of the common variance of the two populations. Hence obtain a pooled estimate of the common standard deviation.

We now move to the other steps for performing a two-sample *t*-test. The null and alternative hypotheses are:

$$H_0\colon \mu_A = \mu_B \quad \text{(the population means are equal)}$$

and

$$H_1\colon \mu_A \neq \mu_B \quad \text{(the population means are not equal)}.$$

The test statistic is

$$t = \frac{\overline{x}_A - \overline{x}_B}{s_{\mathrm{p}}\sqrt{\dfrac{1}{n_A} + \dfrac{1}{n_B}}}.$$

Example 8   *The test statistic for weight gain of calves*

For the calves experiment from Example 7,

$$t \simeq \frac{0.5125 - 0.676\,666\,7}{0.055\,030\sqrt{\dfrac{1}{4} + \dfrac{1}{3}}} \simeq \frac{-0.164\,166\,7}{0.042\,029\,9} \simeq -3.906.$$

Now, if the null hypothesis $H_0\colon \mu_A - \mu_B = 0$ is true, then we would expect t to be close to zero. So we ask: 'Is -3.906 close enough to zero, or should the null hypothesis be rejected in favour of the alternative hypothesis that the mean weight gains differ?' To answer this we consult a table of critical values.

Table 2 gives the 5% critical values for t distributions with different degrees of freedom. For a two-sample *t*-test with sample sizes n_A and n_B, the number of degrees of freedom is $n_A + n_B - 2$ (the same as the denominator in the formula for s_{p}^2).

Table 2   5% critical values for Student's t-test

Degrees of freedom	Critical value (t_c)	Degrees of freedom	Critical value (t_c)
1	12.706	21	2.080
2	4.303	22	2.074
3	3.182	23	2.069
4	2.776	24	2.064
5	2.571	25	2.060
6	2.447	26	2.056
7	2.365	27	2.052
8	2.306	28	2.048
9	2.262	29	2.045
10	2.228	30	2.042
11	2.201	31	2.040
12	2.179	32	2.037
13	2.160	33	2.035
14	2.145	34	2.032
15	2.131	35	2.030
16	2.120	36	2.028
17	2.110	37	2.026
18	2.101	38	2.024
19	2.093	39	2.023
20	2.086	40	2.021

(Table 2 will be referred to at various points in the unit. A copy of this table can be found in the Handbook.)

Figure 13 shows plots of t distributions for various numbers of degrees of freedom. For comparison, it also plots the normal distribution. If you look at the figure, you will see that when the number of degrees of freedom is small, the corresponding curve is comparatively low in the middle and comparatively high (i.e. further from the horizontal axis) at the extremes. As the number of degrees of freedom increases, the curves get nearer the axis at the extremes. Thus the probability of getting a large (i.e. extreme) value of t (either negative or positive) is bigger when the number of degrees of freedom is small than when it is large.

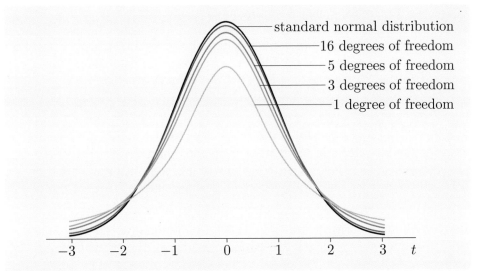

Figure 13 Sampling distribution of the test statistic t, for various numbers of degrees of freedom

---

Example 9 *Critical value for the calves experiment*

Returning to the calves experiment, here $n_A = 4$ and $n_B = 3$. Therefore the number of degrees of freedom is $4 + 3 - 2 = 5$; thus the row of Table 2 to consult is the one with 5 in the 'Degrees of freedom' column. This gives the critical value $t_c = 2.571$.

This means that if the null hypothesis is true, then the probability of obtaining a value of t greater than 2.571 is 0.025, or 2.5%, and the probability of obtaining a value of t less than -2.571 is also 0.025. So if the null hypothesis is true, then the probability of obtaining a value of t less than -2.571 or greater than 2.571 is 0.05, or 5% (see Figure 14).

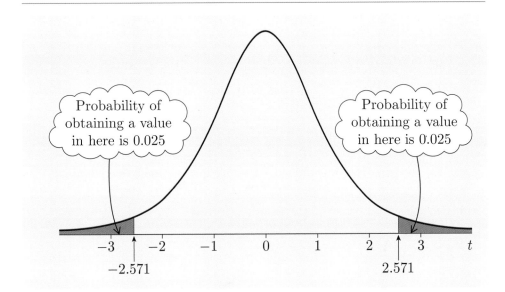

Figure 14 Sampling distribution, under the null hypothesis, of the test statistic t with five degrees of freedom

Activity 11   *Conclusion from the calves experiment?*

In our example, the value of t was calculated to be -3.906. Does this mean that the null hypothesis of no difference between the diets should be rejected at the 5% significance level? What do you conclude?

In general, the null hypothesis should be rejected whenever the calculated value of the test statistic t is further from zero than the critical value, i.e. whenever the value of t, ignoring any minus sign, is greater than or equal to the critical value t_c given in Table 2 for the appropriate number of degrees of freedom.

If you look at the critical values in Table 2 more closely, you may notice that as the number of degrees of freedom increases, the critical value decreases. For example, for 10 degrees of freedom the critical value is 2.228, whereas for 40 degrees of freedom it is 2.021. The reasons for this are illustrated in Figure 13: for small numbers of degrees of freedom, the tails of the distribution of the test statistic t die away less rapidly than for large numbers, so the critical value must be further from zero. This difference can be seen quite clearly (from the curves in the figure) for one or three degrees of freedom, but the curve for 16 degrees of freedom looks very similar to that of the standard normal distribution.

For a larger number of degrees of freedom, the curve (drawn at the scale of the figure) would be indistinguishable from that of the standard normal distribution. However, even these small differences in the curves produce noticeable differences in the sizes of the tails. The tails of these distributions of t all represent a larger proportion of the distribution than do the tails of the standard normal distribution. This larger proportion makes the critical value noticeably larger than 1.96: for 16 degrees of freedom it is 2.120, and for 40 degrees of freedom it is 2.021 (this is smaller than 2.120 but still larger than 1.96). Thus, as the number of degrees of freedom increases, the corresponding critical value decreases: the critical values get closer and closer to 1.96, but they never become smaller than 1.96.

Activity 12   *t-test for ball manoeuvres*

For the ball manoeuvres experiment in Activity 10 carry out a t-test at the 5% significance level to test the null hypothesis

H_0: $\mu_A = \mu_B$ (seeing course or getting instruction are equivalent)

against the alternative hypothesis

H_1: $\mu_A \neq \mu_B$ (seeing course or getting instruction are not equivalent).

Key values for a two-sample t-test

The information you need to know for a two-sample t-test is:

- the sample means ($\overline{x}_A$ and $\overline{x}_B$)
- the sample sizes (n_A and n_B)
- the sample standard deviations (s_A and s_B) or the pooled standard deviation (s_p) or the corresponding variances.

Activity 13   *Plant heights*

This concerns an experiment to investigate the heights of two different varieties of lupin: *Lupinus arboreus* and *Lupinus hartwegii*. Here are the summaries of the data from two samples: one of each of these varieties. All the plants were grown at the same time in similar conditions in a nursery, and the height of each (in metres) was measured on the same day.

Lupinus arboreus:
- sample size $n_A = 5$
- mean $\overline{x}_A = 1.252$
- standard deviation $s_A = 0.051$.

Lupinus hartwegii:
- sample size $n_B = 6$
- mean $\overline{x}_B = 1.023$
- standard deviation $s_B = 0.038$.

Carry out a t-test on these samples to investigate whether there is a significant difference between the heights of the two varieties. (With summary data like these, you cannot check whether the heights are normally distributed – but assume that they can be.)

(a)   (b)

Examples of (a) *Lupinus arboreus* and (b) *Lupinus hartwegii*

Before asking you to analyse the data from the experiment that you are conducting, we will say a little more about the connection between two-sample z-tests and two-sample t-tests, to help show the rationale behind the latter.

The test statistic of the two-sample z-test is

$$z = \frac{\overline{x}_A - \overline{x}_B}{\mathrm{SE}},$$

where

$$\mathrm{SE} = \sqrt{\frac{\sigma_A^2}{n_A} + \frac{\sigma_B^2}{n_B}}.$$

When the t-test is applicable, the two population variances are equal and s_p^2 is an estimate of that common variance. Substituting s_p^2 for both σ_A^2 and σ_B^2 (which are generally unknown) gives

$$\mathrm{SE} = \sqrt{\frac{s_\mathrm{p}^2}{n_A} + \frac{s_\mathrm{p}^2}{n_B}} = s_\mathrm{p}\sqrt{\frac{1}{n_A} + \frac{1}{n_B}}.$$

Then the above test statistic for the two sample z-test becomes

$$\frac{\overline{x}_A - \overline{x}_B}{s_\mathrm{p}\sqrt{\dfrac{1}{n_A} + \dfrac{1}{n_B}}},$$

which is the test statistic for the two-sample t-test.

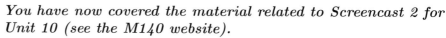

You have now covered the material related to Screencast 2 for Unit 10 (see the M140 website).

3.4   Analysis of mustard seedling data

The analysis of your mustard seedling data will form part of the tutor-marked assignment covering this unit. When your mustard seedlings have grown sufficiently, you should collect data on them, following the instructions in Subsection 2.6. Using these data, you will be able to test whether light affects root growth.

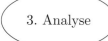

3. Analyse

Even if you have not got 10 measurements from each group, you can still carry out the test – provided you have at least two measurements from each group!

You should have 10 measurements from seedlings grown in the light (Group A) and 10 from seedlings grown in the dark (Group B): all from seedlings whose stems you cut. Before carrying out the t-test on these data, you should consider whether you can assume that the populations satisfy the necessary distributional conditions. The only way you can do this is by examining the data that you have collected. We shall now demonstrate how to do this using the following data, which we hope are not too different from yours.

In Table 3, measurements which are bold were obtained from seedlings whose stems were cut during their growth. A cross indicates a seed which did not germinate.

Table 3 Lengths of roots (in mm) obtained in a mustard seedlings experiment

Seedlings grown in light					Seedlings grown in dark				
21	**39**	27	**31**	×	**22**	×	21	×	39
×	21	26	**13**	12	20	×	**16**	**20**	×
52	**39**	×	11	**55**	14	**32**	**28**	×	**36**
50	×	8	**29**	17	24	**41**	20	**17**	**22**

Activity 14   *Stemplots of seedling data*

Prepare separate stemplots of the lengths of the roots for each of the two samples of 10 cut seedlings from the given data (i.e. of the values which are bold).

Activity 15   *Sample variances of seedling data*

Calculate the sample variance of root-length for the sample of seedlings grown in the light. Do the same for the sample grown in the dark. Can we treat the samples as coming from populations with equal variances?

From the stemplots, the two samples of data each look as if they could have come from populations with a normal distribution. Also, our rule of thumb says we may treat the population variances (and hence also their standard deviations) as being equal. (Also, the spreads of the observations seem similar in the two stemplots, suggesting the populations have similar variances.) With such small samples it is not possible to be more precise than this, but there is certainly no strong evidence that the distributional conditions required for the *t*-test are not satisfied. Nor, again because they are so small, would there be any such evidence even if the samples were less symmetric. Thus Activities 14 and 15, together with a large amount of similar data about living things collected by scientists, suggest that we can apply the *t*-test to these samples of data.

The following summarises the procedure for calculating the test statistic.

Calculation of the test statistic for the two-sample t-test

Denote the two samples by A and B, and their sizes by n_A and n_B.

1. Calculate $\sum x_A$, $\sum x_B$, $\sum x_A^2$ and $\sum x_B^2$.

2. Calculate the sample means $\bar{x}_A = \sum x_A / n_A$ and $\bar{x}_B = \sum x_A / n_A$.

3. Calculate

$$\sum x_A^2 - \frac{\left(\sum x_A\right)^2}{n_A}$$

and divide it by $n_A - 1$ to obtain s_A^2. Similarly, divide

$$\sum x_B^2 - \frac{\left(\sum x_B\right)^2}{n_B}$$

by $n_B - 1$ to obtain s_B^2.

4. Divide the larger of s_A^2 and s_B^2 by the smaller to check whether it is less than 3. If this is the case, it is sensible to assume a common population variance.

5. Calculate a pooled estimate s_p^2 of the common population variance:

$$s_p^2 = \frac{(n_A - 1)s_A^2 + (n_B - 1)s_B^2}{n_A + n_B - 2}.$$

6. Calculate the test statistic:

$$t = \frac{\bar{x}_A - \bar{x}_B}{s_p \sqrt{\dfrac{1}{n_A} + \dfrac{1}{n_B}}}.$$

Round this to three decimal places.

After completing this section and collecting your seedling data, you are in a position to analyse the results of your experiment!

Exercises on Section 3

Exercise 3   *Hay and barley*

Another experiment on calves, similar to that in Example 7, was carried out to compare a diet H including hay with a diet B including barley straw. The average weight gain (kg per day) over five weeks after the birth-date was again measured for each calf. The results for the two diets are summarised here.

Hay:

* sample size $n_H = 20$
* mean $\bar{x}_H = 0.542$
* standard deviation $s_H = 0.081$.

Barley straw:

* sample size $n_B = 19$
* mean $\bar{x}_B = 0.554$
* standard deviation $s_B = 0.088$.

Carry out a t-test on these sample data to test whether the two diets differ in their effect on average weight gain. (Assume that the weight gains of calves are normally distributed.)

Exercise 4   *Comparing production lines*

A manufacturer wishes to compare the performance of two biscuit production lines, A and B. The lines produce packets of biscuits with a nominal weight of 300 grams. Two random samples of 15 packets from each of the two lines are weighed (in grams). The sample data are summarised as follows.

Line A:

* sample size $n_A = 15$
* mean $\bar{x}_A = 309.8$
* standard deviation $s_A = 3.58$.

Line B:

* sample size $n_B = 15$
* mean $\bar{x}_B = 305.2$
* standard deviation $s_B = 4.73$.

Carry out a t-test on these sample data to test whether the two production lines produce packets of different average weight. (Assume that the weights of packets of biscuits produced by each production line are normally distributed.)

4 The t-test for one sample and matched-pairs samples

In this section we shall introduce a version of the t-test that can be used to analyse a single sample of suitable data when the sample size is not large. We then show how this test can be adapted to produce a useful test for data from experiments involving matched pairs. The method is almost identical to the one-sample z-test that we use when the sample size is large and the population standard deviation is unknown. (That test was the topic of Subsection 5.2 of Unit 7.) The test statistic is calculated in the same way, but now we compare it with the tabulated critical values of a t distribution, rather than the critical values of a normal distribution.

4.1 The one-sample t-test

The t-test described in Subsections 3.2 and 3.3 is used to compare two unrelated (i.e. unpaired) samples. We pointed out there that in many ways the procedure is similar to the z-test for the difference between two population means. You may have wondered whether there is a one-sample t-test that resembles the one-sample z-test, but which can be used with a small sample of data. The following example will be used to address this question.

Example 10   *A small sample of tomato plants*

A tomato grower decides to try out a new fertiliser on one variety of outdoor bush tomato plants that he grows. Previously this variety has produced an average yield of 4 kg of tomatoes per plant. The grower wants to investigate whether this average yield would change if he switched to the new fertiliser. He has room to experiment with only five plants on the new fertiliser. The yields of tomatoes from each of these five plants, in kg, are:

   3.6   3.2   3.1   2.6   3.9

If the population mean of the yield (in kg per plant) using this new fertiliser is denoted by μ, then the grower's null hypothesis is that μ is the same as the average yield used to be. In symbols:

   H_0: $\mu = 4$.

His alternative hypothesis is that the new fertiliser changes the average yield. In symbols:

   H_1: $\mu \neq 4$.

If the sample size had been large in Example 10, then the grower could have used the one-sample z-test; however, the sample is certainly not large enough. He could use the sign test, provided he changed his hypothesis to refer to the population median rather than the mean. However, these data are measurements, and the sign test takes account only of whether each data value is above or below a particular number. Thus the sign test does not use all the information in the data. It is possible to use much more of this information by using a *t*-test. It must be stressed, though, that this can be done only if it is reasonable to assume that the population distribution is normal. Our tomato grower might well feel that this assumption is justified. (Many measurements of living things are normally distributed. For example, the heights of adult men closely follow a normal distribution.)

Activity 16   *Key values from the tomato experiment*

The key values are the sample size n, sample mean $\overline{x}$ and sample standard deviation s. State the sample size and calculate the sample mean and sample standard deviation for the tomato grower's data.

Activity 17   *Could the z-test be used?*

(a) We want to test the hypothesis H_0: $\mu = A$, where $A = 4$, for the tomato grower's experiment. What test statistic would you use if you were trying to apply a *z*-test to his data?

(b) Why is the *z*-test not appropriate here?

In a one-sample *t*-test, the null hypothesis is H_0: $\mu = A$ and the alternative hypothesis is H_1: $\mu \neq A$. These are precisely the hypotheses used in a one-sample *z*-test. The test statistic for this *z*-test is

$$z = \frac{\overline{x} - A}{\text{ESE}}, \quad \text{where ESE} = \frac{s}{\sqrt{n}},$$

as noted in the solution to Activity 17. Replacing z by t gives the test statistic for the one-sample *t*-test.

> The test statistic for the one-sample *t*-test:
> $$t = \frac{\overline{x} - A}{\text{ESE}}, \quad \text{where ESE} = \frac{s}{\sqrt{n}}.$$

Example 11   *t-test statistic for the tomato experiment*

For the tomato grower's experiment, we found in Activity 16 that $n = 5$, $\overline{x} = 3.28$ and $s = 0.247$. Also $A = 4$, as the null hypothesis is H_0: $\mu = 4$. Hence ESE $\simeq 0.496\,99/\sqrt{5} \simeq 0.222\,26$, and the test statistic for a *t*-test is:

$$t = \frac{\overline{x} - 4}{\text{ESE}} = \frac{3.28 - 4}{0.222\,26} \simeq -3.239.$$

This, of course, is precisely the value found in part (a) of Activity 17.

If H_0 were true, then the population mean would be 4, so the sample mean $\overline{x}$ would probably be close to 4. Hence $\overline{x} - 4$ would be near 0, and so t would be near 0. Thus, as with the z-test, values of t sufficiently far from 0 (positive or negative) result in rejection of the null hypothesis. To know whether to reject the null hypothesis, we need a critical value – you will probably not be surprised to learn that this comes from the table of critical values in Table 2 (Subsection 3.3). To use this table we need to know what number of degrees of freedom to look up. For the one-sample t-test the rule is:

> For a sample of size n, the number of degrees of freedom is $n - 1$.

Activity 18   Critical value for the tomato experiment

Find the critical value at the 5% significance level for the tomato grower's test.

Example 12   Comparing the test statistic to the critical value

The rejection rule for the tomato grower is therefore: reject H_0 in favour of H_1 if the sample value of the test statistic t is greater than or equal to 2.776 or less than or equal to -2.776. Since $t = -3.239$, which is less than -2.776, the tomato grower should reject H_0 and conclude that, on the basis of his sample, the average yield with the new fertiliser is not 4 kg per plant. Of course he may have some reservations about this conclusion. Perhaps this year the weather was bad for tomato plants, for example.

Example 13   Using a sign test for the tomato experiment

In order to compare the t-test with the sign test, it is informative to re-examine the data on tomato plants using the sign test. The null hypothesis would be

   H_0: The median yield per plant is 4,

and the alternative hypothesis would be

   H_1: The median yield per plant is not 4.

The yields of the five plants were 3.6, 3.2, 3.1, 2.6 and 3.9, which are all less than 4, so the value of the test statistic is 0.

From Table 8 in Subsection 4.1 of Unit 6 (and repeated in the Handbook), we find that there is *no* value of the test statistic for which we would reject H_0 at the 5% significance level. Hence we would not reject it here.

In Example 12, the t-test rejected the null hypothesis. However, in Example 13, the sign test did not reject the null hypothesis. This is because the sign test uses less information than the t-test. In general, the *t*-test is more likely than the sign test to reject a null hypothesis that is false. (That is, the *t*-test is less likely to make a Type 2 error.) We say that the *t*-test is more **powerful** than the sign test.

> **Power of the *t*-test and the sign test**
>
> The *t*-test is said to be a more powerful test than the sign test because the *t*-test is better at identifying a null hypothesis that is false.

The price that is paid in using the *t*-test (rather than the sign test) is that an extra assumption is needed – we must assume that the sample is from a normal distribution. If this assumption is reasonably close to reality, then it is much better to use the *t*-test.

Here is a summary of the procedure for the one-sample *t*-test.

> **Procedure: the one-sample *t*-test**
>
> The test applies to a sample of data consisting of numerical measurements, when the population from which the data comes can be assumed to have a normal distribution.
>
> 1. Denoting the population mean by μ, the null and alternative hypotheses are:
>
> H_0: $\mu = A$
>
> H_1: $\mu \neq A$.
>
> 2. Calculate the sample mean, $\overline{x}$, and the sample standard deviation, s.
>
> 3. Calculate the estimated standard error:
>
> $$\text{ESE} = \frac{s}{\sqrt{n}},$$
>
>   where n is the sample size.
>
> 4. The test statistic is
>
> $$t = \frac{\overline{x} - A}{\text{ESE}}.$$
>
> 5. The critical value at the 5% significance level is the value of t_c for $n - 1$ degrees of freedom in Table 2 (Subsection 3.3).
>
> 6. Reject H_0 in favour of H_1 at the 5% significance level if
>
>   *   either $t \geq t_c$
>
>   *   or $t \leq -t_c$.
>
>   Otherwise H_0 is not rejected at the 5% significance level.
>
> 7. State the conclusion that can be drawn from the test.

You have now covered the material related to Screencast 3 for Unit 10 (see the M140 website).

4.2   The matched-pairs t-test

In various experiments, **matched pairs** are used to remove the effects of factors that would otherwise be uncontrollable. For example, suppose a shoe manufacture wants to test which of two materials makes heels that last longer. One approach would be to make some pairs of shoes with one material and some with the other. Then let people wear the shoes for two months, after which the wear on the heels of the shoes would be measured. This would answer the question if enough pairs of shoes were used in the experiment. However, differences in wear would reflect not just differences in the materials, but also differences in the amount shoes were used, differences in weights of the people, and so forth.

One way of reducing these latter effects would be to make one heel of a pair of shoes from one material and make the other heel *of that same pair of shoes* from the other material. Then the difference in wear between the left and right shoes of a pair would not reflect differences in usage (assuming the wearer did not hop a lot), nor differences in a wearer's weight, as the same person wore both. In this form of experiment, each pair of shoes would give a matched pair of measurements, and the differences in wear between the left and right heels of a pair of shoes would be the data that are analysed.

Sometimes matching isn't with the same person. Each person in a group is *matched* as closely as possible with a person in another group in terms of age and any other aspects that we might want to control for.

> **Pairing**
>
> In a matched-pairs experiment, items are paired in such a way that the factor of interest (but little else) differs between the two items that form a pair. The statistical analysis is then based on the differences between items within a pair.

Taking differences combines two measurements into one, so that methods for analysing a single sample become appropriate. If the number of pairs is large (over 25), then a one-sample z-test might be used. For smaller samples, a t-test should be used if it can be assumed that the population of differences has a normal distribution.

To illustrate this use of the one-sample t-test, we shall look at some data that come from a paper by Cushny and Peebles, published in 1904. (These data were analysed by Gosset (Student) in the 1908 paper in which he published the results that led to the t-test.) These researchers wanted to investigate whether two different forms, L and R, of a drug, hyoscyamine hydrobromide, differ in their capacity to induce sleep. (Note that hyoscyamine hydrobromide is not now commonly used as a sleep-inducing drug.) They conducted an experiment with ten patients. Five of the patients received form R of the drug first, and their gain in sleep was recorded. After a suitable time had elapsed they were given form L instead and the same measurements recorded. The other five patients received the two drugs in the opposite order.

Activity 19   *Benefits of the experimental design*

The experiment was designed to reduce the effects of two sources of variation that could affect results. What effects were reduced?

The results from the experiment are given in Table 4. A positive figure means that the patient got more sleep with the drug than without; a negative figure means that he or she got less sleep with the drug.

Table 4   Sleep gained (hours) by the use of hyoscyamine hydrobromide

Patient	Form L	Form R
1	+1.9	+0.7
2	+0.8	−1.6
3	+1.1	−0.2
4	+0.1	−1.2
5	−0.1	−0.1
6	+4.4	+3.4
7	+5.5	+3.7
8	+1.6	+0.8
9	+4.6	0.0
10	+3.4	+2.0

Note that patients vary considerably in their responsiveness to both drugs. For example, patient 7 is very responsive to both drugs, whilst patient 5 is much less affected.

It would not be appropriate to analyse these data using the two-sample *t*-test from Section 3 because the data are in matched pairs: there is a pair of sleep-gain measurements for each patient. Making effective use of the matching leads to a more powerful test.

To use the matched-pairs *t*-test on these data, first we find the difference, for each patient, between the hours of sleep gained using form L and the hours gained using form R.

Activity 20   *Forming differences*

For each patient in Table 4, calculate the difference, d, in hours of sleep gained: $L - R$.

The null hypothesis is that the two forms of the drug are equally effective: i.e. on average, it does not make any difference which form a patient receives. If we denote the population mean of the hours of sleep gained with form L by μ_L, and the population mean for form R by μ_R, then the null hypothesis is

$$H_0: \mu_L = \mu_R \quad \text{or} \quad H_0: \mu_L - \mu_R = 0.$$

If the population mean of the difference between the hours of sleep gained with form L and with form R is denoted by μ_d, then $\mu_d = \mu_L - \mu_R$.

Now the null hypothesis is just that the population mean difference is zero:

$$H_0: \mu_d = 0,$$

and the alternative hypothesis is

$$H_1: \mu_d \neq 0.$$

We now have a single sample of 10 numbers, the *differences*, and null and alternative hypotheses about the population mean *difference* of the population from which this sample of 10 *differences* comes. If it is reasonable to assume that the distribution of this population of differences is normal, then we can carry out a one-sample t-test on these differences.

Activity 21   *Testing for a mean difference of 0*

Carry out a one-sample t-test on the differences, using d instead of x in the formulas. What do you conclude?

An unmatched pair

You have now covered the material related to Screencast 4 for Unit 10 (see the M140 website).

The following summarises the procedure for a matched-pairs t-test.

> **Procedure: the matched-pairs t-test**
>
> 1.   Calculate the differences between the two values in each pair.
> 2.   The null and alternative hypotheses are
>
> H_0: $\mu_A = \mu_B$
> H_1: $\mu_A \neq \mu_B$,
>
>   where μ_A and μ_B are the population means of the two populations involved.
>
>   Replace these by the equivalent hypotheses
>
> H_0: $\mu_d = 0$
> H_1: $\mu_d \neq 0$,
>
>   where μ_d is the population mean of the population of differences between the matched pairs.
>
> 3.   If it can be assumed that this population of differences has a normal distribution, then apply the one-sample t-test with $A = 0$ and d instead of x in the formulas, to the sample of differences.

Activity 22   *Comparing weighing machines*

A scientist has two pieces of weighing equipment, A and B, in her laboratory, both of which she suspects may be inaccurate, though she does not know in what way. She decides to begin an investigation into their accuracy by comparing their readings for the weights of different objects. She weighs nine objects on both pieces of equipment, with the following results:

| | Weight in grams | |
Object	Equipment A	Equipment B
1	3.6	3.3
2	4.3	4.4
3	11.4	11.2
4	15.9	15.5
5	16.4	16.6
6	18.7	18.7
7	21.1	20.7
8	21.8	21.4
9	24.1	23.8

The scientist wants to test whether one piece of equipment gives higher weights than the other.

(a)   For each object, calculate the weight given by A minus the weight given by B. Calculate the mean and sample standard deviation of these differences.

(b) Give the hypothesis to be tested and the alternative hypothesis.

(c) Calculate the test statistic.

(d) State the number of degrees of freedom and give the critical value for the test.

(e) What is the result of the hypothesis test?

(f) State your conclusion.

Exercises on Section 4

Exercise 5   *One-sample t-test*

A sample of 12 items has a sample mean of 8.2 and a sample variance of 3.7. Using a one sample t-test (where in each case μ is the mean of the population from which the sample was taken):

(a) test the null hypothesis H_0: $\mu = 10$ against the alternative hypothesis H_1: $\mu \neq 10$;

(b) test the null hypothesis H_0: $\mu = 7.5$ against the alternative hypothesis H_1: $\mu \neq 7.5$.

Exercise 6   *Drug comparison*

Use the matched-pairs t-test to analyse data on the effect of a new drug on the weight of male patients. The data on the five matched pairs of males are given below.

Experiment group (new drug taken)		Control group (old drug taken)		
Patient number	Weight change (N)	Patient number	Weight change (O)	Difference ($N - O$)
8	-7	1	-2	-5
16	-7	2	$+1$	-8
20	-3	4	-3	0
13	-1	10	$+1$	-2
17	-2	14	-5	$+3$

Is there a significant difference between the effect of the new drug and that of the old drug?

5 Confidence intervals from t-tests

As with other hypothesis tests, it is often important to go beyond the test and obtain estimates in the form of confidence intervals. For example, the tomato grower in Subsection 4.1 would probably like an estimate of the yield of tomatoes which he is likely to obtain from the new fertiliser. The new fertiliser might be cheaper or easier to apply than his old fertiliser, and an interval estimate could help him to decide whether it was worth using the new fertiliser, even though it did not match up to the old fertiliser.

There is an underlying structure to many forms of confidence interval. It is common to both confidence intervals for a single population mean and confidence intervals for comparing two population means.

> **Confidence interval for a mean or the difference between two means**
>
> The lower limit of the confidence interval is
>
> > point estimate $-$ (z or t critical value) $\times$ ESE,
>
> and the upper limit is
>
> > point estimate $+$ (z or t critical value) $\times$ ESE,
>
> where ESE is the estimated standard error of the point estimate.
>
> (As noted in Subsection 4.1 of Unit 9, an estimate that consists of a single number (rather than a range of values) is called a point estimate.)

A critical value of z is used if the standard error is known or estimated from a large sample (or samples, when there are two populations). The critical value of a t distribution is used if the standard error is unknown and is estimated for a small sample (or samples).

For z, we use the 5% critical value to construct a 95% confidence interval, and the 1% critical value to construct a 99% confidence interval. For t distributions, only 95% confidence intervals will be constructed by hand in M140, as Table 2 (Subsection 3.3) only gives 5% critical values.

5.1 Confidence intervals from one sample and matched-pairs t-tests

Let us suppose the tomato grower wants a confidence interval for μ, the mean yield (in kg per plant) of tomatoes that he will obtain with the new fertiliser. If he were to calculate a confidence interval based on the z-test, then he would calculate the sample mean $\bar{x}$ and the sample standard deviation s. Then the sample estimate of the standard error is

$$\text{ESE} = \frac{s}{\sqrt{n}},$$

so the 95% confidence interval for μ would be
$$(\bar{x} - 1.96 \times \text{ESE}, \bar{x} + 1.96 \times \text{ESE}).$$

Recall that 1.96 is the critical value for the z-test. However, in the hypothesis test he had to use a t-test rather than a z-test because his sample is small. For this same reason he must also calculate his confidence interval differently – it must be based on the t-test rather than the z-test.

The calculation is almost exactly the same as for the interval based on the z-test, but for one modification: he must use the critical value t_c from Table 2 (Subsection 3.3). This is the same critical value as the one which he used in the hypothesis test in Subsection 4.1: that for $n - 1$, i.e. 4, degrees of freedom.

Thus the 95% confidence interval for μ is
$$(\bar{x} - t_\text{c} \times \text{ESE}, \bar{x} + t_\text{c} \times \text{ESE}),$$
where ESE is still $s/\sqrt{n}$.

From Activities 16 and 18, $\bar{x} = 3.28$, $s \simeq 0.496\,99$, $n = 5$ and $t_\text{c} = 2.776$. So ESE $\simeq 0.496\,99/\sqrt{5} \simeq 0.222\,26$ (as in Example 11). Thus
$$t_\text{c} \times \text{ESE} \simeq 2.776 \times 0.222\,26 \simeq 0.62,$$
rounded to the same level of accuracy as the sample mean. So the tomato grower's 95% confidence interval for the mean yield, in kg per plant, is $(3.28 - 0.62, 3.28 + 0.62)$, which equals $(2.66, 3.90)$.

We can summarise this method as follows.

95% confidence interval for the population mean of a normally distributed population

The confidence interval is $\left(\bar{x} - t_\text{c}\dfrac{s}{\sqrt{n}}, \ \bar{x} + t_\text{c}\dfrac{s}{\sqrt{n}} \right)$,

where n, $\bar{x}$, t_c and s are as in the procedure for the one-sample t-test. Thus t_c is the critical value from Table 2 for $n - 1$ degrees of freedom.

The same argument also applies to the confidence interval from the matched-pairs t-test. So for such intervals, the formula is the same as above but with $\bar{d}$ instead of $\bar{x}$; that is, $\left(\bar{d} - t_\text{c}\, s/\sqrt{n}, \ \bar{d} + t_\text{c}\, s/\sqrt{n} \right)$.

Activity 23   An enthusiastic gardener

An enthusiastic gardener wished to investigate whether sunflowers planted in her garden would indeed grow to a height of 4 metres, as claimed on the seed packet. She collected data on the heights, in metres, of a sample of 15 sunflowers grown in her garden. The results are summarised here.

$$n = 15, \quad \text{sample mean } \bar{x} = 3.60, \quad \text{sample standard deviation } s = 1.18.$$

Calculate a 95% confidence interval for the population mean of sunflowers grown in her garden.

In Subsection 4.2 we examined data on the sleep gain of two forms of a drug, form L and form R. We set $\mu_d = \mu_L - \mu_R$ and in Activity 21 we tested the null hypothesis that $\mu_d = 0$.

Use the solution to that activity to find a 95% confidence interval for μ_d.

As $\mu_d = \mu_L - \mu_R$, the last activity determined a confidence interval for $\mu_L - \mu_R$. In words, μ_d is the population mean of the difference between the hours of sleep gained by the same patient using form L and using form R of the drug hyoscyamine hydrobromide. Thus you have calculated a 95% confidence interval for the mean difference between the hours of sleep gained using the two forms of the drug.

5.2   Confidence intervals from two unrelated samples

The confidence interval for the difference between two population means can be based on critical values of z when we have a large sample from each population. When population standard deviations are unknown, this should not be done if one or both samples are small. Instead, a confidence interval can be based on the t distribution, provided the same conditions are satisfied that are required in the t-test for two unrelated samples. These conditions are:

- Two unrelated samples of independent observations are taken, one sample from each of the two populations of interest.

- The distributions of the two populations are normal, and their standard deviations are equal.

The confidence interval is given by the general form

$$\text{lower limit} = \text{point estimate} - t_c \times \text{ESE}$$

and

$$\text{upper limit} = \text{point estimate} + t_c \times \text{ESE}.$$

To apply this formula, denote the sample sizes by n_A and n_B, the sample means by $\overline{x}_A$ and $\overline{x}_B$, and the sample variances by s_A^2 and s_B^2. The pooled estimate of the common variance is calculated as before:

$$s_p^2 = \frac{(n_A - 1)s_A^2 + (n_B - 1)s_B^2}{n_A + n_B - 2},$$

and then

$$\text{ESE} = s_p\sqrt{\frac{1}{n_A} + \frac{1}{n_B}}.$$

As with the corresponding hypothesis test, the appropriate t distribution has $n_A + n_B - 2$ degrees of freedom, and t_c is obtained from Table 2 (Subsection 3.3). Thus the formula for the confidence interval is as follows.

95% confidence interval for the difference between the population means of two unrelated normally distributed populations with equal standard deviations

The confidence interval is

$$\left((\overline{x}_A - \overline{x}_B) - t_{\mathrm{c}} s_{\mathrm{p}} \sqrt{\frac{1}{n_A} + \frac{1}{n_B}}, \; (\overline{x}_A - \overline{x}_B) + t_{\mathrm{c}} s_{\mathrm{p}} \sqrt{\frac{1}{n_A} + \frac{1}{n_B}} \right),$$

where t_{c} is the critical value from Table 2 for $n_A + n_B - 2$ degrees of freedom.

Example 14   *Confidence interval for calves' weight gains*

The first example in Subsection 3.3 concerned the weight gains of calves fed two different diets, diet A and diet B. We will calculate a 95% confidence interval for the difference in average weight gain (kg per day) on the two diets. Useful summary statistics for these data were obtained in Examples 7 and 9:

$$n_A = 4, \quad n_B = 3, \quad \overline{x}_A = 0.5125, \quad \overline{x}_B \simeq 0.676\,666\,7,$$
$$s_{\mathrm{p}} \simeq 0.055\,030, \quad t_{\mathrm{c}} = 2.571.$$

To apply the above formula, we first calculate

$$t_{\mathrm{c}} s_{\mathrm{p}} \sqrt{\frac{1}{n_A} + \frac{1}{n_B}} \simeq 2.571 \times 0.055\,030 \sqrt{\frac{1}{4} + \frac{1}{3}} \simeq 0.108$$

and

$$\overline{x}_A - \overline{x}_B = 0.5125 - 0.676\,666\,7 \simeq -0.164.$$

Thus the confidence interval for the mean weight gain, in kg per day, is $(-0.164 - 0.108, -0.164 + 0.108)$, which is $(-0.272, -0.056)$.

When calculating a confidence interval for two unrelated samples, we make the assumption that the two populations have variances that are equal. Checking that this assumption was reasonable was unnecessary in Example 14, as we had checked it for our two populations of calves before testing the hypothesis $\mu_A = \mu_B$ in Subsection 3.3. This will be the case whenever construction of the confidence interval is preceded by a hypothesis test. When a hypothesis test has not been carried out, though, the assumption must be examined, using the same rule of thumb as before.

Checking equality of variances

The assumption of equal population variances holds acceptably well if the ratio of the larger sample variance to the smaller sample variance is less than 3. This condition should be checked before forming a confidence interval between two population means on the basis of two unrelated samples, unless the condition has already been checked in the course of a hypothesis test.

Activity 25   *Sun and shade*

The data on heights of sunflowers collected in Activity 23 were for sunflowers grown in a sunny flower bed in the garden, bed A. Sunflowers were also grown in a shady flower bed of the same garden, bed B. The gardener wanted an interval estimate of difference in heights for sunflowers grown in a sunny flower bed compared with sunflowers grown in a shady flower bed.

Results are summarised here.

Sunny:

- sample size $n_A = 15$
- mean $\overline{x}_A = 3.60$
- standard deviation $s_A = 1.18$.

Shady:

- sample size $n_B = 20$
- mean $\overline{x}_B = 2.76$
- standard deviation $s_B = 1.09$.

Check that the assumption of equal population variances holds acceptably well, and calculate a 95% confidence interval for the mean difference between the heights of sunflowers grown in the shady flower bed and those grown in the sunny flower bed.

You have now covered the material related to Screencast 5 for Unit 10 (see the M140 website).

Exercises on Section 5

Exercise 7   *Confidence interval for equipment*

In Activity 22 (Subsection 4.2) you tested a hypothesis about weight readings given by Equipment A and Equipment B. Let μ_d denote the average difference in weight that they give. Using results obtained in Activity 22, form a 95% confidence interval for μ_d.

Exercise 4 (Section 4) concerned the weights of packets of biscuits produced on two production lines. Using results obtained in that exercise, calculate a 95% confidence interval for the difference $\mu_A - \mu_B$, where μ_A and μ_B are the mean weights of packets of biscuits from the two production lines.

6 One-sided alternative hypotheses

Until now, when using z-tests and t-tests we have rejected the null hypothesis if the test statistic is larger in size (positive or negative) than a critical value. Such tests are sometimes referred to as **two-sided hypothesis tests**, and they are much the most common form of hypothesis test.

In some situations, however, we only want to reject the null hypothesis if the test statistic is large and positive, while in other situations, we only want to reject the null hypothesis if the test statistic is large and negative. In both these cases, the alternative hypothesis specifies a direction and is said to be a **one-sided alternative hypothesis**. For a one-sample z-test or t-test, where the null hypothesis is H_0: $\mu = A$, a one-sided alternative hypothesis will have the form

$$H_1: \mu < A \quad \text{or} \quad H_1: \mu > A.$$

Similarly, for a two-sample z-test or t-test, the null hypothesis is H_0: $\mu_A = \mu_B$, while the one-sided alternative hypothesis is

$$H_1: \mu_A < \mu_B \quad \text{or} \quad H_1: \mu_A > \mu_B.$$

A hypothesis test that uses a one-sided alternative hypothesis is said to be a **one-sided test**.

As an example of where a one-sided alternative hypothesis would be appropriate, suppose a student takes a multiple choice test in which each question offers a choice of four answers, of which only one is correct. The null hypothesis might be 'the student just guesses', while the alternative is 'the student knows something'. If the null hypothesis is true, then the student should score about 25%. If he scores much more, we would decide that he was not just guessing, so that the alternative hypothesis is true. If he scores much less than 25%, then we would not favour the alternative hypothesis. Rather, we would conclude that the student was just guessing (so the null hypothesis is true) *and* he was also unlucky! If μ denotes the proportion of questions that the student will get right on average if he takes versions of the test many times, then appropriate hypotheses would be

$$H_0: \mu = 0.25 \quad \text{and} \quad H_1: \mu > 0.25,$$

as μ should be more than 0.25 if the student knows something.

One-sided z-tests and t-tests are performed in exactly the same way as the corresponding two-sided tests, except:

- the critical value changes
- we only consider rejecting the null hypothesis if the value of the test statistic is in the direction specified by the alternative hypothesis.

Here we will only give further detail for t-tests, as this adequately demonstrates the similarities and minor differences between one-sided and two-sided hypothesis tests. Table 5, after the following boxes, gives critical values for one-sided t-tests at the 5% significance level. The number of degrees of freedom are the same as before: $n - 1$ for a one-sample test and $n_A + n_B - 2$ for a two-sample test.

"We prefer to call this test 'multiple choice', not 'multiple guess'."

One-sided t-test for one sample or matched-pairs samples

The null hypothesis is again H_0: $\mu = A$. The test statistic t is calculated as for the two-sided one-sample/matched-pairs t-test:

$$t = \frac{\overline{x} - A}{\text{ESE}}, \quad \text{where ESE} = \frac{s}{\sqrt{n}}.$$

The critical value at the 5% significance level is the value of t_c for $n - 1$ degrees of freedom in Table 5.

If the alternative hypothesis is H_1: $\mu > A$, we reject H_0 at the 5% significance level if $t > t_c$.

If the alternative hypothesis is H_1: $\mu < A$, we reject H_0 at the 5% significance level if $t < -t_c$.

One-sided two-sample t-test

The null hypothesis is again H_0: $\mu_A = \mu_B$. As with the two-sided two-sample test, check that it is reasonable to assume equal variances, and, assuming it is, calculate the test statistic:

$$t = \frac{\overline{x}_A - \overline{x}_B}{s_p \sqrt{\dfrac{1}{n_A} + \dfrac{1}{n_B}}},$$

where

$$s_p^2 = \frac{(n_A - 1)s_A^2 + (n_B - 1)s_B^2}{n_A + n_B - 2}.$$

The critical value at the 5% significance level is the value of t_c for $n_A + n_B - 2$ degrees of freedom in Table 5.

If the alternative hypothesis is H_1: $\mu_A > \mu_B$, we reject H_0 at the 5% significance level if $t > t_c$.

If the alternative hypothesis is H_1: $\mu_A < \mu_B$, we reject H_0 at the 5% significance level if $t < -t_c$.

Table 5 5% critical values for one-tailed Student's *t*-test

Degrees of freedom	Critical value (t_c)	Degrees of freedom	Critical value (t_c)
1	6.314	21	1.721
2	2.920	22	1.717
3	2.353	23	1.714
4	2.132	24	1.711
5	2.015	25	1.708
6	1.943	26	1.706
7	1.895	27	1.703
8	1.860	28	1.701
9	1.833	29	1.699
10	1.812	30	1.697
11	1.796	31	1.696
12	1.782	32	1.694
13	1.771	33	1.692
14	1.761	34	1.691
15	1.753	35	1.690
16	1.746	36	1.688
17	1.740	37	1.687
18	1.734	38	1.686
19	1.729	39	1.685
20	1.725	40	1.684

The result of a one-sided *un*matched pair test? Despite this being a cricket scoreboard, it shows the result of a 2003 *rugby* World Cup match: Australia 142 Namibia 0.

Example 15   *A one-sided one-sample t-test*

The average number of customers that a café serves during lunchtime on a weekday is 80.3. To try to increase this number, it starts to advertise regularly in the local newspaper. In the 20 weekdays following the start of the adverts, the average number of customers was 84.4, and the standard deviation of the number of customers was 9.2. The manager of the café wants to test whether advertising has changed the average number of lunchtime customers, or whether the difference between 80.3 and 84.4 is simply random variation. We have:

$$A = 80.3, \quad n = 20, \quad \bar{x} = 84.4, \quad s = 9.2.$$

The null hypothesis is

$$H_0: \mu = 80.3,$$

and the test statistic is

$$t = \frac{\bar{x} - 80.3}{\text{ESE}} = \frac{84.4 - 80.3}{9.2/\sqrt{20}} \simeq 1.99.$$

The analysis up to this point is the same for a one-sided test as for a two-sided test. For a two-sided test we would specify the alternative hypothesis as $H_0: \mu \neq 80.3$. Suppose, though, that the manager was certain, even before gathering data, that newspaper advertising could do no harm – it would either increase custom or result in no change. Then the manager might choose to use a one-sided test and use the alternative hypothesis

$$H_1: \mu > 80.3.$$

The number of degrees of freedom equals $n - 1 = 19$. From Table 5, the 5% critical value for a one-sided t-test with 19 degrees of freedom is 1.729. This is less than 1.99, the value of the test statistic. Also, the difference between $\bar{x}$ (84.4) and A (80.3) is in the direction consistent with H_1. Hence the null hypothesis is rejected at the 5% significance level.

The manager can conclude that there is moderate evidence that the average number of lunchtime customers has increased since advertising started.

In this next activity you are asked to perform a one-sided matched pairs t-test.

Activity 26   *Benefit of exercise*

An exercise physiologist measured the resting heart rate, in beats per minute, of seven people immediately before they started a one-year exercise program. These readings and their resting heart rate readings at the end of the program are given in Table 6. Assuming that the exercise program will not increase resting heart rate on average, examine the evidence that the exercise program reduces resting heart rate.

Table 6   Resting heart rates before and after the exercise program

| Person | Resting heart rate | |
	Before	After
1	74	71
2	71	68
3	68	66
4	75	72
5	75	70
6	72	73
7	69	67

Comparison of Tables 2 (Subsection 3.3) and 5 shows that the critical value for the one-sided test is less than for the two-sided test. This is true for every possible value of the degrees-of-freedom parameter. For example, when there are 20 degrees of freedom, the critical value is 2.086 for the two-sided test at the 5% significance level but only 1.725 for the one-sided test, and for 5 degrees of freedom it is 2.571 for the two-sided test but only 2.015 for the one-sided test.

Since one-sided tests set a lower threshold than two-sided tests, they are more likely to lead to the null hypothesis being rejected. You might have thought that this would make them popular, as experimenters typically hope to reject the null hypothesis. However, because they yield a lower threshold, an experimenter choosing to use a one-tailed test must be able to defend that choice against the question, *Why didn't you use a two-tailed test?* You should use a one-sided hypothesis test only when it is clear – before looking at the data – that if H_0 is wrong, then there is only one direction in which it can be wrong.

You have now covered the material related to Screencast 6 for Unit 10 (see the M140 website).

Exercise on Section 6

The head teacher of a small primary school is keen to help the children to read more quickly and she hopes this can be achieved by involving parents. At the beginning of the school year she calls a meeting of the parents of the 23 children who have just started school and explains how they can help by listening to their children read at home.

The school considers that a child can read after he or she has successfully completed the first four books in the series they use to teach reading. That year, the number of days taken to learn to read had a mean of 119.2 days and a standard deviation of 29.6 days. In previous years, the number of days till a child could read had a mean of 127.3 days. The head teacher wishes to test whether involving parents affects the mean time in which a child learns to read.

(a) Give the null hypothesis, suggest why a one-sided alternative hypothesis could be considered appropriate, and give such an alternative hypothesis.

(b) Give the values of μ, n, $\overline{x}$ and s.

(c) Calculate the value of the test statistic.

(d) Say whether you reject the null hypothesis. What do you conclude?

7 Computer work: experiments

In this section, you will use Minitab to perform one-sample t-tests, two-sample t-tests and paired t-tests. You will also learn how to use Minitab to calculate confidence intervals that correspond to t-tests. You should now turn to the Computer Book and work through Chapter 10.

Summary

In this unit, we have briefly considered the nature of experiments and their role in advancing knowledge; different kinds of experiment were distinguished. You now (hopefully) know how to grow mustard seeds! You will have found that measuring root lengths is not easy, especially as they are not naturally straight. So you will have seen that measurements cannot be made with perfect accuracy; simply because a number is recorded to the nearest millimetre does not mean that the measurement is made with that level of accuracy.

You also met the family of t distributions and the degrees-of-freedom parameter that relates to them. You have learned a new hypothesis test – the two-sample t-test – and used it to analyse the data from your mustard seed experiment. The test requires an assumption that two populations have the same variance. You have used a rule of thumb for checking this assumption and a method of forming a pooled estimate of their common variance, if their variances can be assumed equal.

The t distribution was also used to perform one-sample tests when the sample size is too small for a z-test. This t-test extends easily to test hypotheses when data are from matched pairs, and you used it for that purpose.

In addition, you have learned to use critical values from t distributions to form confidence intervals for the mean of one population or for the difference between the means of two populations. In the latter case the data might be in the form of matched pairs or it might come from two unrelated samples. You also learned how to use t-tests with one-sided alternative hypotheses, although in most situations two-sided alternative hypotheses should be used.

Finally, you have also used Minitab to perform t-tests and construct confidence intervals based on t distributions.

Learning outcomes

After working through this unit, you should be able to:

- distinguish between experimental and non-experimental forms of inquiry
- distinguish between three kinds of experiments (exploratory, measurement and hypothesis testing)
- appreciate the requirements in setting up, maintaining and completing a small scientific experiment
- recognise both samples and areas of investigation for which it would be unwise to use the t-test
- examine whether it is reasonable to assume that two population variances are equal
- carry out a two-sample t-test for unrelated samples
- carry out a one-sample t-test
- carry out a matched-pairs t-test
- calculate confidence intervals for one-sample and two-sample data from populations satisfying the distributional conditions required by the t-tests
- test a one-sided alternative hypothesis
- use Minitab to perform t-tests and construct confidence intervals when sample sizes are small.

Solutions to activities

Solution to Activity 1

The chef could prepare two pies, one with and one without the new ingredient. Then a reasonable experiment is for a large number of people to try both pies. Each person says which pie they prefer, and the sign test (Unit 6) can be used to test whether one pie is better than the other. (Half the people should try the old pie first, and half should try the new pie first, in case the order in which they are tried matters.)

Solution to Activity 2

One possibility is to use two groups of people, as similar as possible with respect to those features which you think might be relevant to poetry appreciation, such as age, sex and educational background. Also, the people should not have read the poem before. Each person in one group would be asked to read the three-verse version of the poem and rate how good it is on a seven-point scale. Each person in the other group would be asked to read, and rate, the truncated two-verse version. The two batches of ratings could then be analysed.

Solution to Activity 3

(a) *Null hypothesis:*   Microbes do not make food putrefy.

   Alternative hypothesis: Microbes do make food putrefy.

   Test: Prevent microbes from acting on the food.

   Possible results and conclusions: The food does not putrefy; therefore reject the null hypothesis. The food putrefies; therefore the null hypothesis is supported.

(b) *Null hypothesis:*   Sound is not transmitted by the jostling of air molecules.

   Alternative hypothesis: Sound is transmitted by the jostling of air molecules.

   Test: Ring a bell inside a vessel with all the air pumped out.

   Possible results and conclusions: The bell is inaudible; therefore reject the null hypothesis. The bell can be heard; therefore the null hypothesis is supported.

Solution to Activity 4

(a) This activity is designed to answer specific questions by pursuing a specific investigation. Thus it is a scientific experiment if it is conducted properly. (It must use a method that is repeatable.)

(b) For the same reasons as the solution to (a), this is a scientific experiment – if it is conducted properly.

(c) This is not a scientific experiment, as no experiment is being conducted. An example of a scientific experiment would be to buy a particular brand of tea and compare it with your usual brand.

(d) For the same reasons as the solution to (a), this is a scientific experiment – if it is conducted properly.

Solution to Activity 5

In Activity 4, you should have identified three scientific experiments.

- Measuring the distance between the Earth and the Sun, which is a measurement experiment.

- Leaving work an hour later to see if it makes much difference to your travel time to get home, which is an exploratory experiment. It could also be rephrased as a hypothesis-testing experiment, as follows.

  Hypothesis: Leaving work an hour later makes a big difference to your average travel time to get home.

  Prediction: If you leave work an hour later, your average time to get home will change substantially.

  Test: Leave work an hour later for a month and see if your average journey time changes a lot.

  Possible results and conclusions: Average journey time almost unchanged; therefore hypothesis is false. Average journey time goes up (or down) by a lot; therefore hypothesis is supported.

- Investigating whether obesity is caused by overeating, which is a hypothesis-testing experiment. It seeks to test a hypothesis about the cause of a phenomenon, as follows.

  Hypothesis: Obesity is caused by overeating.

  Prediction: Eating a lot will cause people to be obese.

  Test: Measure the weights of people who eat a lot and people who do not, and compare these with their ideal weights, as defined by the BMI (body mass index), for example.

  Possible results and conclusions: People who eat a lot are no more obese than people who do not; therefore hypothesis is false. People who eat a lot are more obese than people who do not; therefore hypothesis is supported.

Solution to Activity 6

In Activity 5, you should have identified two hypothesis-testing experiments.

- Leaving work an hour later to see if it makes much difference to your travel time to get home. Treating this as a hypothesis-testing experiment gives the following.

  Null hypothesis: Leaving work an hour later makes no difference to your average travel time to get home.

Alternative hypothesis: Leaving work an hour later makes a big difference to your average travel time to get home.

Test: Leave work an hour later for a month and see if your average journey time changes a lot.

Possible results and conclusions: Average journey time goes up (or down) by a lot; therefore reject the null hypothesis. Average journey time almost unchanged, so do not reject the null hypothesis.

- Investigating whether obesity is caused by overeating. The statistical hypothesis test is as follows.

Null hypothesis: Obesity is not caused by overeating.

Alternative hypothesis: Obesity is caused by overeating.

Test: Measure the weights of people who eat a lot and people who do not and compare these with their ideal weights, as defined by the BMI.

Possible results and conclusions: Clear evidence that people who eat a lot are more obese than people who do not; therefore reject the null hypothesis. Find that people who eat a lot are no more obese than people who do not; therefore the null hypothesis is not rejected.

Solution to Activity 7

The seedlings need to grow under conditions that are as similar as possible except for the presence or absence of light. It is especially important that the seedlings in the two groups are grown at the same temperature and humidity, and that they are equally spaced from each other, so that they do not suffer from unequal crowding effects. By growing the two sets of seedlings side by side in adjacent pots, it should be possible to control for temperature. By carefully spacing the seeds in the pots, it should be possible to avoid unequal crowding effects.

Darkness will be achieved for one set of seedlings by covering the pot in which they are growing with aluminium kitchen foil. As well as cutting out the light, this is likely to have the effect of raising the humidity in the enclosed air space. It is important that the seedlings grown in the light should experience similar humidity, and this can be achieved by covering their pot as well. The simplest solution is to cover the pot with a piece of clear plastic or a plastic bag. However, aluminium might conduct heat differently from clear plastic, so this might introduce an unwanted difference into the experiment. The difference in temperature conditions induced by the two different coverings will probably be small, especially if the room temperature is fairly constant during the experiment. It is up to you whether you try to devise ingenious ways of reducing this source of error, but it is not worth spending too long looking for ways of improving this particular aspect of the experiment.

There is another, quite subtle, factor that needs to be controlled. Light will affect the stems and leaves of the seedlings, and the stems and leaves of the two groups of seedlings will differ quite strikingly in their appearance as a result. It is possible that these changes in the leaves and stems themselves affect the roots. Perhaps a big stem stimulates the growth of a big root, whereas a small stem does not. If this is so, then you cannot be certain whether any differences which emerge are directly due to the effect of light on the roots, or whether they are due to the effect of the light on the leaves and stems, which in turn affect the growth of the roots. To control for this you should cut off the growing shoots from the seedlings. We suggest that you do not treat all the seedlings in this way. This will allow you to see how long the roots grow on the seedlings which are not cut (details in Subsection 2.5).

Solution to Activity 8

Null hypothesis   Light has no effect on root growth.

Prediction based on null hypothesis   The seedlings grown in the light will not differ in average root length from the seedlings grown in the dark.

Possible results and conclusions   If there is a difference in average root lengths between the two groups of seedlings, then the null hypothesis must be rejected, and the alternative hypothesis – that light does influence root growth – should be accepted. If there is no difference, then the null hypothesis is supported.

Solution to Activity 9

We have two independent sample sets – one set grown in the light and the other in the dark. You have come across two tests that can be applied to two unrelated samples of data. The χ^2 test could be applied, if you were to construct a contingency table from the data by dividing the measurements into categories. However, this test needs fairly large samples, and unless almost all your seeds germinate, it is likely that your samples will not be large enough.

The two-sample z-test can also be used on unrelated samples of data, but, like the χ^2 test, it requires samples larger than those that you have. Thus a different test is needed.

Solution to Activity 10

(a) Sums, and sums of squares:

x_A	x_A^2	x_B	x_B^2
2	4	8	64
7	49	11	121
8	64	3	9
3	9	5	25
5	25	8	64
$\sum$ 25	151	35	283

For Group A, $\bar{x}_A = 25/5 = 5$. Also

$$\sum x_A^2 - \frac{(\sum x_A)^2}{n_A} = 151 - \frac{25^2}{5} = 26,$$

so

$$s_A^2 = \frac{26}{n_A - 1} = \frac{26}{4} = 6.5.$$

For Group B, $\bar{x}_B = 35/5 = 7$. Also

$$\sum x_B^2 - \frac{(\sum x_B)^2}{n_B} = 283 - \frac{35^2}{5} = 38,$$

so

$$s_B^2 = \frac{38}{n_B - 1} = \frac{38}{4} = 9.5.$$

(b) The two sample variances are 6.5 and 9.5. Dividing the larger by the smaller gives $9.5/6.5 \simeq 1.462$. As this is less than 3, it is reasonable to accept that the populations have the same variance.

(c) The pooled estimate of the common variance is

$$\begin{aligned}
s_p^2 &= \frac{(n_A - 1)s_A^2 + (n_B - 1)s_B^2}{n_A + n_B - 2} \\
&= \frac{(5 - 1) \times 6.5 + (5 - 1) \times 9.5}{5 + 5 - 2} = \frac{64}{8} = 8.
\end{aligned}$$

Hence s_p (the pooled estimate of the common standard deviation) is $\sqrt{8} \simeq 2.8284$.

Solution to Activity 11

Yes. The value -3.906 calculated for the test statistic t is less than -2.571 (i.e. it is more extreme than the critical value), so the null hypothesis should be rejected at the 5% significance level. Thus there is moderate evidence that the average weight gain of calves differs between the two diets. As the mean weight gains were 0.5125 in Group A and 0.6767 in Group B, there is some evidence that average weight gain is higher on diet B.

Solution to Activity 12

From Activity 10, $\bar{x}_A = 5$, $\bar{x}_B = 7$ and $s_p \simeq 2.8284$.

$$\begin{aligned}
t &= \frac{\bar{x}_A - \bar{x}_B}{s_p \sqrt{\dfrac{1}{n_A} + \dfrac{1}{n_B}}} \\
&\simeq \frac{5 - 7}{2.8284 \sqrt{\dfrac{1}{5} + \dfrac{1}{5}}} \\
&\simeq \frac{-2}{1.7889} \\
&= -1.118 \quad \text{(rounded to three decimal places).}
\end{aligned}$$

The number of degrees of freedom is $5 + 5 - 2 = 8$. From Table 2 (Subsection 3.3) the critical value is $t_c = 2.306$. So we reject H_0 in favour of H_1 if $t \geq 2.306$ or $t \leq -2.306$. The value of the test statistic -1.118 is nearer to zero than the critical value 2.306, so we cannot reject the null

hypothesis (of no difference between the population means) at the 5%
significance level. Hence there is little evidence that the time taken to
manoeuvre the ball around the obstacle course is influenced by whether the
child saw the course in advance or was told in advance how to negotiate it.

Solution to Activity 13

The null hypothesis is

H_0: $\mu_A = \mu_B$

(the population mean heights of the two varieties are equal),

against the alternative hypothesis

H_1: $\mu_A \neq \mu_B$

(the population mean heights of the two varieties are not equal).

First we check that it is reasonable to assume a common population
variance. The two sample variances are $s_A^2 = 0.051^2 = 0.002\,601$ and
$s_B^2 = 0.038^2 = 0.001\,444$. Dividing the larger sample variance by the
smaller sample variance gives $0.002\,601/0.001\,444 \simeq 1.801$. This is much
less than 3, so assuming a common population variance seems reasonable.

It is estimated as:

$$
\begin{aligned}
s_p^2 &= \frac{(n_A - 1)s_A^2 + (n_B - 1)s_B^2}{n_A + n_B - 2} \\
&= \frac{4 \times 0.002\,601 + 5 \times 0.001\,444}{5 + 6 - 2} \\
&= \frac{0.017\,624}{9} \\
&\simeq 0.001\,958\,2.
\end{aligned}
$$

(This is between $0.001\,444$ and $0.002\,601$, so there is no obvious calculation
error.) We have $s_p \simeq \sqrt{0.001\,958\,2} \simeq 0.044\,252$.

Now

$$
\begin{aligned}
t &= \frac{\overline{x}_A - \overline{x}_B}{s_p \sqrt{\dfrac{1}{n_A} + \dfrac{1}{n_B}}} \\
&\simeq \frac{1.252 - 1.023}{0.044\,252 \sqrt{\dfrac{1}{5} + \dfrac{1}{6}}} \\
&\simeq \frac{0.229}{0.026\,796} \\
&\simeq 8.546.
\end{aligned}
$$

The number of degrees of freedom is 9, so from Table 2 (Subsection 3.3),
the critical value $t_c = 2.262$. Hence H_0 is easily rejected at the 5%
significance level. There is evidence that the varieties differ in their
average heights.

Solution to Activity 14

Stemplot for the *light* sample (Group A):

$$
\begin{array}{c|ccc}
1 & 3 & 7 & \\
2 & 1 & 9 & \\
3 & 1 & 9 & 9 \\
4 & & & \\
5 & 0 & 2 & 5
\end{array}
$$

$$n = 10 \qquad 1 \,|\, 3 \text{ represents } 13\,\text{mm}$$

Stemplot for the *dark* sample (Group B):

$$
\begin{array}{c|cccc}
1 & 4 & 6 & 7 & \\
2 & 0 & 2 & 2 & 8 \\
3 & 2 & 6 & & \\
4 & 1 & & &
\end{array}
$$

$$n = 10 \qquad 1 \,|\, 4 \text{ represents } 14\,\text{mm}$$

Solution to Activity 15

For the sample grown in the light (Group A),

$$\sum x_A = 21 + 39 + 31 + \cdots + 17 = 346$$

and

$$\sum x_A^2 = 21^2 + 39^2 + 31^2 + \cdots + 17^2 = 13\,972.$$

As $n_A = 10$,

$$\sum x_A^2 - \frac{\left(\sum x_A\right)^2}{n_A} = 13\,972 - \frac{346^2}{10} = 2000.4,$$

so

$$s_A^2 = \frac{2000.4}{n_A - 1} = \frac{2000.4}{9} \simeq 222.267.$$

For the sample grown in the dark (Group B),

$$\sum x_B = 22 + 16 + 20 + \cdots + 22 = 248$$

and

$$\sum x_B^2 = 22^2 + 16^2 + 20^2 + \cdots + 22^2 = 6894.$$

As $n_B = 10$ as well,

$$\sum x_B^2 - \frac{\left(\sum x_B\right)^2}{n_B} = 6894 - \frac{248^2}{10} = 743.6,$$

so

$$s_B^2 = \frac{743.6}{n_B - 1} = \frac{743.6}{9} \simeq 82.622.$$

Dividing the larger sample variance by the smaller sample variance gives $222.267/82.622 \simeq 2.69$. As this is less than 3, our rule of thumb says we can assume the samples are from populations whose variances are equal.

Solution to Activity 16

The sample size is $n = 5$. We have

$$\sum x = 3.6 + 3.2 + 3.1 + 2.6 + 3.9 = 16.4,$$

so the sample mean is

$$\overline{x} = \frac{\sum x}{n} = \frac{16.4}{5} = 3.28.$$

Also,

$$\sum x^2 = 3.6^2 + 3.2^2 + 3.1^2 + 2.6^2 + 3.9^2 = 54.78,$$

so

$$s^2 = \frac{1}{n-1} \left(\sum x^2 - \frac{(\sum x)^2}{n} \right) = \frac{1}{5-1} \left(54.78 - \frac{16.4^2}{5} \right)$$
$$= \frac{1}{4} (54.78 - 53.792) = 0.247.$$

Thus, the standard deviation is $s = \sqrt{0.247} \simeq 0.496\,99$.

Solution to Activity 17

(a) The test statistic for a one-sample z-test is

$$z = \frac{\overline{x} - A}{\text{ESE}}, \quad \text{where ESE} = \frac{s}{\sqrt{n}}.$$

For the tomato grower's experiment,

$$\text{ESE} \simeq \frac{0.496\,99}{\sqrt{5}} \simeq 0.222\,26, \quad \text{so } z \simeq \frac{3.28 - 4}{0.222\,26} \simeq -3.239.$$

(b) The z-test is not appropriate here for the same reason that it was not appropriate in Section 3. The sample size is so small that $s/\sqrt{n}$ may not be a good estimate of the standard error. Consequently, for such a small sample size, this test statistic has not got a standard normal distribution.

Solution to Activity 18

The sample size n is 5, so the number of degrees of freedom is 4. Thus from Table 2 (Subsection 3.3) the critical value is 2.776.

Solution to Activity 19

1. Some patients might be more responsive to treatment than other patients. To reduce the effect of variation between patients, each patient received *both* drugs.

2. The order in which a patient receives treatments might have an effect – perhaps patients tend to respond more to the first treatment they receive. To reduce this effect, each of the two drugs was the first that five patients received and the second that the other five patients received.

Solution to Activity 20

Patient	Form L	Form R	Difference $L - R$
1	+1.9	+0.7	+1.2
2	+0.8	−1.6	+2.4
3	+1.1	−0.2	+1.3
4	+0.1	−1.2	+1.3
5	−0.1	−0.1	0.0
6	+4.4	+3.4	+1.0
7	+5.5	+3.7	+1.8
8	+1.6	+0.8	+0.8
9	+4.6	0.0	+4.6
10	+3.4	+2.0	+1.4

Solution to Activity 21

The hypotheses are:

$$H_0\colon \mu_d = 0,$$
$$H_1\colon \mu_d \neq 0.$$

Let d denote the difference $L - R$. First it is necessary to calculate the mean $(\bar{d})$ and standard deviation (s) for the sample of differences.

d	d^2
1.2	1.44
2.4	5.76
1.3	1.69
1.3	1.69
0.0	0.00
1.0	1.00
1.8	3.24
0.8	0.64
4.6	21.16
1.4	1.96
$\sum$ 15.8	38.58

Thus, writing d instead of x in the formulas, the mean of these differences is

$$\bar{d} = \frac{\sum d}{n} = \frac{15.8}{10} = 1.58$$

and the variance is

$$s^2 = \frac{1}{n-1}\left(\sum d^2 - \frac{(\sum d)^2}{n}\right) = \frac{1}{10-1}\left(38.58 - \frac{15.8^2}{10}\right)$$

$$= \frac{1}{9}(38.58 - 24.964) \simeq 1.512\,89.$$

Thus, the standard deviation is $s \simeq \sqrt{1.512\,89} \simeq 1.230\,00$. Hence,

$$\text{ESE} = \frac{s}{\sqrt{n}} \simeq \frac{1.230\,00}{\sqrt{10}} \simeq 0.388\,96.$$

Now, the test statistic is

$$t = \frac{\bar{d} - A}{\text{ESE}}$$

but $A = 0$ since the null hypothesis is $H_0\colon \mu_d = 0$. Thus

$$t = \frac{1.58 - 0}{0.388\,96} \simeq 4.062.$$

The critical value is obtained from Table 2 (Subsection 3.3). The number of degrees of freedom is $n - 1 = 10 - 1 = 9$, so the critical value is 2.262. The value of t is 4.062, which is greater than 2.262. So H_0 is rejected at the 5% significance level.

The conclusion is that the population mean difference is not zero. Thus, on the basis of this experiment it seems that the two forms of hyoscyamine hydrobromide do differ in their effectiveness at increasing sleep. Because the test statistic is positive, there is moderate evidence that form L gives a greater gain in sleep on average.

Solution to Activity 22

(a)

Object	Weight in grams Equipment A	Equipment B	Difference d	d^2
1	3.6	3.3	0.3	0.09
2	4.3	4.4	-0.1	0.01
3	11.4	11.2	0.2	0.04
4	15.9	15.5	0.4	0.16
5	16.4	16.6	-0.2	0.04
6	18.7	18.7	0.0	0.00
7	21.1	20.7	0.4	0.16
8	21.8	21.4	0.4	0.16
9	24.1	23.8	0.3	0.09
$\sum$			1.7	0.75

The mean of the differences is

$$\bar{d} = \frac{\sum d}{n} = \frac{1.7}{9} \simeq 0.188\,89.$$

Also

$$s^2 = \frac{1}{n-1} \left(\sum d^2 - \frac{(\sum d)^2}{n} \right) = \frac{1}{9-1} \left(0.75 - \frac{1.7^2}{9} \right)$$

$$\simeq \frac{1}{8} (0.75 - 0.321\,11) \simeq 0.053\,611.$$

Thus, the standard deviation is $s \simeq \sqrt{0.053\,611} \simeq 0.231\,54$.

(b) The hypotheses are

$$H_0 \colon \mu_d = 0,$$
$$H_1 \colon \mu_d \neq 0.$$

(c) The estimated standard error is

$$\text{ESE} = \frac{s}{\sqrt{n}} \simeq \frac{0.231\,54}{\sqrt{9}} = 0.077\,18,$$

so the test statistic is

$$t = \frac{\bar{d}}{\text{ESE}} \simeq \frac{0.188\,89}{0.077\,18} \simeq 2.447.$$

(d) There are $n - 1 = 8$ degrees of freedom. From Table 2 (Subsection 3.3), the 5% critical value (t_c) for 8 degrees of freedom is 2.306. The test statistic, 2.447, is greater than 2.306, so H_0 is rejected at the 5% significance level.

(e) There is moderate evidence that the population mean difference is not zero. This suggests that the two pieces of equipment systematically differ in the weights they give – A seems, on average, to give higher weights than B, which means that the weighing machines cannot both be unbiased. There is moderate evidence that either equipment A on average gives weights that are too high, or that B on average gives weights that are too low, or that both pieces of equipment are biased (when we do not know the direction or directions of bias).

Solution to Activity 23

The number of degrees of freedom is $n - 1 = 15 - 1 = 14$. From Table 2 (Subsection 3.3), the critical value for 14 degrees of freedom is 2.145.

From this we calculate

$$t_c \frac{s}{\sqrt{n}} = 2.145 \times \frac{1.18}{\sqrt{15}} \simeq 0.65.$$

Thus a 95% confidence interval for the height of sunflowers, in metres, is $(3.60 - 0.65, 3.60 + 0.65)$. This is $(2.95, 4.25)$.

Solution to Activity 24

From the solution to Activity 21, $n = 10$, $\overline{d} = 1.58$ and
$\text{ESE} = s/\sqrt{n} \simeq 1.230\,00/\sqrt{10} \simeq 0.388\,96$. Also, there are $n - 1 = 9$ degrees
of freedom, for which the critical value is $t_c = 2.262$.

From this we calculate
$$t_c \frac{s}{\sqrt{n}} = t_c \times \text{ESE} \simeq 2.262 \times 0.388\,96 \simeq 0.88.$$

Thus a 95% confidence interval for the mean number of hours sleep gained
is $(1.58 - 0.88, 1.58 + 0.88)$. This is $(0.70, 2.46)$.

Solution to Activity 25

We first calculate the two sample variances:
$$s_A^2 = 1.18^2 = 1.3924 \quad \text{and} \quad s_B^2 = 1.09^2 = 1.1881.$$

Dividing the larger sample variance by the smaller sample variance gives
$1.3924/1.1881 \simeq 1.172$. This is much less than 3, so from our rule of
thumb it is reasonable to assume a common population variance.

We estimate this common variance by pooling the sample variances:
$$s_p^2 = \frac{(n_A - 1)s_A^2 + (n_B - 1)s_B^2}{n_A + n_B - 2} = \frac{(15 - 1) \times 1.3924 + (20 - 1) \times 1.1881}{15 + 20 - 2}$$
$$= \frac{42.0675}{33} \simeq 1.2748.$$

So $s_p \simeq 1.1291$.

The number of degrees of freedom is $n_A + n_B - 2 = 15 + 20 - 2 = 33$.
From Table 2 (Subsection 3.3) the critical value for 33 degrees of freedom
is 2.035.

We first calculate
$$t_c s_p \sqrt{\frac{1}{n_A} + \frac{1}{n_B}} \simeq 2.035 \times 1.1291 \sqrt{\frac{1}{15} + \frac{1}{20}} \simeq 0.78$$
and
$$\overline{x}_A - \overline{x}_B = 3.60 - 2.76 = 0.84.$$

Thus the confidence interval for the mean difference in height between the
heights of sunflowers, in metres, is $(0.84 - 0.78, 0.84 + 0.78)$, which is
$(0.06, 1.62)$.

Solution to Activity 26

Let μ_d denote the mean change in resting heart rate over the course of the
exercise program. The null hypothesis is that there is no change in average
resting heart rate:
$$H_0: \mu_d = 0.$$

As it is assumed that the exercise program will not increase resting heart
rate, the alternative hypothesis is one-sided:
$$H_1: \mu_d < 0.$$

The data are paired (there are two values for each person), so a matched-pairs t-test is appropriate. The differences d (after − before) are calculated, and then the sample mean and sample variance of d.

Person	Resting heart rate Before	After	Difference d	d^2
1	74	71	−3	9
2	71	68	−3	9
3	68	66	−2	4
4	75	72	−3	9
5	75	70	−5	25
6	72	73	1	1
7	69	67	−2	4
$\sum$			−17	61

The mean of the differences is

$$\bar{d} = \frac{\sum d}{n} = \frac{-17}{7} \simeq -2.4286.$$

Also

$$s^2 = \frac{1}{n-1}\left(\sum d^2 - \frac{(\sum d)^2}{n}\right) = \frac{1}{7-1}\left(61 - \frac{(-17)^2}{7}\right)$$

$$\simeq \frac{1}{6}(61 - 41.285\,71) \simeq 3.285\,71.$$

Thus, the standard deviation is $s \simeq \sqrt{3.285\,71} \simeq 1.812\,65$.

The estimated standard error is

$$\text{ESE} = \frac{s}{\sqrt{n}} \simeq \frac{1.812\,65}{\sqrt{7}} \simeq 0.685\,12,$$

so the test statistic is

$$t = \frac{\bar{d}}{\text{ESE}} \simeq \frac{-2.4286}{0.685\,12} \simeq -3.545.$$

There are $n - 1 = 6$ degrees of freedom. From Table 5 (Section 6), the 5% critical value (t_c) for six degrees of freedom is 1.943. As −3.545 is less than −1.943, H_0 is rejected at the 5% significance level. Thus there is moderate evidence that the exercise program is associated with a reduction in resting heart rate. (Of course, it may be that the people taking the exercise program also started to have a healthier lifestyle in other ways too, such as a change of diet.)

Solutions to exercises

Solution to Exercise 1

(a) This is designed to answer a specific question by pursuing a specific investigation. Thus it is a scientific experiment provided that it is properly conducted.

(b) This is not a scientific experiment: there is no experiment taking place. It is about gathering information rather than exploring, measuring or testing a hypothesis.

Solution to Exercise 2

(a) Driving a car with all the windows open to see whether petrol consumption is affected is an exploratory experiment. It can be rephrased as a hypothesis-testing experiment, as follows.

Hypothesis: Driving with all the windows open affects petrol consumption.

Prediction: If I drive with the windows open, petrol consumption will change (assuming the windows are usually closed).

Test: See what happens to petrol consumption when you drive with the windows open.

Possible results and conclusions: Petrol consumption almost unchanged, so hypothesis is false. Petrol consumption changes substantially, so hypothesis supported.

(b) Formulating this as a statistical hypothesis test gives the following.

Null hypothesis: Driving with all the windows open does not affect petrol consumption.

Alternative hypothesis: Driving with all the windows open affects petrol consumption.

Test: See what happens to petrol consumption when driving with the windows open.

Possible results and conclusions: Petrol consumption changes substantially; therefore reject the null hypothesis. Petrol consumption almost unchanged, so do not reject the null hypothesis.

Solution to Exercise 3

The null hypothesis is

H_0: $\mu_H = \mu_B$ (average weight gain is the same on the two diets),

against the alternative hypothesis

H_1: $\mu_H \neq \mu_B$ (average weight gain differs between the two diets).

First we check that it is reasonable to assume a common population variance. The two sample variances are $s_H^2 = 0.081^2 = 0.006\,561$ and $s_B^2 = 0.088^2 = 0.007\,744$. Dividing the larger sample variance by the smaller sample variance gives $0.007\,744/0.006\,561 = 1.180$ (rounded to three decimal places). This is much less than 3, so assuming a common population variance is reasonable.

It is estimated as:
$$s_p^2 = \frac{(n_H - 1)s_H^2 + (n_B - 1)s_B^2}{n_H + n_B - 2}$$
$$= \frac{19 \times 0.006\,561 + 18 \times 0.007\,744}{20 + 19 - 2}$$
$$= \frac{0.264\,051}{37}$$
$$\simeq 0.007\,136\,5.$$

(This is between $0.006\,561$ and $0.007\,744$, so there is no obvious calculation error.) We have $s_p \simeq \sqrt{0.007\,136\,5} \simeq 0.084\,478$.

Hence
$$t = \frac{\overline{x}_H - \overline{x}_B}{s_p\sqrt{\dfrac{1}{n_H} + \dfrac{1}{n_B}}}$$
$$\simeq \frac{0.542 - 0.554}{0.084\,478\sqrt{\dfrac{1}{20} + \dfrac{1}{19}}}$$
$$\simeq \frac{-0.012}{0.027\,063\,5}$$
$$\simeq -0.443.$$

The number of degrees of freedom is $20 + 19 - 2 = 37$, so from Table 2 (Subsection 3.3), the critical value $t_c = 2.026$. As -0.443 is (much) closer than the critical value to 0, H_0 is not rejected at the 5% significance level. There is little evidence that average weight gain differs between the two diets.

Solution to Exercise 4

The null hypothesis is

H_0: $\mu_A = \mu_B$ (average weight is the same in the two production lines),

against the alternative hypothesis

H_1: $\mu_A \neq \mu_B$ (average weight differs between the two production lines).

First we check that it is reasonable to assume a common population variance. The two sample variances are $s_A^2 = 3.58^2 = 12.8164$ and $s_B^2 = 4.73^2 = 22.3729$. Dividing the larger sample variance by the smaller sample variance gives $22.3729/12.8164 = 1.746$ (rounded to three decimal places). This is less than 3, so we will assume a common population variance.

The population variance is estimated as:

$$s_p^2 = \frac{(n_A - 1)s_A^2 + (n_B - 1)s_B^2}{n_A + n_B - 2}$$

$$= \frac{14 \times 12.8164 + 14 \times 22.3729}{15 + 15 - 2}$$

$$= \frac{492.6502}{28}$$

$$\simeq 17.595.$$

(This is between 12.8164 and 22.3729, as it should be.) We have $s_p \simeq \sqrt{17.595} \simeq 4.1946$.

Hence

$$t = \frac{\overline{x}_A - \overline{x}_B}{s_p \sqrt{\dfrac{1}{n_A} + \dfrac{1}{n_B}}}$$

$$\simeq \frac{309.8 - 305.2}{4.1946 \sqrt{\dfrac{1}{15} + \dfrac{1}{15}}}$$

$$\simeq \frac{4.6}{1.532}$$

$$\simeq 3.00.$$

The number of degrees of freedom is $15 + 15 - 2 = 28$. Thus, from Table 2 (Subsection 3.3), the critical value $t_c = 2.048$. As 3.00 is greater than 2.048, H_0 is rejected at the 5% significance level. There is moderate evidence that average weight differs between the two production lines – production line A seems to give a higher average weight than production line B.

Solution to Exercise 5

(a) The sample standard deviation, s, is $\sqrt{3.7} \simeq 1.9235$, so

$$\text{ESE} = \frac{s}{\sqrt{n}} \simeq \frac{1.9235}{\sqrt{12}} \simeq 0.555\,27.$$

Hence the test statistic for the t-test is

$$t = \frac{\overline{x} - A}{\text{ESE}} \simeq \frac{8.2 - 10}{0.555\,27} \simeq -3.242.$$

The number of degrees of freedom is $n - 1 = 11$. Thus from Table 2 (Subsection 3.3) the critical value for the 5% significance level is 2.201. As -3.242 is less than -2.201, the null hypothesis is rejected at the 5% significance level. There is evidence that the population mean does not equal 10.

(b) From part (a), we have that $\text{ESE} \simeq 0.555\,27$. When $A = 7.5$,

$$t = \frac{\overline{x} - A}{\text{ESE}} \simeq \frac{8.2 - 7.5}{0.555\,27} \simeq 1.261.$$

There are still 11 degrees of freedom, so the critical value is still 2.201. As 1.261 is nearer than 2.201 to 0, the null hypothesis is not rejected at the 5% significance level. There is little evidence against the hypothesis that the population mean is 7.5.

Solution to Exercise 6

The relevant null and alternative hypotheses are:

$$H_0: \mu_{N-O} = 0$$
$$H_1: \mu_{N-O} \neq 0.$$

We need to analyse the sample of five differences $(N - O)$:

d	d^2
-5	25
-8	64
0	0
-2	4
$+3$	9
$\sum$ -12	102

Thus the mean difference $\bar{d} = \dfrac{\sum d}{n} = \dfrac{-12}{5} = -2.4$.

Thus

$$s^2 = \frac{1}{n-1}\left(\sum d^2 - \frac{(\sum d)^2}{n}\right) = \frac{1}{5-1}\left(102 - \frac{(-12)^2}{5}\right)$$
$$= \frac{1}{4}(102 - 28.8) = 18.3,$$

and the standard deviation is $s = \sqrt{18.3} \simeq 4.2778$. Hence

$$\text{ESE} = \frac{s}{\sqrt{n}} = \frac{4.2778}{\sqrt{5}} \simeq 1.913\,11,$$

and

$$t = \frac{\bar{d}}{\text{ESE}} \simeq \frac{-2.4}{1.913\,11} \simeq -1.255.$$

The number of degrees of freedom is $n - 1 = 4$. Thus the critical value is 2.776. The test statistic -1.255 is closer to zero than the critical value 2.776, so we cannot reject the null hypothesis. Thus there is little evidence of a difference between the new drug and the old drug in their effect on the weight of male patients.

Solution to Exercise 7

We have a matched-pairs sample of data.

From the solution to Activity 22, $n = 9$, $\bar{x} \simeq 0.188\,89$ and $\text{ESE} = s/\sqrt{n} \simeq 0.231\,54/\sqrt{9} = 0.077\,18$.

Also, there are $n - 1 = 8$ degrees of freedom, for which the critical value is $t_c = 2.306$.

From this we calculate

$$t_c \frac{s}{\sqrt{n}} = t_c \times \text{ESE} \simeq 2.306 \times 0.077\,180 \simeq 0.18.$$

Thus a 95% confidence interval for the mean difference in weight, in grams, is $(0.19 - 0.18, 0.19 + 0.18)$. This is $(0.01, 0.37)$.

Solution to Exercise 8

We have two unrelated samples of data. In Exercise 4 we checked that it is reasonable to treat the population variances as being equal. From Exercise 4:

$$n_A = 15, \quad n_B = 15, \quad \overline{x}_A = 309.8, \quad \overline{x}_B = 305.2,$$
$$s_p \simeq 4.1946, \quad t_c = 2.048.$$

To apply the above formula, we first calculate

$$t_c s_p \sqrt{\frac{1}{n_A} + \frac{1}{n_B}} \simeq 2.048 \times 4.1946 \sqrt{\frac{1}{15} + \frac{1}{15}} \simeq 3.1$$

and

$$\overline{x}_A - \overline{x}_B = 309.8 - 305.2 = 4.6.$$

Thus the confidence interval for the mean difference in weight of biscuits, in grams, is $(4.6 - 3.1, 4.6 + 3.1)$, which is $(1.5, 7.7)$.

Solution to Exercise 9

(a) The null hypothesis is that involving parents has not changed the mean time to learn to read, so that it is still 127.3 days. Thus

$$H_0\colon \mu = 127.3.$$

If it is believed that involving parents could not hinder a child learning to read, then μ cannot be more than 127.3, giving the one-sided alternative hypothesis

$$H_1\colon \mu < 127.3.$$

(b) $\mu = 127.3$ (under H_0), $n = 23$, $\overline{x} = 119.2$ and $s = 29.6$.

(c) $t = \dfrac{\overline{x} - \mu}{\text{SE}} = \dfrac{119.2 - 127.3}{29.6/\sqrt{23}} \simeq -1.312$.

(d) There are $n - 1 = 22$ degrees of freedom. As the test is one-sided, the critical value for the 5% significance level with 22 degrees of freedom is -1.717, from Table 5. The value $-1.312 > -1.717$, so we do not reject H_0 at the 5% significance level. Thus the experiment provides little evidence that involving parents reduces the average time taken by children to learn to read.

Acknowledgements

Grateful acknowledgement is made to the following sources:

Cover image: Minxlj/www.flickr.com/photos/minxlj/422472167/. This file is licensed under the Creative Commons Attribution-Non commercial-No Derivatives Licence http://creativecommons.org/licenses/by-nc-nd/3.0/

Subsection 1.2 cartoon: www.funnytimes.com

Subsection 1.2 photo (crying baby): Microsoft Corporation

Subsection 1.2 photo (frozen fruit): Eskymaks / www.shutterstock.com

Subsection 1.2 figure (spraying against malaria), taken from: www.flickr.com/photos/field_museum_library/3608428064/sizes/o/in/photostream/

Subsection 1.3 photo (tea tasting): Janet Leigh / http://www.flickr.com/photos/eastleighnet/8952234371/sizes/o/in/photostream/

Subsection 1.3 photo (Karl Popper), taken from: http://ciudadves.blogspot.co.uk/2011/07/la-falsabilidad-de-karl-popper.html#!/2011/07/la-falsabilidad-de-karl-popper.html

Subsection 3.2 cartoon (null hypothesis): www.xkcd.com. This file is licensed under the Creative Commons Attribution-Noncommercial Licence http://creativecommons.org/licenses/by-nc/3.0/

Subsection 3.3 photo (tea tasting, *t*-test): Thunderbolt / www.flickr.com/photos/darjeelingteas/7221569558/sizes/l/in/photostream/. This file is licensed under the Creative Commons Attribution-Noncommercial-NoDerivatives Licence http://creativecommons.org/licenses/by-nc-nd/3.0/

Subsection 3.3 photo (*Lupinus hartwegii*): Miya.m / http://commons.wikimedia.org/ wiki/File:Lupinus_in_Hokkaido_20080630.jpg. This file is licensed under the Creative Commons Attribution-Share Alike Licence http://creativecommons.org/licenses/by-sa/3.0/

Exercises on Section 3, photo taken from: http://toronto.architectureforhumanity.org/events/2671

Subsection 4.2 cartoon (an unmatched pair): www.cartoonstock.com

Section 6 cartoon (multiple choice): www.cartoonstock.com

Section 6 photo (scoreboard): Hamish Blair / Getty Images

Every effort has been made to contact copyright holders. If any have been inadvertently overlooked the publishers will be pleased to make the necessary arrangements at the first opportunity.

Unit 11
Testing new drugs

Introduction

Curiosity is one of the most striking features of human behaviour. People are constantly meddling with things, taking them to pieces, trying to find out how they work, and seeing what happens when they are altered. This curiosity has proved to be immensely fruitful, for on it depends much of present-day scientific and technological knowledge. Human beings experiment: they actively interfere with their surrounding world, and as a result they learn about its properties and learn to manipulate it to their own ends. It is the theme of experimentation that forms the subject matter of this unit.

The focus in this unit is on one particular aspect of medicine: drug-testing. This is one of the most important areas in which scientific experimentation has been applied. Experiments were discussed quite generally in Unit 10 and, as in that unit, in parts we will concentrate on collecting data (stage 2 of the statistical modelling diagram). However, we shall also use techniques and concepts from earlier units to analyse the data, and we will see that the method of analysis to be used must be taken into account when an experiment is being planned. In drug-testing, and in the whole of scientific experimentation, statistics play a very important role. It is this role that is described in this unit. Also, since an experiment is performed to answer specific questions about the real world, its results must be interpreted in terms of what they say about that world. So this unit also provides further examples of how the statistical ideas you have learnt in M140 fit into the process of making decisions in the real world.

2. Collect

Hundreds of new drugs are put on the market every year. Their manufacturers usually claim that the new product is better than existing ones, either because it is more effective or because it has fewer side effects. But how does a manufacturer discover what the effects of a new drug really are? With the health of thousands or millions of potential consumers at stake, there is certainly no room for serious mistakes. This means that each new drug has to be thoroughly tested, both to ensure that it does have the desired effect, and also to ensure that it does not have undesired side effects. Drug manufacturers therefore have to carry out numerous experiments in which they test the effects of new drugs, usually first on animals, or on tissues taken from animals, and then on human beings. After each stage in the drug-testing procedure, they have to decide whether to continue with the next stage, or whether to reject the new drug. The nature of their decision will be determined in part by the statistical information that they receive about the effects of the drug, as revealed by the tests they have conducted. Examples of questions that a drug manufacturer may ask are as follows.

1. Clarify

What is the average effect of the new drug on, say, body weight?

How variable is this effect?

How does the effect compare with that of other well-known and well-tested drugs?

Of course, many other factors will also be taken into account in deciding whether to continue with further stages of testing: for example, the cost involved, the seriousness and prevalence of the medical conditions for which the drug might be used, and the availability of existing alternatives.

Statistical information has a role in making practical decisions in various aspects of everyday life. Almost always, as in drug-testing, statistical information is just one among many factors that have to be taken into account when coming to a decision. You will see how the relative importance of statistical and other sources of information should be assessed in decision-making. This unit is concerned with the practical side of statistics and decision-making, but in a rather narrow fashion. If a drug company (and the public) is to have any confidence in the data that emerges from the tests it has carried out on a new drug, then those tests must be carried out according to certain rules. If these rules are not observed, then the results of the tests could easily be worthless. We shall describe these rules in some detail.

Much of this unit is devoted to a detailed discussion of the principles of drug-testing but, before this, in Section 1 we outline the various stages of testing a new drug and getting it licensed for use. This first section provides only background information, so you do not have to remember its details, nor will it be assessed, but you may wish to refer back to it when studying the rest of the unit. Section 2 describes the principles and methods used in *clinical trials*, which are one of the important methods of testing drugs on human patients. Then Section 3 looks in detail at the design of some clinical trials. This leads naturally to the analysis of the data obtained from such trials, and Section 4 shows the close relationship between this analysis and the design of the trial. We then consider, in Section 5, some of the limitations of clinical trials and the further work that needs to be undertaken to ensure that the drugs which are marketed are as beneficial as possible to society. In Section 6, the whole process of testing and launching a new drug is illustrated by a case study. Finally, Section 7 directs you to the Computer Book.

This unit, unlike the others in M140, contains many references to its sources of information in 'Harvard style'. This means that the full reference is in a separate References section towards the end of the unit, with only a brief mention such as '(Christiansen, 2006)' or 'SMC (2008)' in the main unit text. You are *not* expected to follow up the detailed reference, but the information is there if you wish to.

1 Drug research and testing

Section 1 is for background information only and will not be assessed.

A new drug goes through a long series of tests on animals and human beings before it can be put on the market. The first stage is screening. Large numbers of chemical compounds are synthesised in the laboratories of drug companies, and it is necessary to identify those which have properties that are likely to be of interest.

Tests are devised which, it is hoped, will predict whether each compound has the desired features. The tests may use bacteria grown in cultures in the laboratory, cells or other material taken from animals or humans, or they may be tests on animals. In view of the large numbers of compounds involved, these tests must be relatively quick and easy to perform. Many compounds are rejected at this stage, but the performance of some indicates that they merit further investigation.

Screening is followed by a much fuller series of tests on those compounds that seem to be of interest. Many aspects of the action of the drug will be looked at. Most drugs have both desirable and undesirable (or toxic) effects. Tests at this stage will indicate both the size of dose of the drug needed to produce the desirable effects and the size of dose that produces the toxic effects. There will also be tests of the possibility that the compound may cause cancer or birth defects.

1.1   The phases of drug-testing

If the drug seems to have desirable effects, if toxic actions are only found at doses much higher than those required to produce these desirable effects, and if there is no tendency to cause cancer or defective offspring, then tests in human beings may be started. Conventionally, the tests on human beings are divided into four phases.

Phase 1: Early clinical pharmacology

The first people to take the drug will normally be healthy volunteers rather than patients, and be closely monitored 24 hours a day within a clinic. The drug will initially be given in single doses that are smaller than those expected to be effective. The biological action and safety of the drug will be evaluated, before the dose is gradually increased. In some of these studies, the amount of the drug in the bloodstream or urine will be measured, so that the rate of absorption of the drug, and its rate of elimination from the body, can be assessed. Later on, studies will be carried out in which the volunteers take the drug repeatedly over a period of time.

Phase 2: Early clinical investigations

These are usually the first studies involving patients with the condition the drug is intended to treat. The aims here are as follows: to get an idea of the best dose to use; and to study the efficacy of the drug – that is, its ability to have the effects it is designed to produce. It may be that particular symptoms of the disease respond well to the drug, or that a certain type of patient responds better than others. Thus this phase is largely concerned with forming hypotheses about the action of the drug.

Phase 3: Comparative studies

In this phase the hypotheses formed in phase 2 are tested. To do this, comparative studies, called **clinical trials**, are needed. Treatment with the new drug is compared with existing therapy or, sometimes, with no treatment. A series of different dosages and dosage schedules (i.e. how often the drug is taken) are compared. A wider variety of patients will also be treated, including, for example, elderly patients and those suffering from more than one disease. This phase completes the work necessary to register the drug (i.e. to obtain permission to market it).

Phase 4: Post-marketing studies

This phase includes studies to provide further evidence about the safety of the drug. These use a larger sample of patients than can be obtained before marketing. It also includes various market research studies.

Although both scientific experiments and statistical analysis are important during each of these four phases, they are particularly well illustrated in clinical trials carried out during phase 3 (and sometimes phase 2). This unit therefore concentrates on these clinical trials.

1.2   The licensing of a new drug

EUROPEAN MEDICINES AGENCY
SCIENCE MEDICINES HEALTH

All medicines, whether available only on prescription or freely over-the-counter, must be licensed. A Europe-wide licence may be granted by the European Commission after evaluation, by the Committee for Medicinal Products for Human Use (CHMP) or another specialist committee within the European Medicines Agency (EMA). The CHMP is composed of one member from each EU country, all of whom are specialists in the field (including physicians, pharmacists, pharmacologists and toxicologists). The CHMP advises on whether a new drug should be licensed, basing its decisions on scientific criteria that determine whether new medicines meet safety, efficacy and quality requirements evidenced by clinical trial results. For each drug that is granted authorisation for a licence, the CHMP publishes a European public assessment report. This provides details of the assessment process and states the grounds on which the committee recommended authorisation. It also gives a summary of the product characteristics, the product's labelling, and the patient information leaflet.

The EMA is concerned not only with applications to market new drugs and to use old drugs for new purposes. It also has an important role in the monitoring of drugs that are already on the market. From time to time a doctor will come across a complaint, an illness or perhaps a death which he suspects may be caused by a drug. There is a Europe-wide database,

EudraVigilance, where reports of adverse drug reactions are held. These reports are carefully monitored, and where necessary, the EMA advises the European Commission to change a medicine's licence. These methods of gathering information about the unwanted effects of drugs are discussed in more detail in Section 5.

Once a drug has been launched, doctors are allowed to prescribe it to patients who meet the criteria of the licence. However, for prescribing in Britain under the National Health Service (NHS), a treatment for a specific condition must be approved by the National Institute for Health and Care Excellence (NICE) in England, Wales and Northern Ireland or the Scottish Medicines Consortium (SMC) in Scotland before doctors are freely allowed to prescribe it. These bodies evaluate the cost-effectiveness and efficacy of treatments to provide approval and guidance of their use under the NHS.

Example 1   *NICE and sorafenib*

The drug sorafenib (marketed as Nexavar), used in the treatment of liver and kidney cancers, was licensed by the European Commission in 2006. The licence was approved on evidence from two phase 3 clinical trials (EMA, 2007a and 2007b) comparing sorafenib with treatment containing no medication. The first trial involved 602 liver cancer patients. The second trial involved 903 kidney cancer patients in whom previous cancer treatment had stopped working. Sorafenib was shown to increase the length of time patients survived in both trials by an average of 2.8 and 3.4 months respectively. The drug was found to have several unwanted side effects, but the benefit to patient survival was considered to outweigh the risks.

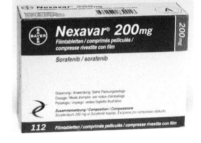

Sorafenib is a very expensive treatment. The cost of treatment is not a consideration in the drug licensing approval process. However, when the drug was evaluated by NICE (2009, 2010) and SMC (2008), it was not found to be cost-effective, so sorafenib was not approved for prescribing under the NHS.

2   Clinical trials

In this section, we shall discuss in some detail the experiments that need to be conducted to test drugs. As already mentioned, such experiments are called clinical trials. First we shall describe one of the first-ever clinical trials, carried out in 1747 by a physician serving in the Royal Navy, James Lind (1716–1794).

James Lind (1716–1794)

Example 2   *James Lind's scurvy experiment*

James Lind (see Lind, 1753) carried out an experiment to test various treatments for scurvy, a disease now known to result from vitamin C deficiency. Scurvy patients develop spots, spongy gums, weak knees and generally feel unwell. As scurvy advances, patients may develop open wounds with pus, jaundice, fever and loss of teeth, and eventually die. Scurvy was once common among sailors on board ships away at sea for periods longer than it was possible to store most fresh fruit and vegetables, and it resulted in many deaths.

On 20 May 1747, James Lind was the surgeon on board the HMS Salisbury patrolling the Bay of Biscay. At the time, the cause of scurvy was unknown, but Lind had reviewed the available literature on scurvy to learn as much as he could. Lind took 12 patients with scurvy, as similar as possible, all with 'putrid gums, the spots and lassitude and weakness of their knees'. They were fed the same general diet, but this was supplemented with an additional treatment:

- two were given a quart of cider daily
- two were given 25 drops of elixir of vitriol (sulfuric acid) three times per day
- two were given two spoonfuls of vinegar three times per day
- two were given half a pint of sea-water daily
- two were given two oranges and one lemon
- two were given bigness of a nutmeg (a spicy paste) three times per day.

Lind observed 'most sudden and visible good effects' on the two patients given oranges and lemons; both were fit for duty at the end of six days.

2.1 Drug-testing by experiment

At first sight, nothing would seem simpler than testing the effects of a drug. Simply give a person suffering from the relevant disease a dose of the drug, and see what happens. There are many reasons – some obvious, others quite subtle – why such a simple procedure might not work. To discover some of these reasons, the following activities consider the use of aspirin to treat headaches.

Activity 1   *Was it the aspirins?*

Suppose that you have a headache, and take two aspirins. An hour later the headache has gone. What do you conclude about the effectiveness of aspirin as a pain-killer?

Activity 2   *Any better?*

Suppose that you took a group of 20 people, all with headaches, and gave them each two aspirin. An hour later, 16 of them said they had no headache. What do you now say about the effectiveness of aspirin as a pain-killer?

Even without treatment, headaches will often go away after a while. To gain a better idea of whether aspirin helps headaches go away in the above type of test, you need another group of people with headaches who do not take aspirin. You can then compare the recovery rate of those who take aspirin with the recovery rate of those who do not.

Such a comparison, between a group that does undergo some form of treatment and a group that does not, is fundamental to drug-testing. It is also fundamental to many other kinds of scientific investigation, as you have already seen in Unit 10. Such a comparison is an experiment. In such an experiment, the group that receives the experimental treatment is referred to as the **experimental group**, and the group that does not receive the experimental treatment is referred to as the **control group**.

In an ideal experiment, the experimental group and the control group resemble each other in every respect except for the one being tested. If this ideal were achieved for the aspirin experiment, and you found that all of the experimental group (the aspirin-tested people) recovered from their headaches within an hour, whereas none of the control group did, then you could be virtually certain (barring an extraordinary fluke) that the aspirin had really cured the headaches.

However, it is by no means an easy task to make sure that the experimental and control groups resemble each other in every respect apart from the one being tested.

Activity 3   *Using a control group*

Consider an experimental group of headache sufferers who have been given aspirin, and a control group who have not. How do the two groups differ other than in the presence or absence of the drug in the body?

'I couldn't afford a control group so I decided to go with an out-of-control group.'

> Treating a patient can quite commonly appear to have a therapeutic effect (or can *actually* have a therapeutic effect), even when the treatment contains no medication and should be ineffectual. This is called the **placebo effect**.

People have all sorts of expectations about medicines that they receive from the doctor, as well as about other types of treatment. These are derived from their own past experiences, from the attitudes of their friends and family, and also from the attitude and expectations of the doctor.

These attitudes can have an important influence on the outcome of treatment. This is by no means confined to neurotic or suggestible people, or to hypochondriacs. Placebo effects, as you might expect, tend to be most noticeable in mild conditions, but they cannot be neglected, even in quite severe conditions. Diabetes and asthma, for example, have both been shown to be sensitive to such effects.

Activity 4   Controlling for the placebo effect

How can the placebo effect be overcome in the experiment on aspirin in Activity 3?

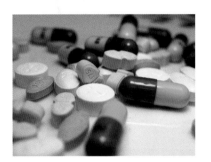

> A dummy treatment that superficially resembles the treatment being tested but contains no active ingredient is called a **placebo**.

A clinical trial (i.e. experiment) in which the control group takes a placebo is called a **placebo-controlled trial**. There is one ethical problem with placebo-controlled trials: patients go to their doctors to get treatment, not dummies. If you assume that the patients agree to take part in a drug-testing experiment, you may be able to think of circumstances where there would be no ethical problem in using a placebo as a control. Three such circumstances spring to mind:

- Where no effective treatment exists for the disease in question.
- Where the condition is mild.
- Where the new treatment is an addition to an existing treatment so that the comparison is between old treatment plus placebo and old treatment plus new treatment.

Placebo-controlled trial

In a placebo-controlled trial, there is a treatment group and a control group. People in the treatment group receive the treatment being tested, while those in the control group are given a placebo.

In the case of a serious, or fairly serious illness, where an effective treatment already exists, there would obviously be no justification for leaving a person untreated. What should be done in such a case? The answer is that the existing treatment rather than a placebo should be given to the control group.

Such questions are, of course, ethical and they can be answered only by taking up a particular ethical position. The position implied in the answers given above is that it is necessary to do the following:

- Minimise the possibilities of causing harm and lack of benefit to a person from a clinical trial.

- Maximise the knowledge gained about the effectiveness and risks of the drugs.
- Make sure that the person being treated knows what is happening and agrees to take part in the trial (this is called **informed consent**).

Some examples will illustrate these issues more clearly.

Example 3 *Smoking cessation therapies*

There have been many trials of smoking cessation therapies (treatments to help people stop smoking) that are placebo-controlled. Many smokers quit without treatment, and some study participants may be more likely to quit because they expect the new therapy to help. It has been argued that placebo-controlled trials are unethical because quitting smoking is an important change that improves health, and several well-accepted therapies have been shown to increase cessation rates. Others argue that most people in the control group would not take any therapy to help them stop smoking if they were not in the study, and a placebo effect could help them quit smoking.

Example 4 *Common cold*

The common cold is incurable in the sense that no known drug can kill the viruses that cause it. On the other hand, drugs are available that can alleviate the symptoms (such as sneezing, headache, watering eyes, blocked nose). If a drug company develops a new drug that they think will kill the virus, then they would want to test it on an experimental group of people with colds, and to use as a control group people who had colds but were not taking any existing drugs that relieve the symptoms. In this way they could clearly distinguish the effects of the new drug and would not feel too unhappy about asking the control group to suffer their colds without treatment.

Activity 5 *Placebo for scurvy*

Would it have been ethical for James Lind to include a placebo group in his experiment on scurvy patients?

2.2 Measurement

You may remember that in Subsection 2.1, to assess the effectiveness of aspirin, we suggested that people should be asked whether or not they still had a headache one hour after taking two aspirin or two placebos.

Activity 6   *A good question?*

Suppose you are designing a placebo-controlled trial to test aspirin's effectiveness at reducing headaches. For comparing the treatments, what problems might there be in asking each subject if the headache is still present one hour after taking the tablets?

'This doesn't look good. I'm afraid you've developed an immunity to placebos.'

As noted in the solution to Activity 6, there are a number of ways that aspirin and a placebo might differ, both with regard to changes in the severity of the headache and the time the headache lasts. Some of these differences would be missed by asking a single yes/no question of the form 'Did you still have a headache an hour after taking the tablets?'.

To get round this problem, you might ask the people to rate their headache on a scale such as this:

- 0 – None. No headache.
- 1 – Mild. The headache is there but it does not bother me much.
- 2 – Moderate. The headache is definitely a nuisance.
- 3 – Severe. The headache is so bad that I can hardly think of anything else.

You could ask them to rate their headaches on this scale before taking aspirin, and then every 15 minutes over a period of, say, 4 hours.

What is the purpose of taking a rating before treatment? This is done because the aspirin might improve a headache without completely curing it, and this would still be better than nothing. It is possible to judge improvement only if you know how bad the headache is to start with.

Activity 7   Is a subjective scale OK?

Judging the severity of a headache is not easy. The measure is, by its
nature, subjective. People do not find it easy to assess their own
discomfort very accurately, or reliably. Does this matter?

Although many symptoms, like pain, must be assessed subjectively, others
are amenable to quantitative and, relatively speaking, more objective
measurement. Your doctor can, for example, measure your blood pressure
or your pulse-rate and express these measurements in widely understood
quantitative terms (units of pressure or beats per minute). If you receive
some form of treatment that alters your blood pressure or pulse-rate, then
these changes can also be expressed in quantitative terms. Measurements
such as these are **objective measurements**, in contrast to the
subjective measurements mentioned earlier.

'Objective' is, of course, a relative term. Different doctors using exactly the
same equipment on the same patient might well obtain slightly different
values of the quantity they are measuring, simply because they use the
equipment in slightly different ways. Different doctors using different
pieces of equipment would be still more variable in the measurements they
produced. Although objective measurements are more cut-and-dried than
subjective measurements, this does not mean that they possess absolute
accuracy, nor that they are necessarily, under all circumstances, of greater
value to the doctor than subjective measurements. Nor does it mean that
objective measurements are free from placebo effects. Objective
measurements can be just as susceptible to placebo effects as subjective
ones. You are probably aware that if you are anxious your heart rate (the
number of beats per minute of the heart) is likely to go up, as is your
blood pressure. The outcome of objective measurements can be influenced
by the expectations and attitudes of the patient to treatment almost as
much as can subjective measurements. Therefore, whether the effectiveness
of the treatment is measured objectively or subjectively, it is important
that the clinical trial be properly designed using a control group.

Activity 8   Beta-blocker and placebo

Suppose that a research laboratory is setting up a clinical trial of the
effect of a beta-blocker on blood pressure. One group of people takes the
beta-blocker tablet, whilst the other group takes a dummy tablet (a
placebo). Does it matter if the people know which kind of tablet they are
taking?

A clinical trial in which individuals do not know whether they are taking
the drug or the placebo, is called a **blind trial**.

Activity 9 *Should the doctor know who gets the placebo?*

For the clinical trial in Activity 8, what about the doctors who are giving the treatment to the patient: does it matter if they know which people receive which treatment?

If the doctors in a research laboratory are comparing two treatments, then they may also have expectations. They may be actively involved in the research project and be enthusiastic about one of the treatments. Such enthusiasm can be conveyed to the patients and change their expectations. Or a doctor might be sceptical about one of the treatments. This too can be conveyed to the patients and affect the outcome of the trial. (We shall use *trial* as short for *clinical trial* throughout this unit now.)

As well as such direct effects on the patients, there are effects caused by the doctors' involvement in assessing the outcome, i.e. their attitudes may affect their assessment of the outcome. They may, for example, tend to assess the patients on a new drug as doing better than those on a placebo; or, because they are aware of this possibility, they may bend over backwards to be fair, over-compensate, and so assess the patients on a placebo as better. Each of these effects will tend to shift the results in a particular direction (but they may partially cancel each other out). Such effects are examples of **bias**.

Activity 10 *Bias in James Lind's scurvy experiment*

When James Lind conducted his experiment on scurvy patients, his two worst patients 'with tendons in the ham rigid (a symptom none of the rest had)' were given a half pint of sea-water daily as their treatment. There were only two patients assigned to each of six treatments. How might this have biased his results on the sea-water treatment in a particular direction?

The doctors who give the treatment should therefore also be ignorant of the nature of the treatment being given. (This may be difficult to achieve in practice, especially if the patient's reactions to the drug are obvious to the doctor.)

A trial where neither patients nor doctors know which treatment is administered, is called a **double-blind trial**. A study in which the patient is blind but the doctor is not, or vice versa, is sometimes called a **single-blind trial**.

As far as is possible, all controlled clinical trials are double-blind trials. You may wonder how anybody knows which kind of tablet a patient is receiving in a double-blind trial. Usually a third party, such as a pharmacist who is independent of the doctors and patients, keeps a record of which tablets have been administered by which doctors to which patients.

Her attempt to stay blinded
was ruined by the sign-building
side-effect of the treatment.

As we have already said, James Lind's 1747 experiment is credited as being the first-ever clinical trial. According to Bhatt (2010), the first double-blind clinical trial was not carried out until 1943. The trial investigated a treatment for the common cold.

Activity 11   *Blinding in James Lind's scurvy experiment*

In James Lind's 1747 experiment on scurvy, all patients were kept in the same space. James Lind hand picked his 12 patients, assigned their treatments and assessed their outcome. Though conditions on board a ship would have been difficult, how might it have been possible to achieve blinding in this experiment?

All of the problems discussed so far in connection with the aspirin experiment relate to the question:

How can you make a correct assessment of the effect of a drug on an individual?

This may seem at first to have little to do with statistics, but, as we shall shortly explain, statistics play an important part in helping doctors to analyse the results of clinical trials. Moreover, the kind of statistical analysis that is best suited to a particular experiment depends very much on the kind of control group that is used, on whether the doctor has taken objective or subjective measurements, and on other similar factors.

Such factors (the nature of the control group, the kinds of measurement, etc.) are known collectively as the **design of the experiment**. One of the main purposes of this unit is to show that the design of an experiment and its statistical analysis go hand-in-hand. Before coming to this, however, one other major feature of drug-testing experiments has to be discussed: the variability of the people to whom the tests are administered.

You have now covered the material related to Screencast 1 for Unit 11 (see the M140 website).

2.3 Variability

Clinical trials need both experimental and control groups of people. But how many people are needed in each group to assess the effect of a drug?

Activity 12   *An unsatisfactory experiment*

Suppose that two people suffering from headaches were available and you gave one of them aspirin and the other placebos. Why would this be an unsatisfactory experiment?

Another unsatisfactory experiment

Three sources of variability are readily distinguished.

- Variability in the disease itself.

- Variability in the response: even when patients are suffering from a similar severity of disease, their response to the drug may vary.

- Inaccuracy in the method of measurement: as we saw in Subsection 2.2, subjective measurements of sensations like pain are necessarily imprecise, and even objective measurements are limited in their accuracy by imperfections in the measuring instruments and in the people who operate them.

The relative importance of these factors will differ from trial to trial, but the total variability will very often be substantial compared to the effect of the drug itself. To illustrate this problem, we look at an example of blood glucose measurements.

Example 5   *Blood glucose*

Blood glucose levels were measured throughout the day in 24 healthy volunteers under controlled conditions in a clinic. All volunteers ate the same breakfast at 7:30, the same lunch at 12:30 and their choice of dinner at 18:00. In this study (Christiansen, 2006), all subjects were monitored by two devices and an average measurement was taken. Figure 1 shows blood glucose measurements from the two separate devices (SCGM 1 and SCGM 2) for one volunteer.

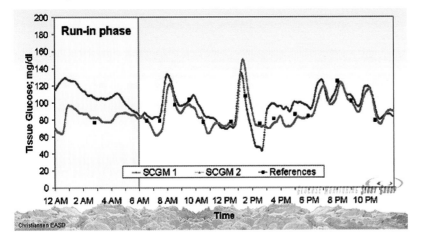

Figure 1   Measurements of blood glucose on two devices

(Source: Christiansen, 2006)

Figure 1 shows variation in measurements between the two different devices, and illustrates that blood glucose peaks after meals. For instance, the blood glucose value after lunch at 12:30 is approximately double its value just before lunch.

Activity 13   *Measuring blood glucose*

Given that the blood glucose level can vary so widely within a single day, what precautions need to be taken when testing the effect of a drug on the blood glucose level?

Where possible in a study, measurements should be taken with all study participants in a similar state, using the same instruments in the same lab. In Figure 2, blood glucose levels for 21 of the volunteers in the study in Example 5 are plotted over a 24-hour period.

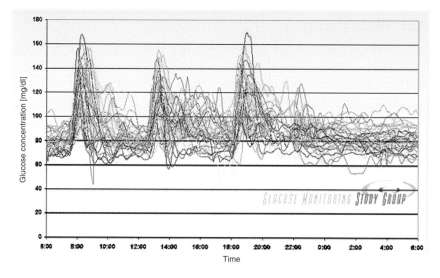

Figure 2   Blood glucose levels of 21 healthy volunteers

(Source: Christiansen, 2006)

It is clear that there is enormous variation in blood glucose levels between these 21 healthy volunteers at the beginning of the day before any food is eaten, and also resulting from the effect of eating food. Thus there is wide variation in 'normal' blood glucose, so in studies of drugs to treat diabetes, researchers must try to decipher differences between drugs from variation between study participants.

Often there are known reasons for differences in the physiology between individuals: for example, height. Factors known to influence an adult's height include sex, ethnicity and nationality, and health and nutrition during development. These factors are called **sources of variation**, and when recorded, can be used to explain variation to some extent.

A jazz band improvising: another source of variation

Example 6 *Heart rates*

Consider a trial to assess the effect of a drug on a person's heart rate. Like blood glucose, heart rates vary throughout the day. Although there are other sources of variation in heart rate, the main source of this variation is physical activity. Consequently, it is important that measurements on study participants should be taken at comparable levels of activity.

Interest often focuses on maximum heart rate, even though this is often estimated rather than measured directly. Measuring the maximum rate can be a lengthy and difficult procedure and, moreover, it can be dangerous to subject elderly people with weak hearts to the strenuous exercise required. The estimates are made by measuring heart rate under mild exercise and using the result to predict what the maximum would be. Figure 3 shows the mean maximum heart rate of men and women at different ages.

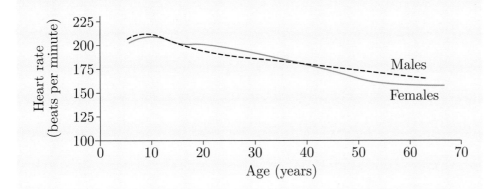

Figure 3 Mean maximum heart rates of men and women at different ages

(Source: Åstrand and Christensen, 1964)

Activity 14 *Factors to control?*

If you wished to reduce the variability in the heart rate of study participants, would it be advisable to ensure that the experimental and control groups were of the same sex, or of the same age, or both?

Figure 3 shows the *mean* maximum heart rate for men and women of *various* ages, but it does not show the *spread* of the maximum heart rates of people of the *same* age. Individuals differ quite widely in their maximum heart rate: individuals of the same age undertaking a similar activity can have somewhat different heart rates. (Heart rate increases with physical activity.)

At each of the ages covered by Figure 3, the population standard deviation of maximum heart rate is about 10 beats per minute. This is a measure of the natural variation in heart rate between people. It is against the background of this natural variation that the effect of any drug on heart rate must be judged. Suppose that a new drug reduced the maximum heart rate, on average, by 3 beats per minute. The drug would have to be tested on a very large sample of people before an effect as small as this could be distinguished from the natural variation in heart rate between people.

Example 7   *Propranolol and heart rate*

Beta-blockers are a group of drugs primarily used in the treatment of high blood pressure, angina pectoris and some other conditions of the heart and the blood's circulatory system. Figure 4 shows how heart rate is affected by one beta-blocker, propranolol.

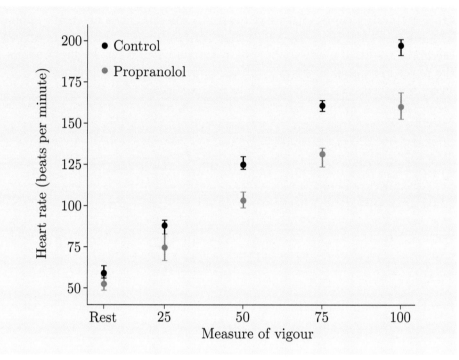

Figure 4   The effect of propranolol on heart rate

(Source: Ekblom et al., 1972)

The effect varies according to the vigour of people's activity. Each orange dot denotes the mean of the heart rates of four people when they were given propranolol. Each black dot denotes the mean of the heart rates of the same four people when they received no drug. The vertical line through each dot denotes the spread of those four measurements.

When the subjects (people) are resting, the effect of the drug is hardly detectable: the mean of the heart rates of the subjects after they have received the drug is slightly lower than that for the same subjects when they have not, but the spreads of the individual heart rates (indicated by the vertical line through each data point) is large enough to mask this effect. When the subjects are undertaking more vigorous activity, the effect of the drug becomes much more noticeable and, when they are engaged in extremely vigorous activity, the difference is very large and could easily be detected despite the spread of the individual heart rates also being larger than when the subjects are at rest.

Propranolol

Propranolol was the first successful beta-blocker developed. In 1988, Sir James Black (1924–2010) was awarded the Nobel Prize in Medicine for its discovery. Newer beta-blockers are now used to treat high blood pressure, but propranolol is still used to treat other conditions.

Variability is the main reason why experimenters need to use statistics. Drug companies do not just want to know what happens to those patients who take a new drug in one particular clinical trial. They want to know the effect their drug would have on a much wider population: for example, the population of all people in the UK who might, now or in the future, suffer from a particular disease. They cannot test the drug on all the members of this population (some of them might not even have the disease yet!), so the drug is tested on a sample of people from the population, and the experimenters must make an inference from the results for this sample back to the population.

If people did not vary at all, then the experimenters could find out all they needed to know by trying out their drug on just one person. They would have no need for statistics: a situation that, no doubt, they would greatly welcome! However, people vary greatly, and small effects are often important in medical contexts, so the need for statistics in drug-testing is paramount.

Exercises on Section 2

Exercise 1   *Measurement scale*

Which of the following features can be measured only on a subjective scale and which can be measured on an objective scale?

(a) Weight loss.

(b) Appetite.

(c) Sore throat.

(d) Indigestion.

Exercise 2 *Controlling factors in a double-blind trial*

Several volunteers agree to take part in a clinical trial of a new drug which, it is hoped, will relieve depression. The volunteers are divided into two groups whose compositions in terms of age and sex are as similar as possible. Double-blind trials of the drug are carried out.

(a) What sources of variability between the experimental and control groups might not have been controlled by this procedure?

(b) Why might it not be justifiable to expect that the results obtained from this clinical trial would apply to all people suffering from depression?

(c) How might some of the problems that you have identified in parts (a) and (b) be overcome?

Exercise 3 *Sources of bias?*

In a large-scale clinical trial of a new anti-depression drug, several experimenters assess the drug's effect on patients by interviewing them. Each experimenter uses a standardised questionnaire to assess the severity of a patient's symptoms. What sources of bias in assessing the effect of the drug might there be in such a trial?

3 Design of clinical trials

2. Collect

Now that you have been introduced to some of the fundamental problems in designing and carrying out clinical trials (and other experiments), it is possible to go further and look at certain aspects of their design in more detail. Briefly, the two main requirements for a well-designed clinical trial are as follows.

• It must eliminate all known forms of bias as far as possible.

• It must be as sensitive as possible – that is, it must, without requiring a large number of patients or a large amount of time, have a good chance of accurately detecting any difference between the treatments being tested despite the variability of patients.

3.1 Crossover design

A simple way of eliminating a great deal of the variability in a trial is to give each person taking part both treatments. In this way, individuals act as their own controls. This procedure eliminates a lot of the variability that arises when different individuals act as experimental and control subjects. As an example, suppose that doctors wish to compare the effect of a beta-blocker with that of a placebo on blood pressure over a short period (e.g. two months). They could give each patient the placebo for eight weeks and then give them the active drug for eight weeks, measuring each patient's blood pressure before they started and during the two treatment periods. Of course, they would want to eliminate the possibility of a placebo effect that was greater at the beginning than at the end of treatment, so they would give half of the patients the placebo first, followed by the active treatment, whereas the other half would get the active treatment first followed by the placebo (see Figure 5). A similar design could be used to compare two different beta-blockers (see Figure 6). This kind of design is called a **crossover trial**. (Strictly speaking, it is a *two-period crossover trial*.) A crossover trial is thus one in which, during the course of the experiment, each subject crosses over from receiving one treatment to receiving the other, or vice versa.

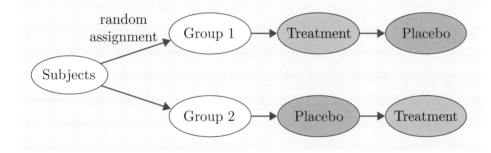

Figure 5   Crossover trial to compare a beta-blocker with a placebo

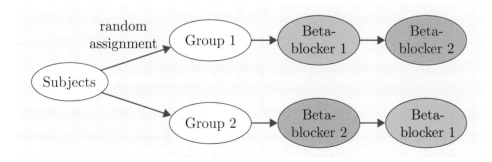

Figure 6   Crossover trial to compare two beta-blockers

Activity 15 *Unusual assumption of a crossover trial*

What unusual assumption is made in the crossover trial design? Write down one case where this assumption is not valid.

If doctors were comparing two antibiotics to treat a bacterial infection, then there would be no point in using a crossover trial because they would expect their patients, or at least some of them, to be cured by the treatment. Therefore the group of patients entering the second period, after receiving antibiotics in the first, will not be in the same condition as when they started the first period. Besides curing the patient, any effect of the drug that tends to last beyond the treatment (that is, any **carry-over effect**) will confuse the issue, so that drugs should usually be given for some time before measurements are made.

Thus the crossover design is most suited to **chronic conditions** (conditions that are relatively long-lasting) such as high blood pressure, diabetes or arthritis, and is not well suited to conditions which are given to spontaneous ups and downs. Consequently the crossover trial is of rather limited application but, when it is suitable, in many cases it is the best design to use.

Activity 16 *Can a crossover design be used?*

State whether a crossover design would be appropriate for the following trials.

(a) Type 1 diabetes is a chronic condition in which patients have high blood sugar. It cannot be cured but it can be controlled by giving insulin. However, insulin can cause hypoglycaemia, where blood sugar becomes too low. A trial is to be set up to compare two different regimens of insulin administration to control type 1 diabetes in patients. The outcome measurement is the number of hypoglycaemic episodes.

(b) A trial on scurvy and two diet supplements, similar to James Lind's experiment. Scurvy can be cured if vitamin C is included in the diet, but without this, scurvy will eventually result in death. The main outcome measurements are whether or not a patient is cured and the time it takes to be cured.

You have now covered the material related to Screencast 2 for Unit 11 (see the M140 website).

3.2 Matched-pairs design

Even if it is impossible to give both treatments to each individual, it is often possible to pair individuals into *matched pairs* by identifying particular features of the individuals or of the disease from which they are suffering, that are likely to be important to the outcome of any treatment. The doctors can then give one treatment to one member of the pair and the other treatment to the other member (see Figure 7).

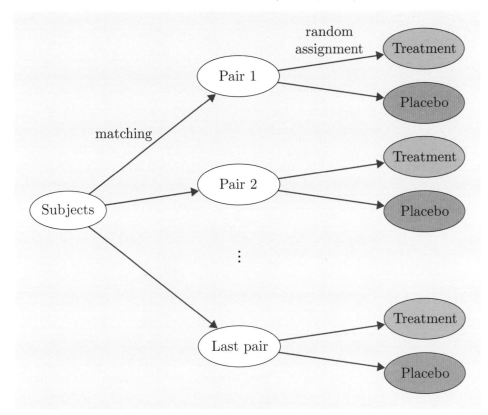

Figure 7 Matched-pairs design with a placebo

A trial that is designed in this way is called a **matched-pairs trial**. Examples of factors that might be matched are age, sex, severity of illness, length of time the patient has suffered from the illness, and the presence of other illnesses. Such a trial can be very useful but again has serious limitations. If a doctor finds an elderly lady suffering from a mild illness of one year's duration, can another be found with whom to match her? How long will the doctor have to wait until a suitable match is found? Another problem is whether there is enough information about which factors really do affect the outcome of a treatment. If it does not matter whether the patient is a man or a woman, then there is no point in matching patients by sex. If, on the other hand, people of different blood groups respond differently to the treatment, then failure to match patients by blood group would reduce the usefulness of the clinical trial.

Twins make ideal matched pairs

A matched-pairs trial is more appropriate for fairly common, long-lasting disease for which special clinics exist, or lists of patients are available. Examples are diabetes and asthma. In this case, the patients can be selected and matched (i.e. paired) before the trial starts. In diseases where patients turn up and need to be treated more or less at once, a matched-pairs trial is harder to organise.

Activity 17 *Organising matched pairs*

Organise the following eight patients into matched pairs. Match using the following order of importance: sex, smoking status, age.

1.   Male, smoker, aged 43,

2.   Female, non-smoker, aged 41,

3.   Male, non-smoker, aged 47,

4.   Female, non-smoker, aged 49,

5.   Male, smoker, aged 44,

6.   Male, smoker, aged 46,

7.   Male, non-smoker, aged 45,

8.   Male, smoker, aged 48.

You have now covered the material related to Screencast 3 for Unit 11 (see the M140 website).

3.3 Group-comparative design

Very often it is not possible to use either a crossover or a matched-pairs trial: the medical condition involved may not be long-lasting (this rules out a crossover trial) and patients cannot be neatly divided into pairs according to factors thought to influence response to treatment (this rules out a matched-pairs trial). There is then little choice but simply to divide the patients into the two groups and to give one treatment to the patients in one group and the other treatment to those in the other (Figure 8). The principle behind this division into groups should be to ensure that each group is *representative* of the population being studied, and that the allocation of treatments to patients is decided at random.

For example, if gender and age were thought to influence a person's response to treatment, then care would be taken so that the control group and the treatment group each contained similar male-to-female ratios and that each group had similar age profiles. Within these restrictions, patients would be allocated to the treatment group or control group at random. This is discussed further in the next subsection and forms the basis of the **group-comparative trial**. It can be used in a very wide variety of situations and it is the most commonly used design of clinical trial.

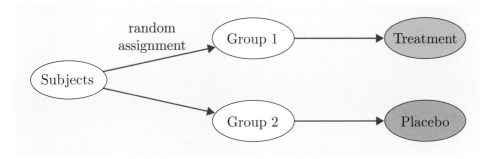

Figure 8 Group comparative design with a placebo

You have now covered the material related to Screencast 4 for Unit 11 (see the M140 website).

3.4 Randomisation

Each of the three designs of trial described in Subsections 3.1 to 3.3 involves an allocation process in which some decision has to be taken concerning the patients involved in the trial. For example:

- In a crossover trial to compare a new drug with a placebo, you need to decide, for each patient, whether they receive the drug first and then the placebo or vice versa.

- In a matched-pairs trial to compare two drugs, after pairing the patients you need to decide, within each pair, which patient is given which drug.

- In a group-comparative trial to test a new drug, you need to decide, for each patient, whether they should be in the experimental group or the control group.

We shall now explain the importance of using random methods in these allocation processes, using a group-comparative design. Similar reasoning can be applied to other designs of clinical trial and similar random methods of allocation can be devised. The use of such random methods is called **randomisation**: it is an important part of the design of clinical trials and of other experiments whose results are to be analysed using statistics.

If individuals with a particular trait are more likely to be selected for the experimental group, while study participants of another kind are more likely to be selected to receive the control, whether this selection is conscious or not, any comparison of the two groups may be biased. This is known as **selection bias**, and the most important reason for randomisation is to eliminate this bias. The process of randomisation may also facilitate *blinding* the identity of treatments to the study investigators and participants. Finally, using random methods to allocate treatments allows the use of probability theory to express how likely it is that any difference in outcome between groups occurred by chance.

As described briefly above, designing a group-comparative trial involves finding a procedure for allocating patients to the two groups. Choosing representative groups is a similar problem to that of choosing a representative sample for a survey (covered in Unit 4). For a survey, the sampling method should produce a sample of the required size. Similarly, it would be bad in a clinical trial if a very large number of the patients ended up in one group and only a few in the other.

Suppose that you wish to test a new drug against an existing drug. Sometimes, when the effects of the control treatment (the existing drug) are particularly well known, experimenters use a control group that is considerably smaller than the experimental group, but, on the whole, it seems reasonable to insist that the numbers of people in the two groups should be approximately equal. One way of achieving this would be to allocate alternate patients to the two groups (experimental and control). This method is similar to systematic random sampling (see Subsection 2.2 of Unit 4) and is sometimes the best method. However, there is a danger that the doctors observing the patients might discover that this method had been used; for example, if the odd-numbered patients did not do so well as the even-numbered patients, or if alternate patients developed a particular side effect. The trial would not then be a double-blind trial.

Activity 18   *Avoiding patterns in treatment allocation*

How could the danger described above, that the doctors observing the patients discover the allocation to the two groups, be reduced?

There are several ways in which a patient could be randomly allocated to the experimental or control group. Perhaps the simplest method is to toss a coin for each subject. If it comes down 'heads', then the patient is allocated to the experimental group; if 'tails', then the patient goes in the control group. In practice, a random number generator on a computer would be used in place of the coin.

In Unit 4 (Subsection 1.3) you saw that random samples tend to be representative. In practice this means that, if the number of patients is large enough, then the use of random numbers to allocate them to experimental and control groups generally results in the two groups being fairly similar in all their features, including features that might not have occurred to the experimenter as being important. For instance, the ratio of males to females will be about the same in the two groups, as will the proportions of people of different ages, etc. However, often it makes sense to build balance into a trial design, and we will briefly explain why this is and how it is done. (You have already seen in Activity 10 (Subsection 2.2) the kind of problem that can occur if there is not balance.)

If a trial is small, there is a risk that the control and treatment groups may have very uneven numbers. One solution to this would be to decide the number of participants in the study beforehand, so the number to be allocated to each group is known and these can be randomly ordered. This would be similar to putting the appropriate number of 'A's and 'B's into a bag and withdrawing the letters to assign the groups.

A trial may be carried out over several different locations, such as different clinics, known as **centres**, or over several time periods, for example, spring admissions and winter admissions. It is preferable to balance numbers assigned to the treatment and control groups within each centre and/or time period. Similarly, the investigators may decide that it is important to balance allocation to groups for other important variables, such as age or disease progression. This is achieved using **stratified randomisation**, with **strata** defined for centre, time period, age or disease progression status as necessary. (Stratified *sampling* was described in Subsection 4.2 of Unit 4.) Each **stratum** is treated as if it has its own separate mini-trial, and randomisation for each stratum is carried out independently. This is only achievable with sufficient numbers of trial participants within each stratum.

The following summarises the three different designs of clinical trial that have been considered in this section.

- The crossover trial. Each person acts as his or her own control: during the course of the trial, each person crosses over from having one treatment to having the other, or vice versa.

- The matched-pairs trial. Each person in one group is matched as closely as possible with a person in the other group.

- The group-comparative trial. People are allocated randomly to two groups, usually in such a way that the two groups contain approximately the same number of people.

The following box summarises their drawbacks and advantages.

- The crossover trial eliminates the variability that would arise from using different people in the experimental and control groups, but it cannot be used when the experimental treatment irreversibly alters a patient's condition, nor is it suited to short-lasting diseases.

- The matched-pairs trial eliminates much of the variability that arises from using different people as experimental and control subjects, but it can be difficult to achieve a good match between the experimental and control groups.

- The group-comparative trial does not eliminate the variability that arises from using different individuals in the experimental and control groups, but it is relatively easy to set up.

Exercises on Section 3

Exercise 4   *What type of trial is being used?*

State which of the three designs of trial is being used in each of the following experiments: a crossover, a matched-pairs or a group-comparative design.

(a) Ten pairs of identical twins are found. The experimenter allocates one of each pair of twins at random to the experimental group and one to the control group. He administers a new drug to the experimental group and a placebo to the control group.

(b) Eighty people suffering from arthritis are divided randomly into two groups. One group receives a new drug, the other a placebo.

(c) Another eighty people suffering from arthritis are divided randomly into two groups. One group receives a new drug for three months and then a placebo for another three months. The other group receives the placebo for three months and then the drug for three months.

Exercise 5   *What type of trial should be used?*

Of the three designs of clinical trial, which would be most appropriate to use in each of the following tests?

(a) To test a drug which alleviates an unpleasant and long-lasting symptom of a disease (e.g. pain) without curing the disease.

(b) To test a drug which improves a condition that is rare and requires immediate treatment.

(c) To test a drug which helps people to give up smoking.

'Your doctor will be here in a minute, I'm a placebo.'

4 Analysing the data

In this section we shall describe the type of analysis commonly used for data from clinical trials like those in the last section. This will include more general points concerning the collection and analysis of data from scientific experiments.

4.1 What analysis?

Imagine that a research laboratory has completed a clinical trial of a new drug. The researchers decided the design for their experiment, selected the patients and used the appropriate random allocation process. They then administered the appropriate treatments (one experimental and one control) to the correct patients at the correct time and measured the effects, i.e. they collected the data. They now want to investigate whether the experimental treatment really differs from the control treatment in its effect on patients. How should they analyse this data?

3. Analyse

It would be appropriate to use hypothesis testing. Units 6–10 described several statistical tests that can be used to investigate whether a hypothesis like this is tenable.

Activity 19   *The null and alternative hypotheses*

Suppose that a drug company wishes to compare the effect of a new drug on headaches with that of an existing drug. In the terminology of Unit 7 (Subsection 1.3), what would be the null hypothesis, and against what alternative hypothesis should the null hypothesis be tested?

Activity 20   *A one- or two-sided test?*

Section 6 of Unit 10 discussed one-sided and two-sided hypothesis tests. Would a one-sided or a two-sided test be more appropriate to test the hypotheses given in Activity 19?

You might have thought that a one-sided test would be appropriate in Activity 20, on the grounds that the drug company would not be interested in testing a drug unless they were fairly certain that it could not be less effective than an existing treatment. However, even if the company do think that, the results of their experiment have to be made available to the European Medicines Agency (EMA) for scrutiny, and the EMA do not wish to rule out the possibility that the new drug is worse than the old by using a one-sided test.

4.2 Hypothesis testing

You have already met several hypothesis tests, and there are many others available. In analysing data from experiments like those described in Section 3, each test does roughly the same job. The experimenter sets up a null hypothesis of no difference (in median or mean) between two populations. The data consist of measurements made on samples from each of the two populations. The outcome of the hypothesis test is that the null hypothesis either *is* or *is not* rejected, on the basis of a test statistic calculated from the observed data from the two samples. Section 4 of Unit 6 and Subsection 1.3 of Unit 10 describe the process of hypothesis testing, which is summarised in Figure 9.

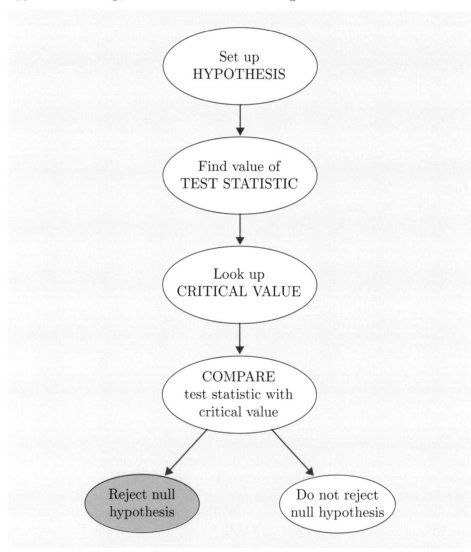

Figure 9 Steps in a hypothesis test

To use a test, the experimenter might decide the significance level, which is the probability of incorrectly rejecting the null hypothesis when it is actually true. Alternatively, the *p*-value (significance probability) given by the test might be used to evaluate the strength of evidence against the null hypothesis.

In the present context, if the clinical trial produces two batches of measurements, one on the effect of the new drug on headache pain and the other on the effect of the existing drug, then a hypothesis test at a given significance level will help to decide whether the two drugs differ in their effects when they are applied to the population from which the samples were chosen.

It is important to remember that what the doctor, scientist, or anyone else decides to do with the result of a hypothesis test is a matter of human judgement, not statistics. One factor influencing this decision should be the significance level of the test, so the user of the test must decide what significance level to use. In science and medicine there is a strong convention of using a 5% significance level, but there is nothing sacred about 5%. There may be occasions when it is sensible to use a different significance level: for example, 1% or (occasionally) 10%.

The following table was given in Section 5 of Unit 6 for the interpretation of p-values. Although the interpretation should inform subsequent decision making, deciding future actions is more complex than simply examining a p-value.

Table 1 Interpretation of p-values

p-value	Rough interpretation
$p > 0.10$	Little evidence against the hypothesis
$0.10 \geq p > 0.05$	Weak evidence against the hypothesis
$0.05 \geq p > 0.01$	Moderate evidence against the hypothesis
$0.01 \geq p > 0.001$	Strong evidence against the hypothesis
$0.001 \geq p$	Very strong evidence against the hypothesis

The critical region is smaller for a hypothesis test at the 1% significance level than at the 5% significance level – if the null hypothesis is rejected at the 1% level then it will also be rejected at the 5% significance level. This has the following obvious consequences. (See Subsection 5.2 of Unit 8, on errors.)

- The probability of a type 1 error is less if a 1% significance level is used, than if a 5% significance level is used; that is, there is a smaller chance of incorrectly rejecting the null hypothesis when it is really true.

- Other things being equal, the probability of a type 2 error will be greater using a 1% significance level than using a 5% significance level; that is, using a 1% significance level you are more likely to accept the null hypothesis when it is really false.

Overall then, a test using a 1% significance level is more cautious about rejecting the null hypothesis than is the same test using a 5% significance level. When deciding the significance level to use in a particular trial design, doctors and other scientists have to take into account all the medical, ethical, social and financial implications of the clinical trials that they are planning and of the decisions that they have to make.

Table 2   Type 1 and type 2 errors

	H_0 true	H_0 false
H_0 not rejected	Correct	Type 2 error
H_0 rejected	Type 1 error	Correct

All the hypothesis tests that were introduced in Units 6–10 involved the assumption that the data came from samples chosen at random from the populations of interest. In drug-testing, although random methods are used (e.g. to allocate patients to the experimental and control groups), it is not common to use the kind of random sampling methods described in Unit 4 to choose the patients who are going to take part in the trial. Indeed, it is usually impossible to do so.

Example 8   *Influenza*

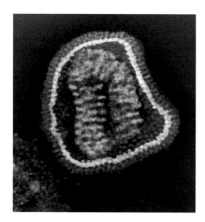

Influenza virus

Suppose that a drug company wants to know about the effect of a new drug on the symptoms of influenza in people living in the UK. The company could select two random samples of people from the population of the UK, giving the people in one sample the new drug and those in the other sample an existing treatment. However, unless everyone in both samples already had influenza, there would be nothing to measure. Since it would not be considered ethically acceptable to infect the people in the samples with influenza, this approach will not work.

The experimenters must choose the groups for this trial from people who already have influenza, and proceed as if these people are a random sample from the population of people in the UK who might have caught influenza. This should result in sound inferences back to this population, because the groups will usually form samples that are representative of the population even if they are not strictly random samples.

In practice, experimenters are often not very precise in specifying exactly to which populations their results refer. This is reflected in a common, but misleading, piece of jargon which you may well have heard. An experimenter might say casually that the experimental and control groups in his experiment *differed significantly*. By this they probably mean the following.

> 'I have carried out a hypothesis test, using the null hypothesis that the populations from which my two groups were chosen did not differ in their means, medians (or some other measure). The result of the hypothesis test was that the null hypothesis of no difference was rejected.'

Thus, to say that two samples differ significantly is to infer something about the populations from which those samples were drawn. Another point to remember is that a difference which is significant in this sense may be of no practical significance whatsoever.

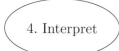

4. Interpret

You may also see the following type of sentence in a report of a scientific experiment.

'The two groups differed significantly ($p < 0.05$).'

This has a similar interpretation, but gives the significance level: there is evidence that the groups come from populations whose means are not identical, on the basis of a hypothesis test using a significance level of 5%.

Although there are many hypothesis tests available, this does not mean that researchers can choose any test they like, because each test requires certain conditions to be fulfilled before it can be used, and these conditions vary from one test to another. In particular, when choosing a test it is important to ask the following questions.

- What type of data has the experiment produced?
- Does the design of the experiment involve matching (i.e. pairing) the subjects in the two groups?

We shall now consider both questions in the following two subsections. In Subsection 4.3 we will consider the types of data. Then in Subsection 4.4 we will consider how the design of the experiment affects the choice of test.

4.3 Types of data

In earlier parts of the module you have met different kinds of data. First, there are **categorical** (or **nominal**) **data**. This form of data arises when there are several mutually exclusive categories and each item or person belongs in exactly one of the categories. Here, the data do no more than identify the category each item or person belongs in. For example, you could ask parents what medicine they used when their child last had a temperature, and record their answers as paracetamol, ibuprofen, none or other. There is very little quantitative information contained in the response of a single parent. You cannot say that a paracetamol-containing medicine is quantitatively different (e.g. larger or smaller) from an ibuprofen-containing medicine. You can, however, count the number of parents who fall into each category.

Various hypothesis tests are available that can be applied to categorical data: the tests introduced in this module are the sign test (Sections 4 and 5 of Unit 6) and the χ^2 test (Section 4 of Unit 8). The sign test could be used to examine, say, whether paracetamol or ibuprofen was preferred by more parents. The χ^2 test could be used to examine, for example, whether the medicine preference for children in one group of parents differed significantly from another group of parents.

Another type of data, called **ordinal data**, contains more quantitative information than categorical data. A Likert scale, introduced in Unit 4 (Subsection 3.1), is an example of a measure that gives ordinal data. A researcher asks patients to rate their sleep quality on a scale from 1 to 4, with 4 signifying that their sleep quality is very good, 3 fairly good, 2 fairly bad and 1 that it is very bad. Here one can say that a rating of 4, for example, is quantitatively different from a rating of 2. It is obviously higher. Data on an ordinal scale like this can therefore be ordered, but it is not really possible to do anything more ambitious with them than that. It would not really be possible to say that a person who rated their sleep as 3 had three times the quality of sleep than a person who rated it 1! It would not even be possible to say that the difference between ratings of 3 and 4 was the same as the difference between ratings of 1 and 2; to be precise, it does not make sense to subtract these ratings.

There are specific hypothesis tests available for ordinal data, though they are not taught in this module. It is possible to analyse ordinal data as nominal data, though information about ordering is lost.

Measurements on an interval scale (**interval scale data**) contain still more quantitative information. Data of this kind are what you might think of as real measurements, since they are actual quantities in definite units, such as height in centimetres, age in years, heart rate in beats per minute and so on. Here it does make sense to say that, for instance, the difference between two people's heights of 147 cm and 151 cm is the same as the difference between 185 cm and 189 cm.

Again, there are statistical techniques which are suitable for testing hypotheses about interval scale data. These include z-tests, described in Unit 7, and t-tests, described in Unit 10.

Examples of all three types of data occur in medicine.

Activity 21   *Types of data*

For each of the following, say whether the recorded information gives categorical, ordinal or interval scale data.

(a) Body temperature (in °C).

(b) Pain, rated on a four-point scale from mild to severe.

(c) A woman of childbearing age's reproductive state: pregnant or not pregnant.

(d) Systolic blood pressure (in mmHg).

You have now covered the material related to Screencast 5 for Unit 11 (see the M140 website).

4.4   Which test?

Nominal data that can be easily categorised and placed in a contingency table arise frequently from clinical trials. For example, the number of test subjects meeting some criteria that determines whether a drug is successful can easily be tabulated. In Unit 8, you met contingency tables and were shown how to apply the χ^2 test. The χ^2 test can also be applied to clinical trial data.

Interval scale data from clinical trials are quite commonly analysed using z-tests or t-tests. A number of such tests have been described in Units 7 and 10:

- The two-sample z-test and two-sample t-test, which are used to test the null hypothesis that the means of two populations are equal.

- The one-sample z-test and one-sample t-test, which are used to test the null hypothesis that a population mean equals some specified value.

- The matched-pairs z-test and matched-pairs t-test, which are used to test the null hypothesis that the mean difference between two responses is equal to zero. (Recall from Subsection 4.2 of Unit 10 that the matched-pairs z-test and matched-pairs t-test are just the corresponding one-sample tests performed on the differences within pairs.)

The appropriate z- or t-test to use will depend on the number of samples, the sample size or sample sizes, whether or not the data are matched, and what assumptions are satisfied. These issues have been discussed in Units 7 and 10 and will be returned to in Unit 12. Here we will only mention again the relationship between matching and clinical trial design.

Section 3 described the advantages and difficulties of using both a crossover trial and a matched-pairs trial. When each subject acts as his or her own control, or when each can be paired with a control subject who is similar in those features known to be important to the experiment, then it is possible to eliminate a lot of unwanted variability from the experiment. Both of these trial designs produce data which are in the form of matched pairs. In a crossover trial, there are two measurements for each person: one for each treatment. These are clearly paired. With a matched-pairs trial, the data from each person are paired with the data from the other half of the matched pair.

The following summarises the above discussion, regarding choice of statistical test.

Choice of hypothesis test, based on data and design

Type of data	Design	Test
Categorical		χ^2
Interval scale	Group comparative	two-sample z- or t-test
Interval scale	Matched pairs	matched-pairs z- or t-test
Interval scale	Crossover	matched-pairs z- or t-test

Exercises on Section 4

Exercises 6 and 7 will refresh your memory of the χ^2 test that you met in Unit 8 and the t-test that you met in Unit 10. They illustrate how these tests can be applied to data from clinical trials. For convenience, Table 28 from Unit 8 and Table 2 of Unit 10 are reproduced below. (Versions of these tables are also given in the Handbook.) These give critical values for these tests.

Table 3   Table of critical values of χ^2

Degrees of freedom	Critical values of χ^2 at significance level	
	5%	1%
1	3.841	6.635
2	5.991	9.210
3	7.815	11.345
4	9.488	13.277
5	11.070	15.086
6	12.592	16.812
7	14.067	18.475
8	15.507	20.090
9	16.919	21.666
10	18.307	23.209
11	19.675	24.725
12	21.026	26.217

Table 4 5% critical values for a two-sided Student's t-test

Degrees of freedom	Critical value (t_c)	Degrees of freedom	Critical value (t_c)
1	12.706	21	2.080
2	4.303	22	2.074
3	3.182	23	2.069
4	2.776	24	2.064
5	2.571	25	2.060
6	2.447	26	2.056
7	2.365	27	2.052
8	2.306	28	2.048
9	2.262	29	2.045
10	2.228	30	2.042
11	2.201	31	2.040
12	2.179	32	2.037
13	2.160	33	2.035
14	2.145	34	2.032
15	2.131	35	2.030
16	2.120	36	2.028
17	2.110	37	2.026
18	2.101	38	2.024
19	2.093	39	2.023
20	2.086	40	2.021

Exercise 6 *Testing a new contraceptive pill*

A drug company wished to test the efficacy of a new oral contraceptive by trying it out on volunteers. So 2000 volunteers were allocated randomly to two groups: the experimental group of 1000 women took the new contraceptive whilst the control group of 1000 women took an existing contraceptive. At the end of a one-year period, each woman taking part in the test was recorded as either having conceived or not. Suppose that only one of the 1000 women taking the new contraceptive had conceived by the end of the year, whereas 15 out of the 1000 women taking the existing contraceptive had conceived.

(a) What type of data is involved?

(b) Tabulate the data in an appropriate contingency table.

(c) Write down the appropriate null and alternative hypotheses.

(d) Carry out the test.

(e) What do you conclude?

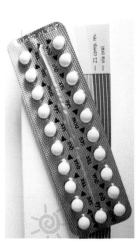

Eight people took part in a crossover trial whose purpose was to discover whether a new drug alters people's heart rate. The trial was a double-blind trial and the control treatment was to give each person a placebo. The data from this trial are in Table 5.

Table 5 Heart rates of eight participants in a crossover trial

| | Heart rate (beats per minute) | |
Subject	Drug	Placebo
1	90	105
2	82	88
3	95	90
4	80	89
5	88	80
6	75	110
7	83	84
8	90	100

(a) What type of data is involved?

(b) What hypothesis test is appropriate for these data?

(c) What distributional assumptions are necessary in order to use this test?

(d) Write down the appropriate null and alternative hypotheses.

(e) Carry out the test. What do you conclude? Does the new drug alter people's heart rate?

5 Drugs in society

Much of the discussion in this unit so far has been about the effectiveness of a drug. Another, equally important, aspect of drug-testing is assessing the unwanted effects of drugs. In this section we shall describe some ways in which these are discovered, and look at the problems involved in ensuring that drugs are as safe as possible.

5.1 Side effects

The unwanted effects of drugs, **side effects**, can be of a number of different kinds. Here are some examples.

- A drug may make people feel drowsy, suffer from hallucinations or have headaches. Such effects may be mild or serious. Even if they are only mild, however, they may cause patients to stop taking the drug and thus reduce its usefulness, especially if the disease itself is not very serious.

- A drug may interfere with the function of particular organs in the body. It might speed up the heart, damage the liver or cause birth deformities. Many of the serious hazards of drugs are of this kind and may be permanent, but effects of this kind may also be milder.

'Listen, when the side effects of this medication kick in, you'll forget what was wrong in the first place!'

Certain unwanted effects of drugs are common. For example, many people taking the pain-reliever codeine may become constipated. Other effects are rare. Clearly a non-serious, uncommon effect is of little importance. It is not at all worrying if, one in a thousand times, a drug causes a headache. But if a drug causes serious liver damage one in a thousand times, then it is most probably not a useful drug. The question of how important an unwanted effect is depends not only on the severity of the effect but also on the severity of the disease being treated. Severe liver damage as a consequence of a treatment for a headache would be unacceptable, whereas if a drug company developed a cure for rabies (which is almost invariably fatal once its symptoms become apparent), then even a treatment with a side effect which killed one in ten of the recipients would be considered a major advance. Whether or not the benefits of a new drug outweigh the risks is precisely what the experts at the EMA aim to establish in order to make their decision on a new drug approval. (Liver damage has indeed been linked to the over-the-counter pain-relief drug paracetamol, but only after overdose or constant long-term use.)

Sometimes investigators in clinical trials have a pretty good idea of what side effects they expect from a new drug. There may be suggestions from preliminary experiments on animals that a particular effect may be a problem; other related drugs may show such an unwanted effect; or the standard treatment may have an undesirable side effect which, it is hoped, will not occur with the new treatment. In all these cases, it is necessary to devise a method of measuring the effect in question.

This process is similar to that described in Subsection 2.2 for measuring the desired effects of drugs.

Sometimes investigators have some idea of the effects for which they are looking, but do not know them exactly. It is well known that quite a lot of drugs have effects, such as headache, constipation and tremor symptoms, which are not uncommon in the population as a whole, whether or not drugs have been taken. In many clinical trials the severity of such symptoms is entered on a checklist of symptoms which, it is known from past experience, are often connected with drug treatment. An example checklist is given below.

Symptom checklist

Symptom	Noticed in past two weeks?	Severity of symptoms on 0–3 scale*
Heart pounding		
Sleepiness		
Headache		
Sweating		
Dizziness		
Trembling		
Blurred vision		
Eye strain		
Difficulty passing urine		
Constipation		
Diarrhoea		
Nausea		
Vomiting		
Indigestion		
Lack of appetite		
Funny taste in mouth		
Dry mouth		
Difficulty in breathing		
Rash		
Itchiness		

* 0 = absent, 1 = mild, 2 = moderate, 3 = severe

'I didn't experience any of the side effects
listed in the enclosed literature.
Should I be concerned?'

Very occasionally in clinical trials, serious unexpected adverse events occur. (An **adverse event** is a side effect that has a negative effect on a patient.) These are events such as death, life-threatening events, hospitalisation, birth defects and disablement. If it is probable that the unexpected adverse event was caused by the drug being tested, then investigators must report the event to the authorities. Throughout the EU, these are entered into a single electronic system called EudraVigilance. Investigators will consider whether the trial should be stopped. During the earlier phases of testing, investigators will stop the trial immediately if adverse reactions are severe.

Example 9   *Phase 1 trial of TGN1412*

An extreme and exceptional case occurred during 2006, when the very first phase 1 trial of a new drug, TGN1412, designed to target the immune system, had to be stopped. The drug was administered in doses 500 times lower than that found to be safe in animals. However, soon after the trial started, six volunteers were hospitalised: four had multiple organ failure and all six experienced cytokine release syndrome, which caused severe inflamation of the skin. Fortunately all the volunteers survived, the last being released from hospital after three months, though one had to have fingers and toes amputated and it was reported that they all remain at a long-term increased risk of developing an immune-system-related illness. The incident was put down to 'unpredicted biological action in humans'. (See Suntharalingam et al., 2006 and Expert Scientific Group, 2006.)

Example 10   *Phase 2 trial of fialuridine*

In 1993, five patients died during a phase 2 trial of the new anti-viral drug fialuridine, designed to target hepatitis B. No sign of toxicity was detected during phase 1 trials, in which 67 subjects received fialuridine for two or four weeks. Then in the thirteenth week of the phase 2 trial, one patient suddenly developed hepatic toxicity (liver damage by chemical). The trial was stopped. Even after stopping the drug, seven patients went on to develop hepatic toxicity; five died and two survived after liver transplants. This severe delayed reaction could not have been predicted; fialuridine had gradually accumulated in liver DNA. (See McKenzie et al., 1995.) Any similar new drug would now be tested on animals for a longer period, to check for this type of damage.

5.2   Unexpected side effects post-licence

A completely different problem is presented by those side effects that are not discovered until after a drug has been licensed. A well-publicised example of this was the drug thalidomide (see Thalidomide Society, 2006). This was a sedative introduced in the UK in 1958. When taken by women in early pregnancy, it sometimes produced very severe effects on the physical development of the unborn children. A more recent case was the drug efalizumab, used to treat chronic psoriasis (red, scaly patches on the skin), which was withdrawn in 2009 after some reports on fatal infections in long-term users; we shall return to this example later. Yet another historical example was the drug practolol, a beta-blocker, which shall now be described in more detail.

Example 11   *Withdrawal of practolol*

Practolol (marketed as Eraldin) was introduced in 1970 as a beta-blocker for the management of heart conditions. The particular advantage of practolol was that it appeared to have fewer unwanted effects than other beta-blockers available at that time. The first indications that the drug was not, after all, safe, came in two letters published in the *British Medical Journal* in 1974. The first, by Felix and Ive (1974), described a characteristic rash that had developed in fourteen patients who had received long-term practolol therapy. The second letter, by Wright (1974), also reported a rash, but a few of his patients had also developed conjunctivitis (inflammation of the membrane that covers the front of the eye) – leading to severe and permanent visual impairment. Practolol seemed to be the common feature in all these cases.

The company that marketed this drug, Imperial Chemical Industries (ICI), sent a letter to all doctors and pharmacists in the UK warning them of these possible side effects, requesting information on similar cases, and advising immediate cessation of practolol therapy in any patient developing such symptoms.

As more data were gathered, it became clear that the adverse reaction was definitely associated with practolol. It also appeared that similar reactions did not occur with other beta-blockers. Practolol was finally withdrawn from the market in October 1975. By 1981, there was a total of about 2450 reports from doctors about reactions to the drug, including 40 deaths, 1130 cases of eye damage and 1250 skin reactions. (See also Abraham and Davis, 2006.)

It is important, when judging the number of reported eye reactions in Example 11, to consider the amount of practolol that was used during the period. This type of amount is usually measured in **patient-years**.

> ### Patient-years
>
> If a single patient takes a drug for one year, then that constitutes one patient-year of use of the drug.
>
> If two patients take the drug for six months each, then the usage is half a patient-year each, which again comes to one patient-year. Assuming that the patients take the same dose of the drug each day, the amount of drug consumed by one patient taking it for a year is the same as the amount consumed by two patients over six months, so a patient-year corresponds to the use of a certain amount of the drug.
>
> If twelve patients each take the drug for a month, or if 365 patients each take it for a day, the total usage is still one patient-year.

The total amount of practolol prescribed during the five years of its use amounted to approximately a million patient-years. The question that must be answered is not

How can such occurrences with new drugs be prevented?

but

How can new drugs that have serious side effects be identified quickly?

It is perhaps necessary first to justify the implication that such occurrences cannot be prevented (except by prohibiting all new drugs). A major factor is the length of time during which patients have to use a drug before the symptoms became apparent. With the exception of certain special cases, such as clinical trials of treatments for cancer, few clinical trials last for longer than a year. It is only when drugs are marketed that they are used for longer periods. One could argue that drugs should be tested in clinical trials for as long as it is proposed to use them in treatment. This would cause great delays in introducing drugs, but for some drugs this probably does not matter. Practolol, however, was a significant advance for many patients, because it provided genuine relief for people suffering from potentially fatal heart conditions. Few would wish to delay a drug that showed a good prospect of saving lives on the grounds of unlikely, although untested, possibilities of unknown risks.

Another obvious factor is simply the rarity of the effect. If a drug causes severe damage to only one in a thousand of the people who take it, then quite a lot of people may have to take it before even the first case will be seen, and even more must take it before it can be known with any certainty that it is the drug that is causing the effect.

Example 12   *Withdrawal of efalizumab*

Efalizumab (marketed as Raptiva) was approved by the EMA in 2004 for the treatment of chronic psoriasis, a disease that attacks the immune system and causes red, scaly patches on the skin. Short-term clinical trials showed efalizumab to be safe, though there was a question over the risk of infection with long-term use.

By the end of 2008, the drug manufacturers had made the EMA aware of a number of cases of serious infections in long-term users, most notably four long-term users who had developed a fatal brain infection (progressive multifocal leukoencephalopathy), three of whom had died.

In February 2009 the CHMP met to review the risks and benefits of efalizumab; its benefits in the treatment of psoriasis were only modest, whereas there was a risk of serious side effects. The CHMP recommended suspension of the drug's licence unless a subgroup of patients could be identified in which the benefits outweighed the risks. In May the drug licence holders voluntarily withdrew efalizumab, and in June the EMA withdrew the licence (EMA, 2009; see also DeFrancesco, 2009, Seminara and Gelfand, 2010).

There are other factors that can easily prevent a relatively rare side effect being quickly detected. One is that not all the cases that occur are notified to the workers carrying out the follow-up; another is that the patients involved are often using more than one drug.

Although it is vital to carry out thorough, well-designed clinical trials of drugs, and although statistical techniques can help to decide whether or not the drug is useful, these trials and statistical techniques cannot, by themselves, guarantee that a drug will be trouble-free when it is marketed. The greater the discrepancy between the conditions in which the clinical trials of a drug are conducted and the conditions in which the drug is actually used, the greater the chance that unpredicted side effects of the drug will appear. When testing a drug, the statistical analysis of data from clinical trials helps a drug company to decide whether to apply for a product licence to market that drug, but further data needs to be collected after marketing the drug. In order to monitor how the drug actually performs once it has been marketed, some form of post-marketing surveillance is needed.

children's HOLIDAY MAGIC project

Another CHMP doing medical good; this one provides music for children in hospitals in the USA over Christmas.

5.3 Post-marketing surveillance

The pharmaceutical industry and national regulators throughout the EU submit all adverse drug reaction reports to EudraVigilance (the central electronic system). This includes both individual case safety reports, which are submitted if an individual patient has a serious adverse reaction to a licensed drugs in general use, and unexpected serious adverse reactions that occur during clinical trials of unlicensed drugs. The aim of such a system is to allow any potential drug safety issue to be detected and investigated as early as possible.

Where necessary, these drug safety signals are referred to the EMA. Within the EMA there is a separate committee who look at all aspects of drug safety, called the Pharmacovigilance Risk Assessment Committee (PRAC). Their responsibilities include scrutinising referrals from the EudraVigilance system, monitoring the system's effectiveness and maintaining a list of drugs that should be subject to additional monitoring. PRAC will make recommendations to the CHMP and other committees on whether a drug's licence should be changed or withdrawn.

The trouble with a method like this is that doctors will not, generally, suspect an adverse drug reaction when they see something unfamiliar but will, quite rightly, send the patient to the appropriate specialist. So the reports submitted to EudraVigilance will tend to be biased towards the symptoms that doctors expect to see as adverse reactions. So a less expected reaction is likely to be missed until a sharp-witted specialist, who sees enough cases, notices that more patients suffering from a particular condition are taking a particular drug than would be expected. In the case of the connection of both rash and conjunctivitis with practolol, there were distinct, unfamiliar features to alert a specialist that something unusual was happening. The situation is much more difficult when a drug causes a disorder that is common in the whole population.

How can the situation be improved? All, or a sample, of the patients taking the drug for a period after the drug comes onto the market can be monitored. Such studies are sometimes called phase 4 trials, and it is a further responsibility of PRAC to assess and evaluate these population-based studies.

Example 13 *Withdrawal of rofecoxib*

Rofecoxib (marketed as Vioxx) is a drug that was used to target arthritis and other pain-causing conditions. It was withdrawn after population-based studies had shown an increased risk of heart attack and stroke.

The drug came onto the market in 1999. A study was published in 2000, comparing the effectiveness and side effects of rofecoxib and another drug used to treat arthritis, naproxen (Bombardier et al., 2000). It found that the incidence of heart attacks was four-fold higher in the rofecoxib group. Rofecoxib's manufacturer, Merck Sharp & Dohme, responded by claiming that the difference was due to naproxen having a protective effect on heart attacks.

In 2000, Merck commenced a three-year study whose primary aim was to assess the effectiveness of rofecoxib for a new purpose, but it had the additional aim of assessing cardiovascular risk. It was found (Bresalier et al., 2005) that the rate of a serious cardiovascular event such as a heart attack or stroke, after 18 months on rofecoxib, was 1.71 events per 100 patient-years versus 0.38 events per 100 patient-years for study participants taking a placebo. The drug was voluntarily withdrawn from the worldwide market by Merck in 2004. (See also Dieppe et al., 2004.)

How are population-based studies carried out? One method is to select a group of patients taking the drug, and to follow them up by means of regular medical checks, interviews and records of hospital admissions. Such a group is called a **cohort**. A control group (cohort) may also be selected, which is matched with this group in as many respects as possible, but those in the control cohort are not taking the drug.

Activity 22   *Selecting groups for post-marketing studies*

The procedure for selecting cohort groups in post-marketing studies is similar to the selection of groups for a clinical trial. Is the selection procedure identical to that used in a clinical trial? If not, in what important ways is it different?

Selecting experimental and control groups after, rather than before, they have received a treatment is unsatisfactory because many factors other than the drug treatment will be different for the two groups, though investigators will try to take these factors into account. This is also a very expensive method of surveillance, and studies may take a long time to carry out; for example, it took four years before rofecoxib was withdrawn. Depending on the size of the population monitored, rare side effects may still go undetected. Other study designs are available that can be used more economically to study rare side effects.

Another approach, called **record linkage**, consists of obtaining access to a patient's medical record so that links, other than those already known, between various ailments and the drugs being taken can be spotted. This approach does not require doctors to actively report information on their patients, but only requires them to permit researchers to have access to the records. For this reason it has many attractions, but it also raises the highly controversial issue of the privacy of medical records.

None of these methods can completely prevent damage to patients from the unexpected actions of drugs. All they can do is reduce the time it takes to spot the effect so that the drug can be withdrawn, or its use limited, as soon as possible.

6   Case study

The following case study describes the progress of a particular drug through the different phases of test. Do not worry if you do not follow all the medical details.

Patients who have just had a hip or knee replacement are at high risk of blood clots forming in the veins of their legs, which can be dangerous if the clot moves to a major organ such as the lungs. Likewise, patients with an abnormal heartbeat, called 'atrial fibrillation', have a high risk of blood clots which can cause a stroke. Patients at high risk of blood clots are prescribed anticoagulant drugs, which prevent blood from clotting. The main safety concern with any drug that prevents blood from clotting is that patients may bleed excessively. Clinical testing of any new anticoagulant needs to establish an acceptable trade-off between blood clot prevention and bleeding.

Dabigatran (marketed as Pradaxa) is one such anticoagulant. Dabigatran was granted marketing authorisation by the European Commission in 2008 after positive evaluation by the CHMP (EMA, 2008, 2013). We will describe all the clinical studies carried out in humans before the drug was approved.

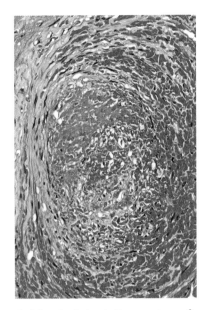

A blood clot at the centre of a blood vessel

6.1   Phase 1 of testing dabigatran

> In phase 1, the drug is usually given in increasing doses to healthy volunteers so as to evaluate biological action and safety.

After pre-clinical testing, which included testing on rats and rabbits, two phase 1 studies with healthy male volunteers were carried out. (See Stangier et al., 2007.)

In the first study, 40 subjects were randomised to one of five groups and, within each group, subjects were randomised so that two received placebo and six received a single dose of dabigatran. The first group received one 10 mg dose; in the other four groups, the single dose was, respectively, 30 mg, 100 mg, 200 mg and 400 mg. Blood samples were taken from patients to observe the rate at which the drug was eliminated from the body.

In the second study, again with 40 volunteers, doses were given three times daily for seven days. The first group received doses of 50 mg and subsequent groups were given higher doses up to 400 mg.

At a dose of 400 mg three times a day, some volunteers bruised where they had been punctured by needles, and some had bleeding gums. The main safety concern was the occurrence of a *major* bleed. Major bleeds are classified according to a strict definition; any bleeding not classified as a major bleed is considered to be a *minor* bleed. No major bleeds were observed during the phase 1 testing.

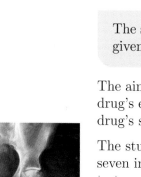

'That's great, but it was supposed to be a laxative.'

6.2   Phase 2 of testing dabigatran

> The studies in phase 2 are usually the first studies in which the drug is given to patients with the condition that the drug is designed to help.

The aims of the first study in patients (called BISTRO I) were to check the drug's effectiveness, form hypotheses about the optimal dose and assess the drug's safety, in particular with respect to bleeding.

The study was conducted over nine months across 11 sites in Sweden and seven in Norway. (See Eriksson et al., 2004.) Dabigatran was given for six to ten days to patients after a hip replacement operation, with patients divided into groups according to when they entered the study. The first group to enter the study received two doses of 12.5 mg each day and the dose was steadily increased for subsequent groups. The ninth group received two doses of 300 mg each day.

Guidelines were carefully set up in advance with regards to stopping the study if the number of patients with bleeding problems became too high as dose size increased.

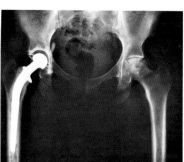

An X-ray image of a patient after a hip replacement

132

- All major bleeds were recorded, and if 5% or more of patients experienced major bleeds the study would be stopped.

- Any other bleeding, no matter how small, was recorded as a minor bleed. However, some bleeding from the surgical hip replacement site was expected, so only excessive bleeding there was recorded.

The other issue was blood clots, which the drug was meant to prevent. Under guidelines for this, the dose level was to be increased for the next group of patients to the next dose up if 20% or more of patients who received the current dose experienced a blood clot.

There were 314 patients enrolled on the study, with 289 receiving at least one dose and 262 patients completing the study, including a follow-up check four to six weeks after surgery. Although no patients experienced a major bleed, the study was stopped at a dose of 300 mg twice daily because two patients experienced minor bleeding from multiple sites. Drug safety and bleeding was evaluated in all 289 patients who received at least one dose, but data to assess drug effectiveness in preventing blood clots were only available for 225 patients.

Some results are given in Table 6. It can be seen that few patients had a blood clot, but minor bleeds were common. The total number of events is given in the last row.

Table 6   Number of bleeds and clots in the dabigatran phase 2 trial

Dose regime		Data on bleeds		Data on clots	
Level (mg)	Times per day	No. of patients	Minor bleeds	No. of patients	Clots
12.5	2	27	2	24	5
25	2	28	9	21	2
50	2	30	18	27	4
100	2	40	33	31	6
150	1	41	39	33	3
150	2	29	26	21	2
200	2	28	22	21	4
300	1	46	41	33	2
300	2	20	16	14	0
Total		289	206	225	28

Example 14   *Does dosage effect the number of minor bleeds?*

As there were no major bleeds, obviously there is no evidence that the dose regime affects the chance of a patient having a major bleed, but there is the question of whether daily dose level affects the number of minor bleeds. The numbers are quite small, so to examine this we will combine results into three categories:

- total daily dose less than or equal to 100 mg
- total daily dose 150 mg or 200 mg
- total daily dose greater than or equal to 300 mg.

Thus, for the first category there are $27 + 28 + 30 = 85$ patients, of whom $2 + 9 + 18 = 29$ had minor bleeds, so that $85 - 29 = 56$ patients had no bleed. Results for the three groups give the following contingency table:

Table 7   Number of patients with minor bleeds and number without minor bleed, by daily dose level

	Total daily dose			Total
	≤ 100 mg	150 or 200 mg	≥ 300 mg	
With minor bleed	29	72	105	206
Without bleed	56	9	18	83
Total	85	81	123	289

The null and alternative hypotheses are:

H_0: Total daily dose of drug and the number of patients having a minor bleed are independent.

H_1: There is a relationship between the total daily dose of drug and the number of patients having a minor bleed.

Recall from Subsection 4.2 in Unit 8, the Expected values are calculated from

$$E = \frac{\text{Row total} \times \text{Column total}}{\text{Overall total}},$$

which gives the following Expected table.

	Total daily dose		
With minor bleed	60.5882	57.7370	87.6747
Without bleed	24.4118	23.2630	35.3253

Note that the Expected values are greater than 5, so it is appropriate to use the χ^2 test.

The Residuals are obtained from

Residual = Observed − Expected.

Thus, for example, the Residual for the first cell is $29 - 60.5882 = -31.5882$. The following is the Residual table.

	Total daily dose		
With minor bleed	−31.5882	14.2630	17.3253
Without bleed	31.5882	−14.2630	−17.3253

For the first cell, the contribution to χ^2 is given by,

$$\chi^2 \text{ contribution} = \frac{(\text{Residual})^2}{\text{Expected}}$$
$$= \frac{(-31.5882)^2}{60.5882} \simeq 16.4688.$$

Repeating the calculation for all six cells results in this χ^2 table:

	Total daily dose		
With minor bleed	16.4688	3.5234	3.4236
Without bleed	40.8743	8.7449	8.4972

Hence the value of the χ^2 test statistic is

$$16.4688 + 3.5234 + 3.4236 + 40.8743 + 8.7449 + 8.4972 \simeq 81.532$$

The number of degrees of freedom for a 2×3 contingency table is $(2-1) \times (3-1) = 2$.

Hence, from Table 3 (Exercises on Section 4), the critical value at the 5% significance level is 5.991, and at the 1% significance level it is 9.210.

Since the test statistic, 81.532, is much greater than the 1% critical value, 9.210, we reject H_0 in favour of H_1 at the 1% significance level and conclude that there is strong evidence of a relationship between the total daily drug dose and the number of patients having a minor bleed. Looking at the data in Table 7 (or at the Residual table), bleeds seem less likely when the daily dose is 100 mg or less compared with when it is 150 mg or more.

Activity 23   *Does dosage effect the number of blood clots?*

One purpose of phase 2 is to start to learn whether the drug is effective. The purpose of dabigatran is to reduce the risk of blood clots. Table 6 gives data on the number of blood clots by dose regime. Combine the dose categories into three groups, using the same dose regime groups as in Example 6. Form a contingency table appropriate for testing whether the total daily dose of drug and the number of patients having a blood clot are independent. Perform the test and report your conclusion.

Phase 2 testing continued with a larger study, called BISTRO II, that shared the same aims as the BISTRO I study (Eriksson et al., 2005).

It was a double-blind randomised controlled trial of 1973 patients who had just undergone a hip or knee replacement across 60 centres in Europe and two centres in South Africa. Given the inconclusive results of the BISTRO I study and the need for sensible dosing schedules to be determined for phase 3 testing, patients in the treatment group were randomised to one of four dosing schedules: 50 mg twice a day, 150 mg twice a day, 300 mg once a day and 225 mg twice a day. Patients randomised to the control group were given an existing treatment proven to reduce the risk of blood clots, enoxaparin.

Activity 24   *Use a placebo as the control treatment?*

Why would it be unethical to compare dabigatran with placebo?

Activity 25   *Double-blind trial – How?*

Dabigatran is given orally in capsule form, while enoxaparin is given as an injection. How do you suppose it was possible to achieve blinding?

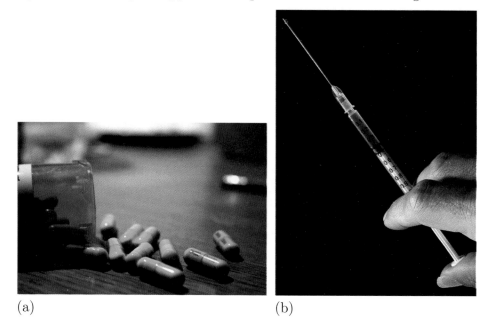

(a)   (b)

Figure 10   (a) A drug in capsule form; (b) an injection of a drug

Activity 26   *Questions of interest?*

For each question that you identify in (a) and (b), state the null hypothesis that should be tested.

(a) What are the main questions involving only dabigatran that should be examined after the data have been gathered?

(b) What are the main questions to examine in comparing dabigatran with enoxaparin?

A summary of some of the main results is given in Table 8. It shows the number of patients experiencing major or minor bleeds and the number experiencing blood clots. Data on bleeds relate to all patients who received at least one dose of a drug in the trial – just under 400 patients for each drug/dosage regime. Data on the number of clots determine the efficacy of a treatment and are only given for those patients who completed the trial – about 300 patients for each drug/dosage regime.

Table 8   Number of bleeds and clots with dabigatran and enoxaparin in BISTRO II

Drug, dose and daily frequency	Data on bleeds			Data on clots	
	No. of patients	Major bleeds	Minor bleeds	No. of patients	Clots
Dabigatran 50 mg: twice	389	1	18	302	86
Dabigatran 150 mg: twice	390	16	31	282	49
Dabigatran 300 mg: once	385	18	37	283	47
Dabigatran 225 mg: twice	393	15	38	297	39
Enoxaparin 40 mg: once	392	8	25	300	72
Total	1949	58	149	1464	293

Statistical analysis showed that, compared with enoxaparin, the rate of occurrence of clots was significantly lower with dabigatran when it was administered at 150 mg twice daily ($p = 0.04$), 300 mg once daily ($p = 0.02$) or 225 mg twice daily ($p = 0.0007$). Looking at Table 8, there is a suggestion that taking dabigatran at these higher doses increases the risk of a major bleed, compared with enoxaparin, but in fact the differences are not statistically significant at the 5% significance level.

When administered in twice-daily doses of 50 mg, dabigatran had significantly lower rates of major bleeds than at other levels, and a significantly lower rate than enoxaparin. However, at that dosage dabigitran seemed no better (and possibly worse) than enoxaparin at reducing the rate of clots.

The conclusion of the BISTRO II study team was that, with dabigatran, both the effectiveness (reduction in the rate of clots) and safety (rate of bleeding events) depended on the dose level. They also concluded that the three highest doses of dabigatran were significantly more effective than enoxaparin at reducing the rate of blood clots, although at these levels there appeared to be an increase in bleeds.

6.3   Phase 3 of testing dabigatran

In phase 3, treatment with the new drug is compared with existing therapies in a wider range of contexts.

There were three large phase 3 studies initiated in 2004, with results published in 2007. Their study set-up and aims were similar to the BISTRO II trial: patients who were undergoing hip or knee replacement were randomised to the treatment group, receiving dabigatran, or the control group, receiving enoxaparin, and effectiveness and safety outcomes, particularly bleeding, were compared. Given the study team's conclusions on dosing after the BISTRO II trial, dabigatran was administered once per day at a dose of either 150 mg or 220 mg.

One of the three studies, called RE-MOBILIZE, was carried out in North America, where the recommended dose of enoxaparin after hip or knee replacement is 60 mg/day, different from the 40 mg dose used throughout Europe (RE-MOBILIZE Writing Committee, 2009). The results of the RE-MOBILIZE trial were of less relevance to the CHMP in deciding whether dabigatran should be licensed within Europe, so will not be described further here.

In one of the other two trials, called RE-MODEL, a total of 2101 knee replacement patients located at one of 105 centres in Europe, Australia or South Africa were randomised to one of the two treatment groups (150 mg or 220 mg dabigatran) or the control group (40 mg enoxaparin) (Eriksson et al., 2007a).

In the third trial, called RE-NOVATE, a total of 3494 hip replacement patients located at one of 115 centres in Europe, Australia or South Africa were randomised (Eriksson et al., 2007b).

Results of the latter two trials are given in the tables below. For instance, in the 220 mg dose of dabigatran group in the RE-MODEL trial (Table 9), the numbers 10/679 mean that, of the 679 patients for whom data are available, 10 of these had a major bleed. There were fewer data for blood clots than for the safety outcomes, because for some patients the relevant data were not collected or were inadequate.

Table 9 Number of bleeds and clots or death with dabigatran and enoxaparin in RE-MODEL (knee replacement)

| | Drug and dose | | |
| | dabigatran | | enoxaparin |
	220 mg	150 mg	40 mg
Major bleeds	10/679	9/703	9/694
Minor bleeds	60/679	59/703	69/694
Blood clots or death	183/503	213/526	193/512

Table 10 Number of bleeds and clots or death with dabigatran and enoxaparin in RE-NOVATE (hip replacement)

| | Drug and dose | | |
| | dabigatran | | enoxaparin |
	220 mg	150 mg	40 mg
Major bleeds	23/1146	15/1163	18/1154
Minor bleeds	70/1146	72/1163	74/1154
Blood clots or death	53/880	75/874	60/897

In Tables 9 and 10, the proportions of people with blood clots or who died are slightly lower with the 220 mg dose of dabigatran than with enoxaparin. For example, in the 220 mg dose of dabigatran group of the RE-MODEL trial, 183 patients out of 503 patients had a blood clot or died (though only 1 patient died in this treatment group), corresponding to 36.4% of patients. In the enoxaparin group, 193 out of 512 patients had a blood clot or died (there was also only 1 death in this group), corresponding to 37.7% of patients. Also, the proportions of people with bleeds are slightly lower with the 150 mg dose of dabigatran than with enoxaparin. However, the study investigators found no statistically significant difference between the effectiveness or safety of either dose of dabigatran and enoxaparin.

In addition to the three phase 3 studies mentioned above, a further phase 3 study, called RE-LY, looked at the effectiveness of dabigatran in preventing stroke in patients with atrial fibrillation (a heart condition which, as mentioned right at the start of this case study, is one where it was hoped dabigatran would be useful). (Connolly et al., 2009, and see also correction in Connolly et al., 2010.) This study, initiated in 2005, was a very large worldwide study in which 18 113 atrial fibrillation patients were randomised to one of two dabigatran dosing schedules or to a control group. The dabigatran dosing schedules were 110 mg or 150 mg, twice daily, while the control group were given the most commonly used existing anticoagulant treatment for this condition, warfarin. The study design was like a cohort study: patients were followed over time, for a median of two years, with several follow-up visits initially, then every four months until the end of the study. Treatments were not blinded. Data were collected on all medical conditions, however minor.

The main aim of the study was to evaluate the effectiveness of dabigatran at reducing the risk of stroke, and to look at the safety of long-term use of the drug with a particular emphasis on bleeding. The trial took several years to run, and results were published in 2009. We will not show a table of the results here as they are more difficult to interpret: the length of time in the study differed between patients, so person-time had to be taken into account. The main findings were:

- At a dose of 110 mg twice daily, dabigatran was as effective as warfarin in reducing the risk of stroke, with a lower risk of major bleeds.

- At a dose of 150 mg twice daily, dabigatran was more effective than warfarin in reducing the risk of stroke, with a similar overall risk of major bleeds. The risk of any type of bleeding was lower, but the risk of gastro-intestinal (stomach and intestine) bleeding was higher.

6.4 Marketing authorisation and use

During 2007, the CHMP considered the evidence from the RE-MODEL and RE-NOVATE trials in deciding whether or not to recommend dabigatran for licensing in Europe. The CHMP concluded that dabigatran was as effective as enoxaparin in preventing blood clots, and safety profiles were similar. It was noted that dabigatran was more convenient for patients than enoxaparin because it is taken orally, rather than given as an injection.

The CHMP considered that the benefits of dabigatran outweighed its risks and recommended to the European Commission that it be given marketing authorisation for use after hip and knee replacement surgery. This was granted in March 2008. After completion of the RE-LY study, marketing authorisation for stroke prevention in patients with atrial fibrillation followed in August 2011.

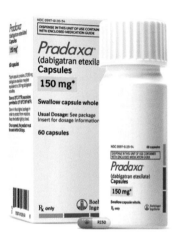

Dabigatran is convenient to use as it can be taken orally in a capsule that acts immediately and requires no monitoring. Partly for this reason, it is considered to be an important new anticoagulant. Two alternative anticoagulants have been mentioned, enoxaparin and warfarin. Enoxaparin is available only as an injection, making it a more invasive treatment. Warfarin is taken orally, but its use requires an initial phase of *normalisation* which requires frequent blood tests. Standard practice is to give patients an anticoagulant for several weeks after hip or knee replacement, but their hospital stay might be less than five days. It follows that dabigatran is more convenient for both patients and medical staff.

The cost-effectiveness of dabigatran for use after hip or knee replacement was reviewed by NICE during 2008. While dabigatran is a more expensive drug than other existing treatments, its convenience means it takes up less clinical time. NICE approved dabigatran as an available option for preventing blood clots after hip or knee replacement surgery on the NHS (NICE, 2008). It also recommended further clinical trials to compare dabigatran with other existing anticoagulants.

6.5 Surveillance

Phase 4 studies use larger samples of patients than can be obtained before marketing. They aim to obtain further evidence about the safety of the drug.

At the end of 2011, the EMA published a press release (EMA, 2011) on the safety of dabigatran. There were worldwide reports of bleeding on the drug, which in a few cases led to death. Excessive bleeding is a well-known risk with any anticoagulant, and evidence from the trials suggested dabigatran had a similar safety profile to other anticoagulants. It was noted that with increasing worldwide use and awareness, the total number of adverse events reported tends to increase. However, the EMA recommended that further checks of a patient's health should be carried out before the patient is prescribed dabigatran. The EMA will continue to monitor the safety of the drug.

Exercises on Section 6

Exercise 8 *Analysing the RE-NOVATE trial*

Table 10, which gave results of the RE-NOVATE trial, is reproduced below. Carry out a χ^2 test to test the null hypothesis of no difference between effectiveness in reducing the risk of blood clots (or death) when treated with 220 mg dabigatran and 40 mg enoxaparin. Start by forming a suitable 2×2 contingency table. You may carry out your calculations either by hand or using Minitab.

| | Drug and dose | | |
| | dabigatran | | enoxaparin |
	220 mg	150 mg	40 mg
Major bleeds	23/1146	15/1163	18/1154
Minor bleeds	70/1146	72/1163	74/1154
Blood clots or death	53/880	75/874	60/897

7 Computer Book: clinical trials

In Section 3 you learnt about crossover trials, matched-pairs trials and group-comparative trials. Chapter 11 of the Computer Book tells you how to use Minitab to randomise patients to treatments for these clinical trials. It then gives you more practice at using Minitab to carry out χ^2 tests and t-tests.

You should work through all of Chapter 11 of the Computer Book now, if you have not already done so.

Summary

In this unit we looked at the testing of new drugs. The tests have two main aims: to determine whether a drug is an effective treatment and to make sure it is safe, with no serious adverse side effects. New drugs are tested in clinical trials that use a control group.

Section 2 explained the difficulties of setting up effective controls, and how some of these difficulties can be overcome by using placebos. It distinguished subjective measurements, such as sensations, from objective measurements, to which relatively precise numerical values can be attached. Bias can arise in experiments from the expectations of both the experimenters and the subjects, but it can be removed by blind and double-blind experiments. Problems also arise from the variability of the experimenters and of the people who are the subjects.

Different types of clinical trial were described in Section 3. One type is the crossover trial, where a patient receives both the control (placebo) treatment in one time period and the new drug in a different time period. A second type is a matched pairs trial, where each person given the new drug is matched with a second person who is given the control treatment. Both these forms of trial aim to remove some of the variability between people, either by using each person as his or her own control, or by matching people with similar attributes. A third type of clinical trial is the group-comparative trial. Here people are allocated to the control group and treatment group at random, subject to the restriction that each group should be representative of the population being studied.

Section 4 showed that some medical conditions and ailments require categorical measurements, others ordinal measurements and others are measured on an interval scale. Different statistical tests need to be used for data from these different types of measurement. This unit illustrated the use of t-tests and χ^2 tests in clinical trial analysis.

The problems of detecting the side effects of a drug were discussed in Section 5. Some side effects are expected and these can be measured by experimental procedures similar to those used to measure the desired effects of a drug. Other side effects may not be expected, as in the case of practolol, a drug developed for treating heart conditions which turned out to damage the eye. Clinical trials are necessarily limited in scale and duration, so they may not reveal all the side effects of a drug. Post-marketing surveillance is therefore important, and this section described various methods of post-marketing surveillance, together with problems that are involved in each.

Section 6 worked through all the major stages in the testing of a new drug. Perhaps the overriding messages from this case study are that study designs can be complex and results may not be clear-cut. Also, the process of drug licensing is slow – first reports of dabigatran were published in 2001, yet it took until 2008 to license the drug.

Learning outcomes

After working through this unit, you should be able to:

- understand the need for controls in a clinical trial and how to control for certain factors
- explain what is meant by a placebo and explain how and why placebos are used in clinical trials
- explain some of the ethical questions that have to be answered when assessing whether a group of patients can be given a placebo
- distinguish between subjective and objective measurements in clinical trials
- identify sources of bias in clinical trials and suggest experimental procedures whereby bias can be reduced
- identify sources of variability in clinical trials and recognise when this variability can hamper the interpretation of the results from a clinical trial
- describe crossover, matched-pairs and group-comparative designs of clinical trials
- recognise those investigations in which each of these designs should be used and those in which they should not
- understand some uses of random methods of allocation in the design of an experiment, and their importance
- understand that the design and analysis of a clinical trial (or any scientific experiment) are closely connected
- distinguish between categorical, ordinal and interval scale measurements, and understand their uses in clinical trials
- analyse categorical data from trials using the χ^2 test
- analyse interval scale data from trials using the t-test
- explain why clinical trials may fail to detect all the side effects of a new drug
- describe some methods of post-marketing surveillance, together with their advantages and drawbacks.

References

Abraham, J. and Davis, C. (2006) 'Testing times: The emergence of the practolol disaster and its challenge to British drug regulation in the modern period', *Social History of Medicine*, vol. 19, no. 1, pp. 127–147.

Åstrand P.O. and Christensen, E.H. (1964) 'Aerobic work capacity', in Dickens, F. et al. (eds) 'Oxygen in the animal organism', Pergamon Press, New York, p. 295.

Bhatt, A. (2010) 'Evolution of clinical research: a history before and beyond James Lind', *Perspectives in Clinical Research*, vol. 1, pp. 6–10.

Bombardier, C., Laine, L., Reicin, A., Shapiro, D., Burgos-Vargas, R., Davis, B., Day, R., Ferraz, M.B., Hawkey, C.J., Hochberg, M.C., Kvien, T.K. and Schnitzer, T.J. for the VIGOR Study Group (2000), 'Comparison of upper gastrointestinal toxicity of rofecoxib and naproxen in patients with rheumatoid arthritis', *New England Journal of Medicine*, vol. 343, no. 21, pp. 1520–1528.

Bresalier, R.S., Sandler, R.S., Quan, H., Bolognese, J.A., Oxenius, B., Horgan, K., Lines, C., Riddell, R., Morton, D., Lanas, A., Konstam, M.A. and Baron, J.A. for the Adenomatous Polyp Prevention on Vioxx (APPROVe) Trial Investigators (2005), 'Cardiovascular events associated with rofecoxib in a colorectal adenoma chemoprevention trial', *New England Journal of Medicine*, vol. 352, no. 2, pp. 1092–1102.

Christiansen, J.S. (2006) 'What is Normal Glucose? – Continuous Glucose Monitoring Data from Healthy Subjects' [Online]. Lecture at the Annual Meeting of the EASD, Copenhagen, Denmark. Available at www.diabetes-symposium.org/index.php?menu=view&id=322

Connolly, S.J., Ezekowitz, M.D., Yusuf, S., Eikelboom, J., Oldgren, J., Parekh, A., Pogue, J., Reilly, P.A., Themeles, E., Varrone, J., Wang, S., Alings, M., Xavier, D., Zhu, J., Diaz, R., Lewis, B.S., Darius, H., Diener, H.C., Joyner, C.D. and Wallentin, L. for the RE-LY Steering Committee and Investigators (2009), 'Dabigatran versus warfarin in patients with atrial fibrillation', *New England Journal of Medicine*, vol. 361, pp. 1139–1151.

Connolly, S.J., Ezekowitz, M.D., Yusuf, S., Reilly, P.A. and Wallentin L. for the Randomized Evaluation of Long-Term Anticoagulation Therapy Investigators (2010) 'Newly identified events in the RE-LY trial', *New England Journal of Medicine*, vol. 363, pp. 1875–1876.

DeFrancesco, L. (2009) 'RIP Raptiva?', *Nature Biotechnology*, vol. 27, p. 303.

Dieppe, P.A., Ebrahim, S., Martin, R.M. and Jüni, P. (2004), 'Lessons from the withdrawal of rofecoxib', *British Medical Journal*, vol. 329, pp. 867–868.

Ekblom, B., Goldbarg, A.N., Kilbom, Å. and Åstrand, P.O. (1972) 'Effects of atropine and propranolol on the oxygen transport system during exercise in man', *Scandinavian Journal of Clinical Laboratory Investigations*, vol. 30, pp. 35–42.

EMA (2007a) 'Nexavar®: EPAR - Scientific Discussion' [Online], London, European Medicines Agency.Available at www.ema.europa.eu/docs/en_GB/document_library/EPAR_- _Scientific_Discussion/human/000690/WC500027707.pdf

EMA (2007b) 'Nexavar®-H-C-690-II-05: EPAR - Scientific Discussion - Variation' [Online], London, European Medicines Agency. Available at www.ema.europa.eu/docs/en_GB/document_library/EPAR_- _Scientific_Discussion_-_Variation/human/000690/WC500027710.pdf

EMA (2008) 'CHMP assessment report for Pradaxa' [Online], London, European Medicines Agency. Available at www.ema.europa.eu/docs/ en_GB/document_library/EPAR_-_Public_assessment_report/human/ 000829/WC500041062.pdf

EMA (2009), 'Public statement on Raptiva (efalizumab)' [Online], London, European Medicines Agency. Available at www.ema.europa.eu/ docs/en_GB/document_library/Public_statement/2009/11/WC500009129.pdf

EMA (2011) 'European Medicines Agency updates on safety of Pradaxa' [Online], London, European Medicines Agency. Available at www.ema.europa.eu/ ema/index.jsp?curl=pages/news_and_events/news/ 2011/11/news_detail_001390.jsp

EMA (2013) 'European public assessment report (EPAR) for Pradaxa' [Online], London, European Medicines Agency. Available at www.ema.europa.eu/ema/index.jsp?curl=pages/medicines/human/ medicines/000829/human_med_000981.jsp

Eriksson, B.I., Dahl, O.E., Ahnfelt, L., Kälebo, P., Stangier, J., Nehmiz, G., Hermansson, K. and Kohlbrenner, V. (2004) 'Dose escalating safety study of a new oral direct thrombin inhibitor, dabigatran etexilate, in patients undergoing total hip replacement: BISTRO I', *Journal of Thrombosis and Haemostasis*, vol. 2, pp. 1573–1580.

Eriksson, B.I., Dahl, O.E., Büller, H.R., Hettiarachchi, R., Rosencher, N., Bravo, M.L., Ahnfelt, L., Piovella, F., Stangier, J., Kälebo, P. and Reilly, P. for the BISTRO II Study Group (2005), 'A new oral direct thrombin inhibitor, dabigatran etexilate, compared with enoxaparin for prevention of thromboembolic events following total hip or knee replacement: the BISTRO II randomized trial', *Journal of Thrombosis and Haemostasis*, vol. 3, pp. 103–111.

Eriksson, B.I., Dahl, O.E., Rosencher, N., Kurth, A.A., van Dijk, C.N., Frostick, S.P., Kälebo, P., Christiansen, A.V., Hantel, S., Hettiarachchi, R., Schnee, J. and Büller, H.R. for the RE-MODEL Study Group (2007a) 'Oral dabigatran etexilate vs. subcutaneous enoxaparin for the prevention of venous thromboembolism after total knee replacement: the RE-MODEL randomized trial', *Journal of Thrombosis and Haemostasis*, vol. 5, pp. 2178–2185.

Eriksson, B.I., Dahl, O.E., Rosencher, N., Kurth, A.A., van Dijk, C.N., Frostick, S.P., Prins, M.H., Hettiarachchi, R., Hantel, S., Schnee, J. and Büller, H.R. for the RE-NOVATE Study Group (2007b) 'Dabigatran etexilate versus enoxaparin for prevention of venous thromboembolism after total hip replacement: a randomised, double-blind, non-inferiority trial', *Lancet*, vol. 370, pp. 949–56.

Expert Scientific Group (2006) 'Expert Scientific Group on phase one clinical trials - final report' [Online], The Stationery Office, London. Available at http://webarchive.nationalarchives.gov.uk/20130107105354/www.dh.gov.uk/prod_consum_dh/groups/dh_digitalassets/@dh/@en/documents/digitalasset/dh_073165.pdf

Felix, R. and Ive, F.A. (1974) 'Skin reactions to practolol', *British Medical Journal*, 11 May 1974, p. 333.

Lind, J. (1753) *A Treatise of the Scurvy*, London, A. Millar. Also [online] available at https://archive.org/details/treatiseonscurvy00lind

McKenzie, R., Fried, M.W., Sallie, R., Conjeevaram, H., Di Bisceglie, A.M., Park, Y., Savarese, B., Kleiner, D., Tsokos, M., Luciano, C., Pruett, T., Stotka, J.L., Straus, S.E., and Hoofnagle, J.H., (1995) 'Hepatic failure and lactic acidosis due to fialuridine (FIAU), an investigational nucleoside analogue for chronic Hepatitis B', *New England Journal of Medicine*, vol. 333, no. 17, pp. 1099–1105.

NICE (2008) 'Technology appraisals TA157: Dabigatran etexilate for the prevention of venous thromboembolism after hip or knee replacement surgery in adults' [Online], London, National Institute for Health and Care Excellence. Available at http://guidance.nice.org.uk/TA157

NICE (2009) 'Technology appraisals TA178: Bevacizumab (first-line), sorafenib (first- and second-line), sunitinib (second-line) and temsirolimus (first-line) for the treatment of advanced and/or metastatic renal cell carcinoma' [Online], London, National Institute for Health and Care Excellence. Available at http://guidance.nice.org.uk/TA178

NICE (2010) 'Technology appraisals TA189: Hepatocellular carcinoma (advanced and metastatic) - sorafenib (first line)' [Online], London, National Institute for Health and Care Excellence. Available at http://guidance.nice.org.uk/TA189

RE-MOBILIZE Writing Committee (2009) 'Oral thrombin inhibitor dabigatran etexilate vs North American enoxaparin regimen for prevention of venous thromboembolism after knee arthroplasty surgery', *Journal of Arthroplasty*, vol. 24, pp. 1–9.

Seminara, N.M. and Joel M Gelfand, J.M. (2010) 'Assessing long-term drug safety: lessons (re) learned from Raptiva', *Seminars in cutaneous medicine and surgery*, vol. 29, pp. 16–19. Also [online] available through NIH Public Access at www.ncbi.nlm.nih.gov/pmc/articles/PMC2864916/

SMC (2008) 'Advice: sorafenib (Nexavar)', [Online], Glasgow, Scottish Medicines Consortium. Available at www.scottishmedicines.org.uk/ SMC_Advice/Advice/482_08_sorafenib_Nexavar_/sorafenib_Nexavar_

Stangier, J., Rathgen, K., Stähle, H., Gansser, D. and Roth, W. (2007) 'The pharmacokinetics, pharmacodynamics and tolerability of dabigatran etexilate, a new oral direct thrombin inhibitor, in healthy male subjects', *British Journal of Clinical Pharmacology*, vol. 64, no. 3, pp. 292–303.

Suntharalingam, G., Perry, M.R., Ward, S., Brett, S.J., Castello-Cortes, A., Brunner, M.D. and Panoskaltsis, N. (2006) 'Cytokine storm in a phase 1 trial of the anti-CD28 monoclonal antibody TGN1412', *New England Journal of Medicine*, vol. 355, no. 10, pp. 1018–1028.

Thalidomide Society (2006) 'The history of thalidomide' [Online], London, The Thalidomide Society. Available at www.thalidomidesociety.co.uk/ thalhistory.htm

Wright, P. (1974) 'Skin reactions to practolol', *British Medical Journal*, 8 June 1974, p. 560.

Solutions to activities

Solution to Activity 1

The answer is *nothing at all*. Headaches tend to go away sooner or later anyway. Perhaps your headache would have been gone in an hour even if you had not taken the drug.

Solution to Activity 2

You cannot say much more than in the previous activity. You are more likely to believe that aspirin really works if 16 out of 20 headaches improve rather than if none improve, but you still do not know how many of the headaches would have got better anyway.

Solution to Activity 3

Each member of the experimental group has taken a pill, whereas each member of the control group has not. This may appear to be a trivial difference, but it is not. Every doctor knows that the mere fact of taking a pill can have beneficial effects, irrespective of any active ingredients that the pill may contain.

Solution to Activity 4

The control group can be given dummy tablets which look like aspirin and taste like aspirin but contain no active drug.

Solution to Activity 5

Scurvy is a serious illness that can result in death. Hence it would not have been ethical to give a placebo – all patients needed to be treated.

Solution to Activity 6

Some of the problems are as follows.

- With either treatment, the headache may take more than an hour to go away, but last longer when the placebos are taken instead of the aspirin.

- With either treatment, the headache might be gone after an hour. However, the headache may have gone away in 5 minutes with the aspirin and in 45 minutes with the placebos, for example.

- The headache may be still there but may not be as severe with the aspirin as with the placebos.

Solution to Activity 7

It probably does not. If a drug gives only a degree of relief which is not easily noticeable, then it will not be very useful. Thus it is only quite substantial differences that are likely to be of interest.

Solution to Activity 8

It certainly does matter, because the people will expect the active tablet to work and the dummy tablet to be ineffective. Thus their expectations of the treatment will be quite different in the two cases. So it is important to make sure, as far as possible, that the subjects do not know which treatment they are receiving.

Solution to Activity 9

It still matters, because the doctors also have expectations. They will probably expect the active treatment to be better than a placebo, and their expectations can often affect how the patients respond to the treatment.

Solution to Activity 10

If all treatments were equal, you would expect the two patients given sea-water to take longer to recover from the scurvy, so the results from this group may appear worse than the other treatment groups.

Solution to Activity 11

An independent person could have assigned and given the treatments in a private space. Then James Lind would have been blinded to the treatments. Blinding patients to what treatment they themselves received would not have been possible, but patients could have been blinded to the treatments that other patients received.

Solution to Activity 12

It would be unsatisfactory because people are variable. Not only do different people vary in the extent to which aspirin reduces their headaches, but an individual's response to aspirin can vary from one time to another. For example, perhaps with some people the aspirin produces no relief if the headache is very severe, but banishes it altogether if the headache is slight.

Solution to Activity 13

Measurements should be taken at specific times before and after eating. In studies of drugs designed to control glucose levels in diabetics, it is normal to take blood glucose or similar measurements after fasting as a baseline.

Solution to Activity 14

The measurements for men and women are very similar, so there is little need to ensure that the control and experimental groups are of the same sex. However, the maximum heart rate decreases quite noticeably with age, so it would be important to ensure that the experimental and control groups were either of similar age or contained similar proportions of old and young people.

Solution to Activity 15

It assumes that the effect of the drug is reversible, i.e. that the patient is essentially the same after the treatment has been withdrawn as before it was started. In practice, this assumption would need to be tested and it will not hold if, for instance, the patient is cured by the treatment.

Solution to Activity 16

(a) A crossover trial can be used here. Diabetes is a chronic condition that patients will have for the duration of the trial.

(b) It would not be appropriate to use a crossover design here as scurvy could be cured (or have resulted in death) prior to receiving the second diet supplement.

Solution to Activity 17

Matching first on sex, then smoking status, then age, gives the following pairs: 1 and 5, 2 and 4, 3 and 7, 6 and 8. If the relative importance of sex, smoking status and age changes, these matched pairs will change.

Solution to Activity 18

By allocating patients to the two groups at random.

Solution to Activity 19

The null hypothesis would be that the effect of the new drug is not different from the effect of the existing drug. The alternative hypothesis would be that the effect of the new drug is different from the effect of the existing drug, i.e. that it relieves headache pain either more or less effectively.

Solution to Activity 20

A two-sided test would be more appropriate. There is a chance that the existing drug will be better than the new drug (the existing drug has presumably proved better than competitive drugs in the past), but the drug company hopes that the new drug will be the better drug. They wish to detect differences between the new and the existing drug in both directions. Therefore a two-sided test should be used.

Solution to Activity 21

(a) Body temperature can be measured on an interval scale, giving interval scale data.

(b) As pain can be rated (from mild to severe), these are ordinal data.

(c) There are (two) categories, pregnant and non-pregnant, so the information gives categorical data.

(d) Blood pressure measurements give interval scale data.

Solution to Activity 22

Yes, there is a major difference in the two selection procedures. In post-marketing surveillance, people are allocated to groups *after* the decision is taken as to which patients should be treated with the particular drug.

Solution to Activity 23

Combining results for the three groups gives the following contingency table:

	\leq 100 mg	Total daily dose 150 or 200 mg	\geq 300 mg	Total
Blood clot	11	9	8	28
No blood clot	61	55	81	197
Total	72	64	89	225

The null and alternative hypotheses are:

H_0: Total daily dose of drug and the number of patients having a blood clot are independent.

H_1: There is a relationship between the total daily dose of drug and the number of patients having a blood clot.

The Expected table is as follows:

	Total daily dose		
Blood clot	8.9600	7.9644	11.0756
No blood clot	63.0400	56.0356	77.9244

Note that the Expected values are greater than 5, so it is appropriate to use the χ^2 test.

Residual = Observed − Expected, so the following is the Residual table.

	Total daily dose		
Blood clot	2.0400	1.0356	−3.0756
No blood clot	−2.0400	−1.0356	3.0756

For the first cell, the contribution to χ^2 is given by:

$$\chi^2 \text{ contribution} = \frac{(\text{Residual})^2}{\text{Expected}}$$
$$= \frac{(2.0400)^2}{8.9600} \simeq 0.4645.$$

Repeating the calculation for all six cells results in this χ^2 table:

	Total daily dose		
Blood clot	0.4645	0.1347	0.8541
No blood clot	0.0660	0.0191	0.1214

Hence the value of the χ^2 test statistic is

$$0.4645 + 0.1347 + 0.8541 + 0.0660 + 0.0191 + 0.1214 \simeq 1.660$$

As in Example 14, the number of degrees of freedom is $(2 - 1) \times (3 - 1) = 2$ so, from Table 3 (Exercises on Section 4), the critical value at the 5% significance level is 5.991 and at the 1% significance level it is 9.210.

Since the test statistic, 1.660, is less than the 5% critical value, 5.991, we cannot reject H_0 at the 5% significance level. Hence we conclude that the data provide little evidence of a relationship between the total daily drug dose and the number of patients getting a clot.

Solution to Activity 24

As noted at the start of this section, patients who have undergone a hip or knee replacement are at high risk of blood clots. Blood clots can be dangerous so it would be unethical to give such patients a placebo when there are known, established treatments for reducing the risk.

Solution to Activity 25

Patients in the treatment group were given a placebo injection in addition to the dabigatran capsule, and patients in the control group were given a placebo capsule in addition to the enoxaparin injection.

Solution to Activity 26

(a) The same questions that were examined in BISTRO I should be examined in BISTRO II. Thus the questions to examine are whether the daily dose of drug affects the number of patients having (i) a minor bleed, (ii) a major bleed and (iii) a blood clot.

BISTRO I found evidence that the number of patients having a minor bleed was affected, so we would expect BISTRO II to replicate that result. BISTRO II is a larger trial than BISTRO I so there are more likely to be major bleeds. (There were none in BISTRO I.) Also, because it is a larger trial it may find evidence that drug dosage affects the number of patients suffering a blood clot.

The null hypotheses would be:

(i) H_0: Total daily dose of dabigatran and the number of patients having a minor bleed are independent.

(ii) H_0: Total daily dose of dabigatran and the number of patients having a major bleed are independent.

(iii) H_0: Total daily dose of dabigatran and the number of patients having a blood clot are independent.

(b) The primary aim in comparing the two drugs is to discover whether dabigatran is better than enoxaparin. That is, is there a daily dose level of dabigatran for which it is better than enoxaparin? Thus, for the first dose regime, the question is whether taking 50 mg doses of dabigatran twice a day is better than taking enoxaparin. Here, 'better' relates to the number of patients having (i) a minor bleed, (ii) a major bleed and (iii) a blood clot.

The corresponding hypotheses are:

(i) H_0: The drug taken (50 mg of dabigatran twice a day or enoxaparin) and the number of patients having a minor bleed are independent.

(ii) H_0: The drug taken (50 mg of dabigatran twice a day or enoxaparin) and the number of patients having a major bleed are independent.

(iii) H_0: The drug taken (50 mg of dabigatran twice a day or enoxaparin) and the number of patients having a blood clot are independent.

The question would be repeated for each of the other dose levels of dabigatran that were examined in the trial (150 mg twice a day, 300 mg once a day and 225 mg twice a day).

Solutions to exercises

Solution to Exercise 1

(a) Weight loss can be measured on an objective scale – in kilograms per week, for example.

(b) Certain aspects of appetite can be measured only on a subjective scale. Researchers might wish to know, for example, whether a drug affected people's subjective impression of their own appetite. On the other hand, it is possible to set up objective measures which might accurately reflect these subjective impressions: for example, the amount of food eaten (measured by weight or calorie content) over a certain period of time.

(c) This would probably be measured on a subjective scale. People might be asked to rate the soreness of their throat on a scale of discomfort, or doctors might assess the soreness of the throat on the intensity of the inflammation, or the size of the inflamed area. The inflammation could in theory be measured objectively, but in practice it would probably not be measured in this way.

(d) This would be measured on a subjective scale. People would probably be asked to rate the severity of their discomfort on a numerical scale.

Solution to Exercise 2

(a) The severity and nature of the depression – and the individual's history of depression – may vary greatly. For example, some individuals might be suffering from long-lasting and extremely severe depression, whilst others might be suffering from short-lived and moderate depression. The causes, and therefore the cure, of the depression might thus differ. A woman suffering from post-natal depression might, for example, respond to a drug very differently from a woman suffering from a bereavement. A person with a long history of depressive illness might respond to a drug very differently from a person who is experiencing depression for the first time.

(b) People who volunteer to take part in a clinical trial might not be typical of people in general suffering from depression. For example, severely depressed people might not be willing to volunteer at all. Hence the results of these trials on volunteers might not be representative of the results that would be obtained in the population of depression-sufferers in general.

(c) The problem outlined in part (a) would have to be overcome by making sure that the experimental and control groups were as similar as possible with respect to the severity, nature and history of their depression. The problem outlined in part (b) would have to be overcome by selecting subjects for the clinical trial who were representative of the population of depression-sufferers in general, if this is ethically possible.

Solution to Exercise 3

Despite the use of standardised questionnaires, the patients' responses may be markedly affected by their attitude towards the experimenters, and this attitude is likely to vary from one patient, and one experimenter, to another. For example, the answers that an aggressive experimenter obtained might be different from those that would have been obtained from the same patient by a more polite experimenter.

Solution to Exercise 4

(a) This is an ideal example of a matched-pairs design, but one that is extremely difficult to set up, owing to the difficulty of finding enough pairs of identical twins suffering from the condition of interest.

(b) This is a group-comparative design.

(c) This is a crossover design; each individual crosses over during the course of the experiment from one treatment to the other.

Solution to Exercise 5

(a) A crossover design would be most appropriate here, provided that there was no carry-over effect.

(b) The only possible option here would be a group-comparative design because it would not be ethical to use the extra time required to set up a matched-pairs trial.

(c) A matched-pairs design could be the most appropriate here because it might be possible to obtain a lot of volunteers for the trial and to select pairs that match for age, sex, how heavily they smoke, etc. If enough matched pairs could not be found, then a group-comparative design is best, probably using stratified randomisation so that the control group and treatment group have similar characteristics for factors thought important.

Solution to Exercise 6

(a) The data are categorical.

(b) The data are tabulated in a suitable contingency table below.

	Experimental group	Control group	Total
Conceived	1	15	16
Not conceived	999	985	1984
Total	1000	1000	2000

(c) Null hypothesis (H_0): The effects of the new and old contraceptive on conception are the same.

Alternative hypothesis (H_1): The effects of the new and old contraceptive on conception are different.

Expressing these in a form suitable for the χ^2 test involves looking at the experiment in a slightly different way. The drug company was interested in determining whether the type of contraceptive used has any effect on the number of women who conceived during the one-year period. We should therefore set up the null and alternative hypotheses in terms of these variables as follows.

H_0: The type of contraceptive used and the number of women who conceived during the one-year period are independent.

H_1: There is a relationship between the type of contraceptive used and the number of women who conceived during the one-year period.

(You may have set up the null and alternative hypotheses using slightly different wording. This does not matter as long as you have labelled the variables clearly and the hypotheses convey the same meaning.)

(d) The Expected values are calculated using the method of Unit 8 (Subsection 4.2),

$$E = \frac{\text{row total} \times \text{column total}}{\text{overall total}}.$$

which gives the following table of Expected values.

	Experimental group	Control group
Conceived	8	8
Not conceived	992	992

Notice that all the Expected values are greater than 5, so it is appropriate to use the χ^2 test.

The Residuals are obtained from

Residual = Observed − Expected.

Thus, for example, the Residual for the first cell is $1 - 8 = -7$. The following is the Residual table.

	Experimental group	Control group
Conceived	−7	7
Not conceived	7	−7

For the first cell, the contribution to χ^2 is given by,

$$\chi^2 \text{ contribution} = \frac{(\text{Observed} - \text{Expected})^2}{\text{Expected}}$$

$$= \frac{(\text{Residual})^2}{\text{Expected}}$$

$$= \frac{(-7)^2}{8}$$

$$= 6.125.$$

Repeating the calculation for all four cells results in this χ^2 table:

	Experimental group	Control group
Conceived	6.125	6.125
Not conceived	0.0494	0.0494

where the χ^2 contributions for the 'Not conceived' groups have been rounded to four decimal places.

Hence the value of the χ^2 test statistic is

$$6.125 + 6.125 + 0.0494 + 0.0494 \simeq 12.349.$$

The number of degrees of freedom for a 2×2 contingency table is $(2-1) \times (2-1) = 1$.

Hence, from Table 3, the critical value at the 5% significance level is 3.841, and at the 1% significance level it is 6.635.

Since the test statistic, 12.348, is greater than the 1% critical value, 6.635, we reject H_0 in favour of H_1 at the 1% significance level and conclude that there is strong evidence of a relationship between the type of contraceptive used and the number of women who conceived in the one-year period. In the terminology of Subsection 4.2, the new and old contraceptives have significantly different effects on conception.

(e) Looking at the contingency table in (b), you can see that the new contraceptive results in fewer conceptions. This, together with the result of the hypothesis test, means that the drug company should be satisfied that the new contraceptive was better than the existing one against which they tested it. These results would also be useful evidence to submit with an application for a product licence, provided that they were accompanied by evidence that there were no side effects and that the trials had been carried out carefully – for example, that both groups of women were using the contraceptives correctly. (Many oral contraceptives are effective only if they are taken regularly at the same time every day.)

Solution to Exercise 7

(a) These data are on an interval scale (of beats per minute). Not only is it possible to say that a heart rate of 120 beats per minute is larger than one of 70 beats per minute, it also makes sense to say that it is 50 beats per minute larger.

(b) Since this was a crossover design, the two measurements for each person form a matched pair. (Each pair of measurements consists of the heart rates for one person – when given the drug and when given the placebo.) The sample size is small, so the matched-pairs t-test is appropriate here.

(c) The necessary assumption is that the population distribution of the differences in heart rate reduction (between the placebo and the drug) follow a normal distribution.

(d) The hypotheses for a matched-pairs t-test are:

$$H_0\colon \mu_d = 0 \quad \text{and} \quad H_1\colon \mu_d \neq 0,$$

where d is the difference between the placebo and drug.

(e) The two-sided matched-pairs t-test statistic is found using the procedure in Subsection 4.2 of Unit 10. The first step is to calculate the differences between the pairs of data values, square them, and total these, as in the table below. Here we have subtracted the D (drug) values from the P (placebo) values. You may have subtracted the P values from the D values, in which case your solution will differ slightly from ours. However, you should end up with the same conclusion.

Subject	Heart rate (beats per minute) Placebo	Drug	Difference d	d^2
1	105	90	15	225
2	88	82	6	36
3	90	95	−5	25
4	89	80	9	81
5	80	88	−8	64
6	110	75	35	1225
7	84	83	1	1
8	100	90	10	100
$\sum$	746	683	63	1757

The mean of the differences is

$$\overline{d} = \frac{\sum d}{n} = \frac{63}{8} = 7.875.$$

Also

$$s^2 = \frac{1}{n-1}\left(\sum d^2 - \frac{(\sum d)^2}{n}\right) = \frac{1}{8-1}\left(1757 - \frac{63^2}{8}\right)$$
$$= \frac{1}{7}(1757 - 496.125) = 180.125.$$

Thus, the standard deviation is $s = \sqrt{180.125} \simeq 13.421$. Hence,

$$\text{ESE} = \frac{s}{\sqrt{n}} = \frac{13.421}{\sqrt{8}} \simeq 4.745.$$

Now, the test statistic is

$$t = \frac{\overline{d}}{\text{ESE}}$$

as the null hypothesis is H_0: $\mu_d = 0$. Thus

$$t \simeq \frac{7.875}{4.745} \simeq 1.660.$$

From Table 4, the critical value at the 5% significance level with $n - 1 = 7$ degrees of freedom is 2.365.

Since the test statistic, 1.660, is less than the critical value, 2.365, we cannot reject H_0 at the 5% significance level. In the terminology of Subsection 4.2, the drug and placebo are not significantly different in their effect on heart rate. Thus, from these data there is little evidence that the new drug alters people's heart rate.

(However, the sample of people used is very small, so it might still be worth conducting a larger trial with more people.)

Solution to Exercise 8

The contingency table for the data is as follows:

	Blood clot		Total
	Yes	No	
Dabigatran 220 mg	53	827	880
Enoxaparin 40 mg	60	837	897
Total	113	1664	1777

The null and alternative hypotheses are:

H_0: Daily doses of 220 mg dabigatran and 40 mg enoxaparin are equally effective at reducing the risk of a blood clot.

H_1: Daily doses of 220 mg dabigatran and 40 mg enoxaparin are not equally effective at reducing the risk of a blood clot.

The Expected table is as follows.

	Yes	No
Dabigatran 220 mg	55.9595	824.0405
Enoxaparin 40 mg	57.0405	839.9595

The Expected values are greater than 5, so it is appropriate to use the χ^2 test.

Residual = Observed − Expected, so the following is the Residual table.

	Yes	No
Dabigatran 220 mg	−2.9595	2.9595
Enoxaparin 40 mg	2.9595	−2.9595

The χ^2 table is:

	Yes	No
Dabigatran 220 mg	0.1565	0.0106
Enoxaparin 40 mg	0.1536	0.0104

The χ^2 statistic is therefore

$$\chi^2 = 0.1565 + 0.0106 + 0.1536 + 0.0104 \simeq 0.331.$$

The number of degrees of freedom for a 2×2 contingency table is $(2-1) \times (2-1) = 1$. So, from Table 3 (Exercises on Section 4), the critical value at the 5% significance level is 3.841. As $0.331 < 3.841$ we do not reject the null hypothesis at the 5% significance level. There is little evidence that daily doses of 220 mg dabigatran or 40 mg enoxaparin differ in their effectiveness at reducing the risk of a blood clot.

Acknowledgements

Grateful acknowledgement is made to the following sources:

Figure 1: www.diabetes.co.uk

Figure 2: www.diabetes.co.uk

Figure 10(a): Michael Fenn / Fillmore Photography. This file is licensed under the Creative Commons Attribution Licence http://creativecommons.org/licenses/by/3.0/

Figure 10(b): Armin Kubelbeck / This file is licensed under the Creative Commons Attribution-Share Alike Licence http://creativecommons.org/licenses/by-sa/3.0/

Section 1 photo (laboratory testing), Horia Varlan / www.flickr.com. This file is licensed under the Creative Commons Attribution-Non-commercial Licence http://creativecommons.org/licenses/by-nc/3.0/

Subsection 1.2 EMA logo © EMCDDA, 1995–2012.

Subsection 1.2 photo (Nexavar): courtesy of Bayer Healthcare / www.healthcare.bayer.com

Subsection 1.2 photo (James Lind): courtesy of James Lind Library. This file is licensed under the Creative Commons Attribution Licence http://creativecommons.org/licenses/by/3.0/

Subsection 2.1 photo (headache): open Democracy / www.flickr.com. This file is licensed under the Creative Commons Attribution-Share Alike Licence http://creativecommons.org/licenses/by-sa/3.0/

Subsection 2.1 cartoon (control group): www.causeweb.org

Subsection 2.1 photo (various pills): publisher unknown. This file is licensed under the Creative Commons Attribution-Share Alike Licence http://creativecommons.org/licenses/by-sa/3.0/

Subsection 2.2 cartoon (immunity to placebos): www.causeweb.org

Subsection 2.2 cartoon (research laboratory): www.causeweb.org

Subsection 2.3 photo (jazz band), taken from: www.polarityrecords.com/early-jazz-bands-and-jug-bands-photo-gallery.html

Subsection 3.2 photo (twins): Shawn Welling / www.flickr.com. This file is licensed under the Creative Commons Attribution-Share Alike Licence http://creativecommons.org/licenses/by-sa/3.0/

Exercises on Section 3, cartoon: www.causeweb.org

Subsection 4.2 image of influenza virus: Kat Masback / www.flickr.com/photos/36128932@N03/3338845735. This file is licensed under the Creative Commons Attribution-Share Alike Licence http://creativecommons.org/licenses/by-sa/3.0/

Subsection 4.3 photo (tall/short): Gideon Tsang / www.flickr.com. This file is licensed under the Creative Commons Attribution-Share Alike Licence http://creativecommons.org/licenses/by-sa/3.0/

Exercises on Section 4, photo (contraceptive pills): Beria Lima / www.flickr.com. This file is licensed under the Creative Commons Attribution-Share Alike Licence http://creativecommons.org/licenses/by-sa/3.0/

Subsection 5.1 cartoon (side effects): www.cartoonstock.com

Subsection 5.1 cartoon (no side effects): www.cartoonstock.com

Subsection 5.2 CHMP logo, taken from: http://holidaymagiccd.com/press-release/

Subsection 5.3 photo (stethoscope and keyboard): jfcherry / www.flickr.com. This file is licensed under the Creative Commons Attribution-Share Alike Licence http://creativecommons.org/licenses/by-sa/3.0/

Section 6 image of blood clot: Nephron / This file is licensed under the Creative Commons Attribution-Share Alike Licence http://creativecommons.org/licenses/by-sa/3.0/

Subsection 6.1 cartoon (laxative): www.cartoonstock.com

Subsection 6.4 image of Pradaxa, taken from: www.anh-usa.org/wp-content/uploads/2013/04/

Every effort has been made to contact copyright holders. If any have been inadvertently overlooked the publishers will be pleased to make the necessary arrangements at the first opportunity.

Unit 12

Review

Introduction

This unit is designed to help you consolidate what you have learned in M140. It describes some extensions of ideas you have already met, as well as a small number of new statistical ideas. The aim is to draw together parts of the module that are closely linked, even though they may have been in different units. Each section will review one or two topics and contain a number of activities to help you refresh your knowledge of them.

Another way of drawing material together

- Section 1 reviews descriptive statistics and summary statistics, which were the focus of Units 1, 2 and 3 (Book 1). There is new material in Subsection 1.2, which introduces *growth charts*.

- Section 2 discusses the collection of data through surveys and in experiments, including clinical trials. The material is based mainly on Units 4, 10 and 11, with the addition of material on combining survey methods (Subsection 2.1).

- Section 3 reviews properties of probability given in Units 6 and 8. Also, in Subsection 3.2, the general form of the binomial distribution is introduced. (Unit 6 used a specialised form of this distribution.)

- Section 4 describes the principal steps in a hypothesis test (Unit 6) and considers the χ^2 test of independence in a contingency table (Unit 8).

- Section 5 reviews the properties of the normal distribution and examines hypothesis tests and confidence intervals for making inferences about the mean of a population or the difference between two population means (Units 7, 9 and 10). A two-sample t-test for populations with unequal variances is introduced.

- Section 6 concerns relationships between two variables and reviews regression and correlation, which were the main focus of Units 5 and 9.

- Section 7 uses Minitab to explore binomial distributions and perform two-sample t-tests.

> In planning your study, you should note that there is new (assessable) material in Subsection 1.2, a small part of Subsection 2.1, most of Subsection 3.2 and a large part of Subsection 5.2.

Section 7 directs you to the Computer Book. You are also guided to the Computer Book at the end of Sections 3 and 5. It is better to do the work at those points in the text, although you can leave it until later if you prefer.

1 Summarising data

One reason for summarising data is to be able to report the data succinctly, perhaps quoting its median value or range in order to describe features of the data. As well as numeric summaries, figures such as a boxplot or stemplot can be used for this purpose and are very informative. Another important reason for summarising data, which you saw in later units, is that summary statistics are often all that are needed for performing hypothesis tests or calculating confidence intervals. In this context there is little choice as to how the data should be summarised. For example, the sample mean and the sample size are the information required from the data in order to perform a one-sample z-test.

In Subsections 1.1 and 1.2, numerical statistics for summarising data are described. In Subsection 1.3, we turn to graphical summaries. In Subsection 1.4, we focus on the Retail Prices Index (RPI) and other indexes for summarising data on prices and earnings. All these topics are primarily taught in Units 1 to 3.

1.1 Common numerical summaries

Numbers that are used to summarise data are referred to as *summary statistics*. Usually, the key quantities used to summarise a set of data are its median or mean, along with its interquartile range, standard deviation or variance.

Median and mean

The median is the middle item in a set of data (if the number of items in the batch is odd) or the average of the middle two items (if there are an even number of items in the batch).

The mean is the average value in a set of data, given by:

$$\overline{x} = \frac{\sum x}{n},$$

where n is the number of items in the set of data.

If you have to give just *one* number to summarise a set of data, then the median or mean are the obvious choices – one gives the middle of the data and the other its average. The two are quite close if the data have a fairly symmetric distribution, but will differ more if the data show great skewness. When the data are highly skew, the median is often more representative of the data.

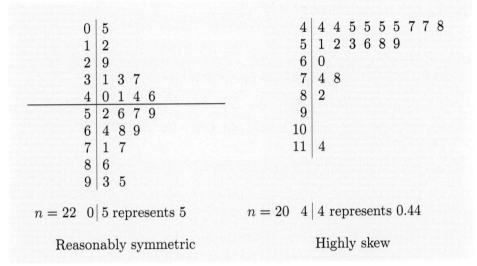

```
  0 | 5                          4 | 4 4 5 5 5 5 7 7 8
  1 | 2                          5 | 1 2 3 6 8 9
  2 | 9                          6 | 0
  3 | 1 3 7                      7 | 4 8
  4 | 0 1 4 6                    8 | 2
  5 | 2 6 7 9                    9 |
  6 | 4 8 9                     10 |
  7 | 1 7                       11 | 4
  8 | 6
  9 | 3 5
```

$n = 22$ 0|5 represents 5 $n = 20$ 4|4 represents 0.44

Reasonably symmetric   Highly skew

Figure 1 Examples of reasonably symmetric and highly skew datasets

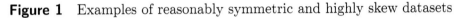

Activity 1 *Time between elections*

Following the *Fixed-term Parliaments Act 2011*, general elections in the UK take place every five years. Before that, an election could be called at any point the Prime Minister wished.

The following are the times (in months) between elections in the years 1970 to 2010:

44,   7,   55,   49,   48,   58,   61,   49,   47,   60.

(a) What is the median of these data?

(b) What is the mean of these data?

(c) Which observation is most responsible for the difference between the median and mean? Would you consider either the mean or median unrepresentative of these data?

The median and mean each describe the *location* of a set of data. They give a value that, in some sense, the data are centred around. The interquartile range, standard deviation and variance are each a measure of the extent to which a set of data is spread out.

Interquartile range

The central half of a set of data lies between the lower quartile and the upper quartile. The distance between these quartiles is the interquartile range.

In the ordered set of data, the lower quartile is at position $(n + 1)/4$ and the upper quartile is at position $3(n + 1)/4$.

Activity 2   *Interquartile range examples*

The following two sets of data have each been ordered from lowest to highest. The first set contains 15 data values and the second contains 20 data values. Determine the interquartile range of each set.

(a) 47, 49, 56, 57, 58, 58, 63, 63, 63, 64, 64, 65, 66, 68, 73.

(b) 13, 15, 16, 16, 17, 19, 20, 20, 20, 20, 21, 21, 21, 22, 23, 24, 26, 27, 28, 29.

Variance and standard deviation

The variance is the squared differences between each data value and the sample mean, added together and divided by $n - 1$ (where n is the sample size).

The standard deviation is the square root of the variance.

Although, from its definition, the formula for the sample variance (s^2) is

$$s^2 = \frac{\sum(x - \bar{x})^2}{n - 1},$$

it is quicker to separately calculate $\sum x^2$ and $\sum x$ and apply the equivalent formula

$$s^2 = \frac{1}{n - 1}\left(\sum x^2 - \frac{(\sum x)^2}{n}\right).$$

Activity 3   *Lowestoft daily temperatures*

The following are the mean daily maximum temperatures (in °C) in Lowestoft for July, in the years from 2002 to 2010:

20.5, 21.6, 19.6, 19.9, 23.7, 20.8, 21.1, 21.2, 23.6.

Determine the variance and the standard deviation of these data.

Victoria Beach, Lowestoft

A disadvantage of the variance is that its scale is not the scale of the original data. For example, suppose the data are the times taken to perform a task and each of these times is typically within 15 seconds of 2 minutes. Then the standard deviation might be, say, 10 seconds. This quantity is readily interpreted and can be related to the data values. In contrast, the variance would be 100 seconds^2, which cannot be related to the data values quite so easily.

The reason the variance is important is that it has good mathematical properties. For instance, to perform a two-sample z-test (Unit 7) requires ESE: the estimated standard error of $\bar{x}_A - \bar{x}_B$. This is calculated, not from the two standard deviations s_A and s_B, but from the variances s_A^2 and s_B^2:

$$\text{ESE} = \sqrt{\frac{s_A^2}{n_A} + \frac{s_B^2}{n_B}}.$$

When a set of data is to be summarised by giving one quantity to indicate its location and another to indicate its spread, we generally give either the mean and standard deviation, or the median and interquartile range. Quoting other pairings, such as the mean and interquartile range, is less common.

The quantities used most commonly in statistical calculations (such as when forming confidence intervals or testing hypotheses) are means, variances and standard deviations. Even when testing whether a population median takes a specified value, we do not need the sample median.

1.2 Numerical summaries used less frequently

This subsection contains new material, not previously covered in M140.

The largest and smallest values in a dataset, E_U and E_L, are quite often recorded in conjunction with other summary statistics so as to give a fuller description of the data. (For example, they are included in five-figure summary tables.) Inspecting the values of E_U or E_L is a useful step in cleaning data prior to statistical analysis as unusual values can highlight major errors in a dataset, perhaps caused by typing errors or other errors in recording the data.

In contrast, the range, $E_U - E_L$, is seldom of interest because it is heavily influenced by the odd high or low value, so is often a poor reflection of the typical spread in a dataset. Similarly, the **mid-range**, $(E_u + E_L)/2$, and mode are seldom used as summary statistics even though they could be used as measures of location – they are generally less representative of the centre of the data than the mean or median, so one of the latter is used instead.

An informative way of giving a detailed summary of a large set of data is to identify some of its percentiles. As well as the median (50th percentile), lower quartile (25th percentile) and upper quartile (75th percentile), some of the deciles (10th, 20th, ..., 90th percentiles) might also be given. Also, in forming confidence intervals and prediction intervals, the $2\frac{1}{2}$ and $97\frac{1}{2}$ percentiles are important as they are the end-points of a 95% interval. While confidence intervals summarise the results of a statistical analysis, rather than simply summarising a set of data, they illustrate that the more extreme percentiles can be of interest. Hence, it is often useful to include percentiles of less than 10% and more than 90% in a detailed summary of data.

To avoid a reader being swamped with numbers, the information from a large number of percentiles might be presented in a diagram. Figure 2 gives an example called a **growth chart**. It shows the distribution of weights in a very large sample of boys in the first year of life. The percentiles that are given are the 0.4th, 2nd, 9th, 25th, 50th, 75th, 91st, 98th and 99.6th.

The type of chart in Figure 2 is given to mothers leaving hospital after giving birth. It should reassure the majority of new parents that their baby is growing normally, while hopefully ringing alarm bells when a baby's weight is unusually high or low. Reading values from the graph shows, for instance, that at 28 weeks old:

- 25% of boys are below 7.5 kg (and 75% are above that weight).

- 9% of boys are below 7 kg.

- 2% are above 10 kg.

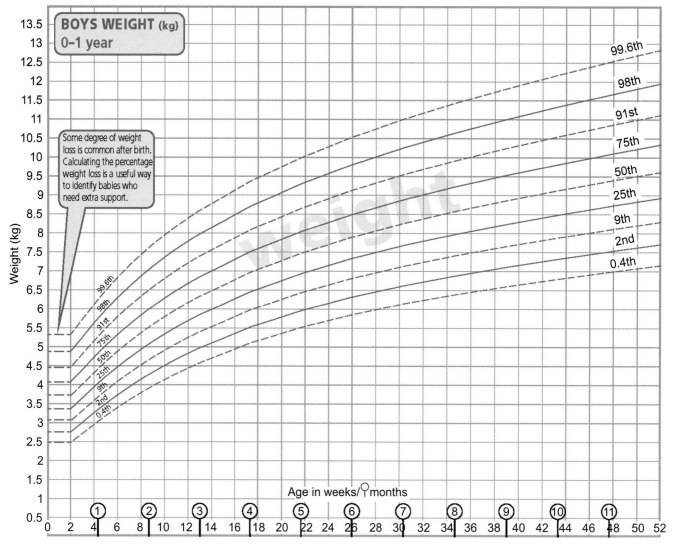

Figure 2

Growth chart showing percentiles of boys' weights in first year of life

Activity 4   *Percentiles from a growth chart*

Use Figure 2 to give the proportion of boys who weigh:

(a) less than 4.5 kg when 10 weeks old;

(b) more than 10 kg when 46 weeks old;

(c) between 6 kg and 7.5 kg when 22 weeks old.

You have now covered the material related to Screencast 1 for Unit 12 (see the M140 website).

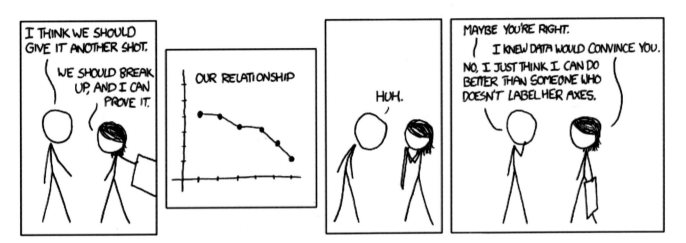

1.3 Graphical summaries

Boxplots and stemplots are commonly used as graphical summaries of data. If there are no unusually large or small data, a boxplot gives precisely the same information as a five-figure summary, except that the boxplot does not give n, the sample size.

Five-figure summary

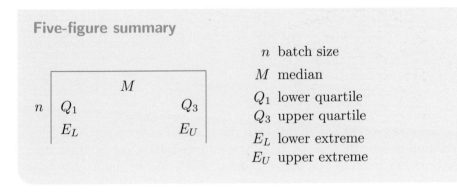

n batch size

M median

Q_1 lower quartile

Q_3 upper quartile

E_L lower extreme

E_U upper extreme

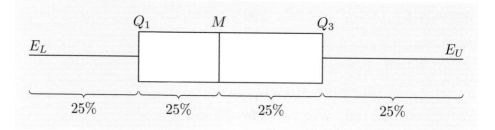

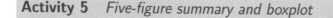

Figure 3 A standard boxplot

Activity 5 *Five-figure summary and boxplot*

The following data were given in part (a) of Activity 2 (Subsection 1.1):

   47, 49, 56, 57, 58, 58, 63, 63, 63, 64, 64, 65, 66, 68, 73.

(a) Produce a five-figure summary of the data.

(b) Produce a boxplot of the data.

(c) Explain whether the boxplot indicates marked skewness in the data.

Details for drawing boxplots are given in Subsection 2.2 of Unit 3.

If there are very large or very small values (relative to the main body of data), then in a boxplot these are marked individually and the whiskers only extend as far as the lower adjacent value (for the left whisker) or the upper adjacent value (for the right whisker).

A stemplot resembles a histogram that has been turned on its side. It shows the shape of the distribution and contains most (or all) of the information in the data. Examples of stemplots are given in Figure 1 (Subsection 1.1). The following is a stemplot of the data in Activity 5.

$$
\begin{array}{r|l}
4 & 7\ 9 \\
5 & \\
5 & 6\ 7\ 8\ 8 \\
6 & 3\ 3\ 3\ 4\ 4 \\
6 & 5\ 6\ 8 \\
7 & 3 \\
\end{array}
$$

$n = 15$ $4 \mid 7$ represents 47

From this stemplot we could give each value with full accuracy – no information is lost. In Activity 6, a little information is lost because the initial data are given to two decimal places, while the stemplot only gives one decimal place.

Activity 6 *Olympic times for the 800 metres*

The following data give the times of 24 athletes in the semi-finals of the men's 800-metre race at the 2012 Olympic Games. (A 25th runner was disqualified.) The times are given in seconds above 1 minute. For example, the fastest time of 1 minute 44.34 seconds is given below as 44.34 seconds. The data values have been ordered from fastest to slowest.

Table 1 800-metre race times, in seconds above 1 minute

44.34	44.35	44.51	44.54	44.63	44.74	44.87	44.93
45.08	45.09	45.10	45.34	45.44	45.63	45.84	45.85
46.14	46.19	46.29	46.66	47.52	48.18	48.98	53.46

(Data source: Official website of the Olympic Movement)

(a) Construct a stretched stemplot of the data, in which each whole second is split between two levels, and one outlier is listed separately.

(b) Comment on the shape of the stemplot.

In summarising data, the following is the order of priority.

1. If data must be summarised by just one number, then a number that represents the location of the data should be given (usually the median or mean).

2. If two numbers are to be used as the summary, then the second number should indicate the spread of the data (usually the interquartile range, standard deviation or variance).

3. Additional information would describe the shape of the data, notably any skewness, and identify the largest and smallest data along with any numbers that are extreme relative to the main body of the data.

Graphical summaries can convey a lot of information in an accessible way.

1.4 Summarising changes in prices and earnings

The Retail Prices Index (RPI) and Consumer Prices Index (CPI) are both used to summarise the overall change in the level of prices paid by people for the goods and services they buy. These price indexes are calculated in similar ways, and here we will focus on the RPI. Both use a very large 'basket of goods' that is designed to reflect the pattern of spending in the UK. Figure 4 shows the make-up of the RPI basket in 2012.

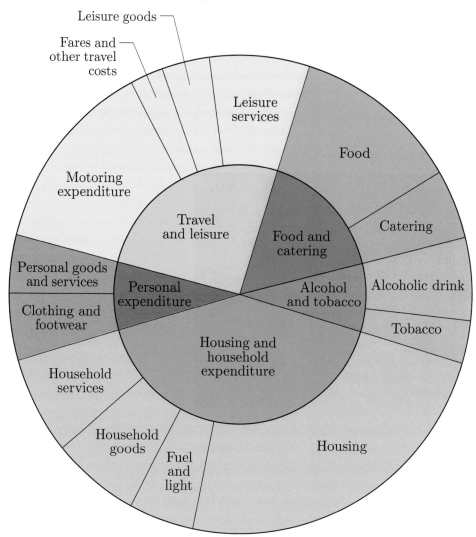

Figure 4   Structure of the RPI in 2012 (based on data from the Office for National Statistics)

As can be seen, the RPI is divided into five broad groupings. The inner ring shows, for example, that the typical household spends about twice as much on the group 'Food and catering' as on 'Personal expenditure'. The five groupings are divided into 14 more detailed subgroups, which are themselves divided into sections.

Certain items within each section are priced. For instance, within the 'Food and catering' group there is a 'Bread' section and the prices of representative items of bread (such as a large white sliced loaf and bread rolls) are monitored each month in a number of shops and supermarkets. For each item, its prices in the current month are compared with its prices in the previous January and a *price ratio* is calculated that fairly reflects how the price of the item has changed across the country.

> ## Weighted mean of price ratios
>
> The weighted mean of two or more numbers is:
> $$\frac{\text{sum of \{number} \times \text{weight\}}}{\text{sum of weights}}.$$
> So the weighted mean of two or more price ratios is:
> $$\frac{\text{sum of \{price ratio} \times \text{weight\}}}{\text{sum of weights}}.$$

1. First, the price ratios of items within a subgroup are combined by taking their weighted mean – using weights that reflect expenditure patterns for the different items. These give a price ratio for each subgroup.

2. Next, the price ratios of subgroups within a group are combined by taking their weighted mean, giving a price ratio for the group.

3. Lastly, group price ratios are combined by taking their weighted mean, giving the *all-item price ratio* for that month.

The weights are determined from survey data on people's expenditures. They are set each January and used for a year. Calculating the all-item price ratio from the group price ratios is illustrated in Activity 7.

Activity 7   *All-item price ratio for 2013*

Group price ratios (r) for August 2013 relative to January 2013 are given in Table 2, where the weights (w) for 2013 are also given. Complete the last column of the table and show that the sum is 1021.086. Hence show that the all-item price ratio for August 2013 (relative to January 2013) is approximately 1.021.

Table 2   Weights and price ratios for August 2013

Group	Price ratio for August 2013 relative to January 2013 (r)	2013 weights (w)	Price ratio × weight ($r \times w$)
Food and catering	1.013	163	
Alcohol and tobacco	1.021	91	
Housing and household expenditure	1.017	419	
Personal expenditure	1.055	83	
Travel and leisure	1.022	244	

(Source: Office for National Statistics)

The RPI in January 2013 was derived from the RPI in January 2012, which in turn was derived from the RPI in 2011, and so on. Hence the RPI is a chained index. To give the chain a starting point, the RPI is set equal to 100 at a base date. The current base date for the RPI is January 1987.

The RPI in any month is obtained through multiplying 'that month's price ratio relative to the previous January' by 'the RPI in the previous January'. For example:

- The price ratio for January 2013 relative to January 2012 (the previous January) was 1.0328 and the RPI in January 2012 was 238.0. Hence the RPI in January 2013 was $1.0328 \times 238.0 \simeq 245.8$.

- As the price ratio for August 2013 relative to January 2013 was 1.021 (from Activity 7), the RPI in August 2013 was $1.021 \times 245.8 \simeq 251.0$.

The change in a person's annual expenditure seldom reflects change in prices, which is the change that the RPI aims to capture. Rather, the change in a person's annual expenditure probably reflects a change in the person's annual income or a change in their personal circumstances. It is for this reason that the RPI requires a notional basket of goods. In contrast, finding the change in a person's annual earnings simply requires knowledge of their earnings. Moreover, information on a person's earnings is usually carefully recorded – a by-product of the UK system of income tax. Hence, constructing an index of earnings does not face the same challenges that the RPI must overcome. There are, however, adjustments that surveys of earnings must make. For example, the Average Weekly Earnings (AWE) index seasonally adjusts figures to allow for the effect of changes in earnings that occur regularly at fixed times of the year. Another example is the Annual Survey of Hours and Earnings (ASHE), which only collects information on paid employees and must make adjustments for the self-employed and unemployed, amongst others. Some detail is given in Unit 3.

2 Collecting data

Throughout this module we have examined samples of data. Sometimes the purpose of a sample is to learn about the population from which it comes, so the sample needs to be representative of the whole population and will usually need to be diverse. Another reason for gathering sample data is to perform an experiment. Then, often, the items selected for the experiment should be as similar as possible, so that differences between treatments (say) are not obscured by random variation between items.

Simple random sampling is the most common method of sampling, and many methods of testing hypotheses or forming confidence intervals assume that the data are a simple random sample from the population of interest. This is true of the *sign test* in Unit 6 where in one activity (Activity 29, Subsection 4.1) we have a random sample of 15 large schools from the East of England region, in another (Activity 34, Subsection 5.1) we have a random sample of secondary school academies from the East of England, and so forth. Similarly, random samples are used in one-sample

z-tests (Unit 7, Activity 26 in Subsection 5.2 and Exercise 17 in Section 5, for example) and to form confidence intervals from z-tests (Unit 9, Activity 18 in Subsection 4.2). In order to compare the means of two populations it is common to take a simple random sample from each population, as illustrated in Unit 7 (Exercises 20 and 21, Section 6) and Unit 10 (Exercise 4, Section 3).

In principle, a simple random sample should be picked by sampling at random from the target population. This requires a list of the target population (or a mechanism that can select members of the target population at random) and is often impractical or impossible. Often a sample is treated as a simple random sample because it was not selected in any special way. For example, in your experiment with mustard seeds in Unit 10, the seeds are treated as a random sample of mustard seeds even though you did not use random number tables to decide which shop to go to for the seeds, or which packet of seeds to buy when you were in the shop.

In Subsection 2.1, we review survey methods that aim to find out about a population by examining just some of the items in the population, or questioning just some of the people in it. In Subsection 2.2, we discuss the collection of data for experiments.

2.1 Survey methods

When a large sample is to be gathered and no list of the population is available, then quota sampling is commonly employed so that characteristics of the population, such as age and gender, are reflected in the sample. For example, interviewers may be told to complete questionnaires with, say, thirty men aged 30–35, forty women aged 50–60, and so forth. This method might even be used when a list of the population is available, as it can be an economical method of gathering reasonably representative data. However, when a list of population members is available, other efficient survey methods can be employed. Also, given a suitable list, proper randomisation can be used to give a simple random sample. The following methods were discussed in Unit 4.

Simple random sampling

In simple random sampling, members are selected one at a time. At each selection, those members of the population who have not already been selected are each equally likely to be the one selected. Thus each selection is independent of earlier selections, except that no member of the population can be selected more than once. The selection might be based on numbers given by a random number table or, more commonly, by a computer's randomisation procedure. In Unit 6, the module team used random numbers generated by Minitab to select a sample of schools from a list of schools in the East of England.

Systematic random sampling

Choosing a sample from a list of the target population is slightly easier using systematic random sampling rather than simple random sampling. If, say, one-seventh of the population is to be included in a systematic

Statisticians fall asleep faster by taking a random sample of sheep.

sample, then every seventh person in the list would be included in the sample, starting from one of the first seven people in the list, chosen at random. The random choice of starting point means that everyone in the population has an equal chance of being included in the sample.

If the population is listed in an order such that similar items or people are grouped together, then systematic sampling may well produce a more representative cross-section of the population than would be obtained by simple random sampling. For example, in an alphabetical listing of people, a husband and wife may well be listed such that one is immediately after the other. Then they would not both be included in a systematic sample, but through chance they might both be included in a simple random sample – which would then over-represent their family.

The following activity is designed to refresh your skills in using random number tables to choose samples for the above two types of survey.

Activity 8 *Random and systematic samples*

Table 3 gives the initials of 68 people who form the target population. The people are grouped in six sets (A, B, C, D, E and F) and have been labelled $01, 02, \ldots, 68$.

Table 3   A population divided into sets A–F

Label	Initials	Set	Label	Initials	Set	Label	Initials	Set
01	C.J.	A	24	R.D.M.	C	47	Z.G.	D
02	R.A.B.	A	25	M.C.	C	48	Y.H.	D
03	A.P.D.	A	26	E.L.	C	49	K.V.M.	E
04	M.A.	A	27	T.P.H.	C	50	P.H.	E
05	E.M.	A	28	I.M.	C	51	J.P.R.	E
06	J.L.	A	29	J.S.	C	52	G.C.T.	E
07	J.D.H.	A	30	C.G.	C	53	D.S.P.	E
08	A.E.G.	A	31	T.R.F.	C	54	H.M.	E
09	E.M.H.	B	32	C.C.T.	C	55	M.J.P.	E
10	T.N.	B	33	D.J.S.	C	56	C.S.T.	F
11	C.T.L.	B	34	S.G.C.	C	57	A.Y.K.	F
12	B.W.S.	B	35	D.L.	C	58	A.H.S.	F
13	J.A.R.	B	36	D.K.B.	C	59	D.B.M.	F
14	J.S.R.	B	37	C.A.M.	C	60	M.A.T.	F
15	S.L.	B	38	R.I.J.	C	61	A.N.D.	F
16	W.N.R.	B	39	W.O.J.	C	62	J.R.H.	F
17	A.C.D.	B	40	A.H.D.	D	63	R.J.C.	F
18	P.J.G.	B	41	P.V.	D	64	G.T.W.	F
19	W.W.S.	B	42	A.L.	D	65	G.K.S.	F
20	H.T.	B	43	L.R.P.	D	66	E.D.	F
21	G.B.Y.	B	44	D.A.F.	D	67	Y.S.H.	F
22	D.W.	B	45	R.H.R.	D	68	M.B.	F
23	M.S.	B	46	A.T.	D			

(a) Calculate the proportion of the population in each set.

(b) Choose a simple random sample of size 17 from the population in Table 3 using the random number table in the appendix to Unit 4, starting at the beginning of row **30**.

How many people in the sample are from set A? How many from each of the other sets? In the sample, which sets are under-represented relative to their size?

(c) Choose a systematic random sample of about a quarter of the population in Table 3. This time, take the first digit in row **10** in the range 1 to 4 as your random start. Analyse the sample with respect to 'set' and comment on how representative it is of the population.

(d) Explain whether you expected the sample obtained in (c) to represent the population better than the sample obtained in (b)?

Stratified sampling

Sometimes a population divides naturally into separate categories/ subpopulations, and items in the same category are likely to be more similar with respect to a quantity of interest than items from different categories. Then the categories are *strata*, provided each member of the population falls in exactly one category and we know (before gathering sample data) which members are in each category.

The approach in stratified sampling is to take a subsample from each stratum and combine the information the subsamples yield. If the quantity of interest is a numerical measurement on an interval scale (such as a length or weight, say), then the information from subsamples is combined as follows to yield an overall estimate of the population mean.

1. Taking each stratum separately, the sample mean and variance of the data in its subsample are calculated. These are estimates of the mean and variance for that complete stratum.

2. A weighted average of the strata means is calculated to obtain an estimate of the population mean. The weights are based on the number of data in each strata. (Formulas for the weights and the standard error of the weighted average are outside the scope of M140.)

If the quantity of interest is a proportion (the proportion of the population who prefer brand X to brand Y, say), then the proportion in each subsample is determined first – to give an estimate of the proportion in each stratum. A weighted average of these proportions is then calculated and taken as the overall estimate of the population proportion.

Cluster sampling

Cluster sampling is almost essential when data are to be gathered through face-to-face interviews and the population of interest is spread across a large geographical area or consists of a large number of locations. Many surveys require interviewers to call at people's homes or workplaces and cluster sampling is a way of reducing the travel involved in conducting the survey. In cluster sampling:

- The large geographical area is divided into small geographical areas – the *clusters*. (Each cluster might be an office block, or a street, say.)

- A limited number of these clusters are selected, preferably at random from all the clusters.

- Cluster samples are obtained by taking a random sample from each selected cluster. (For example, 20% of the people in each cluster might be questioned in the survey.)

- The cluster samples are combined to form a sample from the population.

In forming cluster samples, it is quite common to choose sample sizes so that the same proportion of each cluster is sampled. For example, the survey design might specify that 20% of the people in each selected cluster should be questioned in the survey. As long as the clusters that will be sampled are selected at random, each member of the target population will then have an equal chance of being included in the survey – which seems an attractive property. However, if the clusters in the population differ radically in size, a drawback of this approach is that the total sample size (and hence the cost of the sample) is not known until after the clusters to sample have been selected. There are variants of cluster sampling that are designed to avoid this problem.

With stratified sampling, the strata subsamples must contain the same proportion of each stratum if each member of the target population is to have an equal chance of being sampled. Again, this is quite commonly done in practice, but there can be reasons for preferring alternatives. In particular, from previous surveys it may be known that certain strata display far greater variability than other strata. That is, the variance of the quantity of interest is known to be greater in particular strata. Those strata should then be sampled more heavily than strata in which the variability is less.

Combining survey methods

This is new material, not previously covered in M140.

In practice, it is common to combine different survey methods in designing a survey. To give an example, suppose a sample of staff working in hospitals across the UK is required. If it is thought that regional variations are likely, then the following survey design might be appropriate.

- Divide the UK into regions: say Scotland, Northern England, Wales, the Midlands and so on. Each region is a stratum and hospital staff from each stratum must be included in the sample.

- Within each region there are a lot of hospitals and so, to reduce the travelling a survey interviewer must do, each hospital might be treated as a cluster. Then, within each stratum, cluster sampling would be used to determine which hospitals the interviewer would visit.

- Suppose the survey must question nurses, doctors and administrators.

Cluster sampling?

To ensure a balanced sample is taken, these three categories of staff might be treated as three strata, and a random sample taken from each.

The above survey design might seem unnecessarily complicated, but surveys can be expensive. Moreover, large surveys are often repeated at regular intervals, so efficient and effective design is important. In Unit 2, some information was given about the survey methods used to obtain data for the Retail Price Index (RPI). For the RPI, the UK is divided into twelve regions (strata) and shopping locations in each region are placed within size categories.

- The size categories (another level of strata) are based on factors such as the size of the shopping population, the number of shops, and the drive-time to the shopping centre.

- Location selection takes place separately within each region, using a form of systematic sampling within strata. The outlets in a selected location are listed and the commodities each outlet sells are coded. The outlets are sampled in such a way as to obtain a number of prices for each item in the large basket of goods on which the RPI is based. (Some items in the basket of goods are sampled centrally, rather than through this procedure, but only for about 140 items out of 700.)

This procedure sounds complicated ... and the detail around the separate sampling stages is substantially more complicated!

Activity 9   *Sampling an urban area for interview*

The Social Services department of a large unitary authority wishes to investigate whether disabled people in its urban area are receiving sufficient support. They plan to carry out a sample survey and decide to use as a sampling frame a list prepared for the purpose of collecting the council tax. This list includes every house in the urban area with its address, the house's band for council tax purposes (which is a measure of its estimated selling price), whether the house is owned privately or by the council, and the parish (the urban area is divided into 27 parishes) in which it is situated. The list contains about 60 000 houses.

The Social Services department wants to select a sample of about 3000 houses and will send an interviewer to each selected house. They will ask if any disabled people live at the house and, if so, ask about the support they receive.

(a) Giving reasons for your choices, describe how the Social Services department might use a procedure involving some forms of stratified sampling, cluster sampling and simple random sampling to select the sample of 3000 houses. (It is not necessary to use all the methods.)

(b) State whether your procedure would be likely to increase or decrease the sampling error compared with that of a simple random sample of 3000 houses. What is the main benefit of your proposal compared with simple random sampling?

2.2 Collecting data in experiments

An experiment involves making specific observations under specific conditions in order to answer specific questions. There are many kinds of experiments, including:

- exploratory (Baconian) experiments, which aim to answer questions such as 'What happens if ...?'

- measurement experiments

- hypothesis-testing experiments, which aim to test a specific hypothesis – often one about the cause of a phenomenon.

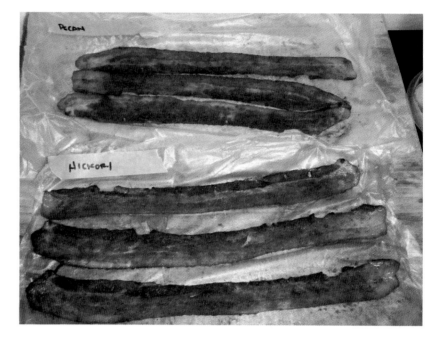

A Bacon(ian) experiment

In M140 we have concentrated on the third type of experiment. Most of the experiments have investigated the effect of a particular treatment of some sort on people, animals, plants or some kind of object. They include whether the roots of mustard seeds grow more in the light than in the dark; whether the weight gain on diet A differs from that on diet B; whether a new drug is more effective than a placebo; and which dose of drug gives the best combination of effectiveness and low risk of adverse side effects. The items or individuals from a population that are included in an experiment are referred to as the *experimental units*. The investigations in M140 often involved comparing experimental units that had been exposed to the experimental treatment (the experimental group) with other experimental units that had not been exposed to the treatment (the control group). Otherwise, the experiments typically involved experimental groups that had been exposed to one of two treatments.

In designing experiments, one aim is to give fair comparison of the different treatments being examined.

You have met various strategies that help achieve this aim.

- Randomisation is the most important of these strategies. This allocates treatments to experimental units by chance, so no treatment can be deliberately favoured by being tested on the more responsive units. Hence, for example, in the mustard seed experiment you tossed a coin to decide which of the two pots of seeds would grow in the dark (step 12 in Subsection 2.3 of Unit 10).

- Apart from the characteristic being examined, the different treatments are made to resemble each other as much as possible. Thus placebos are used in clinical trials (and could be used in other forms of trial) so that 'treatment' and 'no treatment' appear the same to patients. For a similar reason, in the mustard seed experiment, the group of seeds grown in the light were covered with a piece of clear plastic so that they experienced similar levels of humidity as the seeds grown under aluminium foil.

- *Double-blind trials* are used so that knowledge of which treatment a patient is receiving cannot influence a patient's response or a clinician's perception of that response. This again aids a fair comparison of treatments.

Activity 10   *Double-blind trials and placebos*

Very briefly explain which of the following statements about double-blind trials are true and which are false.

A. In a double-blind clinical trial, as many as possible of those carrying out the trial, and of the patients receiving the treatment, must know which patients have received the active drug and which the placebo.

B. In a clinical trial where all measurements being made are objective rather than subjective, it is not necessary to use double-blind procedures.

C. In a clinical trial where all measurements being made are subjective rather than objective, it is not necessary to use double-blind procedures.

D. In a double-blind trial, the doctors who are administering the placebo and the patients who are receiving it all know that it is the placebo, whereas the doctors who are administering the drug begin tested and the patients who are receiving it do not know whether they are dealing with the drug or the placebo.

E. As far as possible, all controlled clinical trials should be double-blind.

F. In a double-blind trial, the patients should never be told of the possibility that they might receive a placebo.

G. In a double-blind clinical trial, neither the patients nor the doctors know which patients have received the drug being tested and which the placebo. However, an appropriate independent person does have this information.

Randomisation of treatments to experimental units will mean that treatment allocation is impartial – no treatment is deliberately favoured. However, differences in the experimental units might favour one treatment over another and so introduce bias. So:

> Another aim in designing experiments is to remove or reduce potential sources of bias.

Thus, for example:

- In the mustard seed experiment the two pots were placed side by side (step 13 of the experiment) so that the two pots were at a similar temperature. For the same reason, you swapped the positions of the two large containers each day (Subsection 2.4 of Unit 10).

- The Clackmannanshire experiment examined three different methods of teaching children to read. Teaching methods are applied to whole classes, rather than individual children, so care was taken in selecting the participating classes and schools to ensure that the children taught by each method were broadly comparable (Subsection 1.3, Unit 8).

- Many experiments (notably many clinical trials) are group-comparative trials in which people/patients are allocated to treatments at random, but with restrictions, so that the overall characteristics of each treatment group are similar for qualities that are thought to matter. If gender and age were thought to influence a person's response to treatment, then care would be taken to ensure that the control group and treatment group (or treatment groups) contained similar male-to-female ratios and that each group had similar age profiles.

Activity 11   *Group-comparative trial of an arthritis drug*

A drug company wishes to carry out a clinical trial on a new drug that, it is hoped, will alleviate the symptoms of arthritis. A design is chosen in which 20 arthritis sufferers are allocated to the trial. Half of the patients are to receive the new drug for four weeks (the experimental group), and the other half are to receive an existing drug for the same period of four weeks (the control group). The ten patients for the experimental group are chosen as a simple random sample from the list of 20. The remaining ten patients form the control group.

Once the allocation has been carried out, the research staff running the clinical trial discover to their dismay that all the patients allocated to the experimental group turn out to be women and all those allocated to the control group turn out to be men.

(a) Explain what characteristics of this experiment make it a group-comparative trial.

(b) Explain why the allocation of all the women to the experimental group and all the men to the control group might upset the validity of the clinical trial.

(c) If the research staff were to abandon this trial and start again with 20 new patients, how might they alter their allocation procedure to ensure that such a problem could not arise?

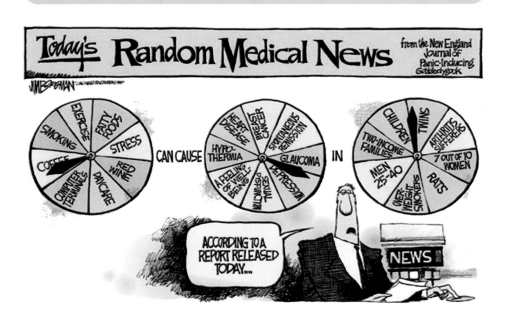

Random variation will affect differences that are observed between treatments, so a third aim when designing an experiment is to try to reduce this variation.

Quite commonly, an experiment is designed to yield pairs of closely related measurements: the difference between the measurements in each pair is calculated and these differences form the data that are used in testing hypotheses or forming confidence intervals. The differences typically have a much smaller variance than the original measurements. The following are instances from earlier units where differences between pairs were formed.

- In Exercise 9 of Unit 6 (Section 5), the change in degree of depression after taking methadone (before − after) was the data used for a hypothesis test of whether methadone had any effect, rather than just the degree of depression after taking the drug.

- Matched-pairs t-tests are based on the differences within pairs of observations. A pair of measurements might be the weights of an object given by two different weighing machines (Activity 22 in Subsection 4.2 of Unit 10) or resting heart rate before and after an exercise program (Activity 26 in Section 6 of Unit 10), for example.

- In clinical trials, matched pairs look at differences between pairs of patients who are closely matched (twins ideally!). One treatment is given to one member of the pair and the other treatment to the other member. Often, though not always, the data will be analysed using a paired t-test.

- In a crossover design, each person taking part in the trial is given both treatments. Thus, each individual acts as their own control, thereby reducing variability. The differences between a person's responses under the two treatments are the data analysed.

When designing an experiment, a common question is: *How much data should be collected?* Often the experimenter is hoping to minimise the amount of data he or she has to collect. However, the experimenter should also consider the amount of time that will be spent preparing for the experiment, analysing the data statistically and then writing reports or papers about the results. These activities will take a significant amount of time – several weeks or months if the work is to be reported as a project or published in a scientific journal. In such cases, gathering data is just a small part of the process – but the quantity of data that is gathered is often crucial to the value of an experiment. The chance of rejecting a null hypothesis that is false is dependent on the amount of data gathered. Hence:

> Good advice for when you are designing an experiment is that you should aim to gather as much data as you reasonably can.

Exercises on Section 2

Exercise 1   *Stratified sampling and cluster sampling*

(a) Consider again the population in Table 3 (Subsection 2.1). Suppose sets A and B can sensibly be considered as one stratum, sets C and D as a second stratum, and sets E and F as a third stratum. A stratified sample is required in which six people are selected from the first stratum, six from the second stratum, and five from the third stratum. (The third stratum is smaller than the others.) Start in row **36** of the random number table (Unit 4 appendix) and pick a stratified sample. Give the labels of the people in the sample.

(b) Suppose that the sets in Table 3 are groups of people who are widely separated geographically, so that cluster sampling is the obvious survey method to use. Restricting your sample to just two of the sets, sample approximately one-third of the individuals in each cluster.

Obtain the sample using the following procedure:

- Label the sets $A–F$ from 1 to 6. Using *single* random digits, and starting at the beginning of row **95** of the random number table, select the two sets to be sampled. These sets are to be sampled in the order in which they are selected.

- Determine the sizes of the samples to take from each cluster by dividing each cluster size by 3 and rounding the results *up* to whole numbers.

- To select individuals for the subsample from the first selected street, use pairs of digits starting at row **72** of the random number table. No person may be selected more than once. To select individuals from the second subsample, continue from the point reached in the random number table after selecting the first subsample, and apply the same procedure again.

List the people chosen in the subsamples.

Exercise 2 *Survey of NHS trust employees*

A large NHS trust wishes to survey a sample of its 6000 employees about job satisfaction. In addition to each employee's payroll number, the employee database also includes information about each employee's age and grade. It is thought that both age and grade might relate to job satisfaction.

(a) Describe how the procedures of stratified sampling and systematic sampling might together be used to choose a sample of size 500 that represents an appropriate balance of the workforce.

(b) Identify two non-sampling errors that may arise in the survey.

Exercise 3 *Other trials of an arthritis drug*

Suppose that, as in Activity 11 (Subsection 2.2), a drug company wishes to carry out a clinical trial to compare the usefulness of two drugs (a new drug and an existing drug) for alleviating the symptoms of arthritis.

(a) Describe briefly how researchers could use a crossover design in a clinical trial comparing the two drugs.

(b) Describe briefly how researchers could use a matched-pairs design in a clinical trial comparing the two drugs.

(c) Which of the two designs would you consider the more suitable? Would a group-comparative trial be better?

3 Probability

In this section, we first review some properties of probability that were given in Units 6 and 8. We then consider the binomial distribution and the probabilities that it gives. You used a specialised form of the binomial distribution to test hypotheses about the median in Unit 6, and here the general form of the distribution is described.

3.1 Basic properties

The data in Table 4 will be used to illustrate the basic properties of probability. It concerns academic statisticians working in UK universities in 2013. They are separated into five age-bands (under 30, 30–39, 40–49, 50–59, and 60 or over) and the table gives the number of them in each job category and age-band.

Table 4   Academic statisticians in UK universities

	< 30	30–39	40–49	50–59	≥ 60	Total
Research Fellow	102	82	31	5	7	227
Lecturer	13	150	59	11	6	239
Senior Lecturer	0	35	70	43	8	156
Professor	0	8	51	66	47	172
Total	115	275	211	125	68	794

'Research fellow' includes research assistants as well as research fellows, and 'senior lecturer' includes readers as well as senior lecturers.

Definition of probability

A simple definition of probability is to equate it to a *proportion*:

Probability = Proportion.

More precisely:

Probability of an event

Let E stand for the event of selecting a person or object with some particular property from a population using random sampling. Then the probability of E is given by

$$P(E) = \frac{\text{Number in population with particular property}}{\text{Total number in population}}.$$

Example 1   *Probability of picking a lecturer*

There are 239 lecturers in the population of 794 academic statisticians in Table 4. Thus, the proportion of lecturers in the population is

$$\frac{239}{794} \simeq 0.301.$$

Hence, if we pick a person at random from the academic statisticians, the probability that we pick a lecturer is 0.301.

Activity 12   *Picking a research fellow*

Suppose an academic statistician is picked at random. What is the probability that the person is:

(a) a research fellow?

(b) aged 30–39?

(c) a research fellow aged 30–39?

Prominent statisticians from the University of Cambridge Statistical Laboratory, 1953

The figure below shows staff and postgraduate students of the University of Cambridge Statistical Laboratory in 1953.

Some of the people shown were already very well known statisticians in 1953, and others became prominent statisticians later. You will hear of some of them if you study statistics further, including David Cox (now Sir David Cox, FRS, FBA), John Wishart (first Director of the Statistical Laboratory), Frank Anscombe and Dennis Lindley, who are respectively third to sixth from the left in the second row.

Conditional probability

Sometimes we want probabilities for subpopulations. For example, Smith (a statistician) has become a professor at the age of 37 and wants to know the probability that an academic statistician is a professor if they are in the 30–39 age-band. Thus academic statisticians aged 30–39 form the subpopulation of interest.

From Table 4, there are 275 in this subpopulation, of whom 8 are professors. Hence among statisticians aged 30–39, the proportion who are professors is

$$\frac{8}{275} \simeq 0.029.$$

Thus

$$P(\text{professor}|\text{aged 30–39}) \simeq 0.029.$$

The conditional probability of A, given B, denoted $P(A|B)$, is the probability that A occurs, given that B occurs.

Activity 13   *Senior lecturer aged 40–49 years old*

Suppose an academic statistician is picked at random.

(a) If the person is aged 40–49, what is the probability that they are a senior lecturer?

(b) If the person is a senior lecturer, what is the probability that they are aged 40–49?

Independence

Independence is an important concept in statistics. Most of the hypothesis tests in M140 require observations to be independent. In particular, this is true of the sign test, the one-sample and two-sample z-tests, and t-tests for one sample or two unrelated samples. In such contexts, the everyday notion of independence corresponds to the statistical definition. We are assuming that the value taken by one (random) observation has no influence on the value taken by any other random observation. That is, as in standard English, two things are 'independent' if they are unrelated.

More precisely, we define statistical independence in terms of probabilities.

Hoping to avoid the difficulties of using conditional probability, Thomas Jefferson writes the Declaration of Independence.

> Two events A and B are statistically independent if the occurrence of one has no influence on the chance of occurrence of the other. Then
>
> $$P(A|B) = P(A).$$
>
> [It can be shown that if $P(A|B) = P(A)$, then $P(B|A) = P(B)$.]

Events that are unrelated are also statistically independent. For example, if you roll a die and toss a coin, the event 'the die gives a three' is both physically independent and statistically independent of the event 'the coin lands heads'. However, statistical independence is a numerical property of probability, and events can be statistically independent without being physically disconnected. This is illustrated in the following example.

Example 2   *Rolling a die*

Suppose an ordinary six-sided die is rolled. Assuming it is unbiased, it is equally likely to roll a 1, 2, 3, 4, 5 or 6. Suppose it is rolled once and consider the following events,

- A: it rolls an even number (i.e. 2, 4 or 6).
- B: it rolls a 4 or more (i.e. 4, 5 or 6).
- C: it rolls a 3 or more (i.e. 3, 4, 5 or 6).

Which of these events are independent? Well,

$$P(A) = \frac{3}{6} = \frac{1}{2}$$

as three of the six possibilities result in A occurring.

Now if we know that B has occurred, then our population of possible outcomes reduces to 4, 5 or 6. Each of these three events is equally likely, and event A occurs if the roll was actually a 4 or 6 (but not if it was a 5). Hence,

$$P(A|B) = \frac{2}{3}.$$

As $P(A)$ does not equal $P(A|B)$, the probability that A occurs is affected by whether or not B occurs. Thus events A and B are not independent.

Suppose, instead, that we know that C has occurred. Then our population of possible outcomes is 3, 4, 5 or 6. Each of these four outcomes is equally likely, and event A occurs if the roll was a 4 or 6 (but not if it was a 3 or 5). Hence,

$$P(A|C) = \frac{2}{4} = \frac{1}{2}.$$

As $P(A)$ does equal $P(A|C)$, the occurrence of C has no influence on the probability that A occurs. Thus events A and C *are* independent, even though the same physical quantity – the outcome of rolling a die – determines them both.

Lastly, for events B and C,

$$P(C) = \frac{4}{6} = \frac{2}{3}$$

as four of the six possibilities result in C occurring. Also, if we know that B has occurred, then our population of possible outcomes is 4, 5 or 6. Regardless of which of these outcomes has occurred, C will occur. That is, C is certain to occur if B occurs, so

$$P(C|B) = 1.$$

As $P(C)$ does not equal $P(C|B)$, the probability that C occurs is affected by whether or not B occurs. Thus events B and C are not independent.

Joint probabilities (the 'and' linkage)

The joint probability of A and B, denoted $P(A \text{ and } B)$, is the probability that both A and B occur together.

Joint probabilities

Let A and B be any two events. Joint and conditional probabilities are linked by the following relationships:

$$P(A \text{ and } B) = P(A) \times P(B|A) = P(B) \times P(A|B).$$

Also, if A and B are independent events [so $P(B|A) = P(B)$], then

$$P(A \text{ and } B) = P(A) \times P(B).$$

Activity 14   *Picking a professor*

Suppose an academic statistician is picked at random.

(a) How many academic statisticians are professors aged 50–59? Hence show that 0.083 is the probability that the randomly picked person is a professor aged 50–59.

(b) What is the probability that the randomly picked person is a professor?

(c) If the randomly picked person is a professor, what is the probability that they are aged 50–59?

(d) Define events A and B as follows.

> A: a randomly picked academic statistician is a professor
>
> B: a randomly picked professor is aged 50–59.

Use (a), (b) and (c) to show that

$$P(A \text{ and } B) = P(A) \times P(B|A).$$

Adding probabilities (the 'or' linkage)

We say that the event 'A or B' occurs if (i) A occurs, or (ii) B occurs, or (iii) *both A and B* occur. The 'or' linkage leads to the addition of probabilities and has a simpler form when events are mutually exclusive.

> Two events are said to be mutually exclusive if they cannot occur at the same time. More generally, any number of events are said to be mutually exclusive if no two of them can occur at the same time.

If events A and B are mutually exclusive, then $P(A \text{ and } B) = 0$, as they cannot both occur at the same time.

> **Addition rules for probabilities**
>
> Let A and B denote two events, mutually exclusive or not. Then
>
> $$P(A \text{ or } B) = P(A) + P(B) - P(A \text{ and } B).$$
>
> If A and B are mutually exclusive,
>
> $$P(A \text{ or } B) = P(A) + P(B).$$

Activity 15   *The great and the good*

(a) Suppose a statistical organisation wishes to invite 'the great and the good' to an event it is hosting. Any UK academic statistician who is a professor or is aged at least 60 will be invited. Using Table 4, explain why 193 UK academic statisticians will be invited. How many people are double-counted if you simply add the number of professors to the number of academic statisticians aged 60 or over?

(b) At a more select gathering, only older professors are invited (professors aged at least 60). How many people from UK universities are invited?

(c) Define events A and B as follows.

  A: a randomly picked academic statistician is a professor

  B: a randomly picked academic statistician is aged 60 or over.

Use (a) and (b) to calculate the probabilities $P(A \text{ or } B)$ and $P(A \text{ and } B)$.

(d) Also calculate $P(A)$ and $P(B)$. Hence show that

  $$P(A \text{ or } B) = P(A) + P(B) - P(A \text{ and } B),$$

in line with theory.

We have focused on the case where there are exactly two events. The following box gives useful results for the case where there are four events, which can be easily generalised to other numbers of events.

Sets of events

If A, B, C and D are independent events, then

  $$P(A \text{ and } B \text{ and } C \text{ and } D) = P(A) \times P(B) \times P(C) \times P(D).$$

If A, B, C and D are mutually exclusive events, then

  $$P(A \text{ or } B \text{ or } C \text{ or } D) = P(A) + P(B) + P(C) + P(D).$$

3.2   The binomial distribution

This subsection contains new material, not previously covered in M140.

You encountered the binomial distribution in Unit 6. It is an important distribution in statistics so here we consider it further.

In Unit 6 (just before Activity 22 in Subsection 3.1), we determined that the number of ways in which a committee of 3 people can be chosen from 10 members of a club is equal to

$$\frac{10 \times 9 \times 8}{3 \times 2 \times 1}.$$

This led to the following result.

Number of combinations

Suppose there are n objects to choose from. Then the number of ways of choosing x objects if the order does not matter is

$$^{n}C_{x} = \frac{n \times (n-1) \times \cdots \times (n-x+1)}{x \times (x-1) \times \cdots \times 1}.$$

(There are x terms in both $n \times (n-1) \times \cdots \times (n-x+1)$ and $x \times (x-1) \times \cdots \times 1$.)

For any value of n, $^{n}C_{0}$ and $^{n}C_{n}$ are defined as being equal to 1.

The result will be used to obtain the probabilities given by a binomial distribution. The following activity will refresh your memory of using it.

Activity 16   *Socks for the weekend*

(a) You have six clean pairs of socks and must pack three pairs in your bag to go away for the weekend. In how many ways could you choose the three pairs to take?

(b) A month later you are going away for a longer break and must pack four pairs of socks. If you have nine clean pairs, how many choices do you have? (Either you have got better at doing the washing or you have bought some more socks!)

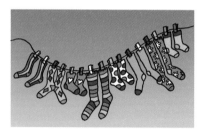

Suppose that a defence lawyer has a success rate of 0.3. That is, in 30% of the trials in which he is the defence lawyer the defendant is acquitted. Let S denote success (the defendant is acquitted) and F denote failure (the defendant is found guilty). Then

$$P(S) = 0.3 \quad \text{and} \quad P(F) = 1 - 0.3 = 0.7.$$

A sequence of five trials might give the sequence $SFFSS$, where this means that the first trial was a success for the lawyer, the next two were failures, and the last two were successes. If we assume that outcomes are independent of each other, then

$$P(SFFSS) = 0.3 \times 0.7 \times 0.7 \times 0.3 \times 0.3 = 0.3^{3} \times 0.7^{2}.$$

Other sequences that gives 3 successes and 2 failures include $SSSFF$ and $FSSSF$, with probabilities

$$P(SSSFF) = 0.3 \times 0.3 \times 0.3 \times 0.7 \times 0.7 = 0.3^{3} \times 0.7^{2}$$

and

$$P(FSSSF) = 0.7 \times 0.3 \times 0.3 \times 0.3 \times 0.7 = 0.3^{3} \times 0.7^{2}.$$

Clearly, the probability of any sequence that gives 3 successes and 2 failures is $0.3^{3} \times 0.7^{2}$. Suppose now, that we want the probability that exactly 3 of the next 5 trials will be a success (in any order). It follows that this probability equals:

(number of sequences of 5 trials giving 3 successes) $\times 0.3^3 \times 0.7^2$.

As $^5C_3$ is the number of sequences of 5 trials giving 3 successes,

$$P(3 \text{ successes in } 5 \text{ trials}) = {}^5C_3 \times 0.3^3 \times 0.7^2$$
$$= \frac{5 \times 4 \times 3}{3 \times 2 \times 1} \times 0.027 \times 0.49$$
$$= 0.1323.$$

Activity 17 *Sales targets*

A salesman has a daily target for the number of sales he should make in a day. Let S denote success (he reaches his target) and F denote failure. Assume that the probability of S on any day is 0.6 (so $P(F) = 0.4$) and that results on different days are independent of each other.

(a) What is the probability that in the next 6 days his sequence of successes and failures is $FSSSFS$?

(b) How many different sequences of 6 days give 4 successes and 2 failures?

(c) What is the probability that the salesman meets his target in exactly 4 of the next 6 days?

(d) What is the probability that the salesman meets his target in exactly 5 of the next 8 days?

The probabilities you calculated in parts (c) and (d) of Activity 17 are probabilities from a **binomial distribution**. More generally, the binomial distribution arises in the following situation.

1.   There is a fixed number of trials, where a trial is an event that can result in success (S) or failure (F). Let n denote the number of trials.

2.   The probability of success in a trial is the same for all trials and the result of any trial is independent of the results of other trials. Let p denote the probability of success and $q = 1 - p$ denote the probability of failure.

3.   Let x denote the number of successes in the n trials. Then the probability distribution of x is a binomial distribution.

In the example with lawyers a 'trial' was actually a real trial. We were interested in the number of successes in 5 trials, so n equals 5, and the probability of success in any one trial was 0.3, so $p = 0.3$ and $q = 0.7$.

In the example with the salesman in Activity 17, a 'trial' was a day's sales performance and success equated to making the daily target. Thus $p = 0.6$ was the probability of success and $q = 0.4$ was $P(F)$. In part (c) of Activity 17, we were concerned with a 6-day period, so n was 6, and we wanted $P(4 \text{ successes}) = P(x = 4)$. In (d), n was 8 and we wanted $P(x = 5)$.

The following defines the binomial distribution.

Binomial distribution

Suppose the result of a trial is success or failure (with no other possibilities). Suppose also that the probability of success (p) is the same in each trial. Put $q = 1 - p$ and let x denote the number of successes in n trials. If trials are independent of each other, then

$$P(x) = {}^{n}C_{x} \times p^{x} \times q^{n-x}.$$

The binomial distribution is the probability distribution of x.

Activity 18   Blood group O

Forty-four per cent of the population of the UK are blood group O. If seven people are picked at random, what is the probability that exactly two of them are blood group O?

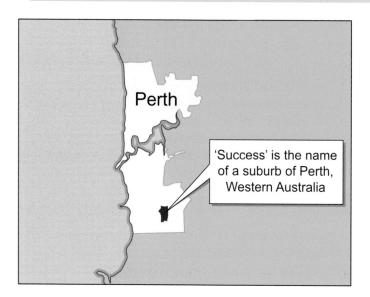

Perth

'Success' is the name of a suburb of Perth, Western Australia

In Unit 6, we were interested in the number of observations in a sample that would exceed the population median. Consider each observation as a trial and equate success to 'the observation exceeds the population median'. Then, if there are x successes and n observations,

$$P(x) = {}^{n}C_{x} \times p^{x} \times q^{n-x}.$$

From the definition of the median, $p = P(\text{success}) = \frac{1}{2}$ and $q = 1 - p = \frac{1}{2}$. Thus the probability that there are x values above the population median in a sample of n observations is

$${}^{n}C_{x} \times \left(\frac{1}{2}\right)^{x} \times \left(\frac{1}{2}\right)^{n-x} = {}^{n}C_{x} \times \left(\frac{1}{2}\right)^{n}.$$

This formula (the formula for a binomial probability when $p = \frac{1}{2}$) is the special case of the binomial distribution used in Unit 6.

You have now covered the material related to Screencast 2 for Unit 12 (see the M140 website).

You have also now covered the material needed for Subsection 12.1 of the Computer Book.

Exercises on Section 3

Exercise 4   *Age and job category independent?*

Consider Table 4 (Subsection 3.1) and suppose an academic statistician is picked at random.

(a) Are the events 'the person is aged 40–49' and 'the person is a lecturer' independent?

(b) Use the formula $P(A \text{ and } B) = P(B) \times P(A|B)$ to obtain the probability that the person is a lecturer aged 40–49.

(c) What is the probability that the person is a lecturer *or* aged 40–49 *or* both?

Exercise 5   *Binomial probabilities*

Suppose the probability of success in a trial is 0.2 and that trials are independent of each other.

(a) If there are four trials, what is the probability that there is exactly one success?

(b) If there are five trials, what is the probability that there are exactly two successes?

(c) If there are seven trials, what is the probability that there are no successes?

Exercise 6   *Relief from headache*

The probability that a person with a headache will feel better within an hour of taking a particular headache tablet is 0.6. If six people with headaches take the tablet, determine the following probabilities, stating any assumptions you make.

(a) The probability that exactly two of them feel better within an hour.

(b) The probability that two or fewer of them feel better within an hour.

4 Hypothesis testing and contingency tables

Hypothesis testing is an important use of statistics. In this section we review the structure of a hypothesis test, illustrating the main ideas by describing the χ^2 test for contingency tables.

The following is the procedure in a hypothesis test.

1. The first step is to state the null hypothesis, H_0, and the alternative hypothesis, H_1. We provisionally assume that H_0 is true and (usually) hope to find that the data cast strong doubt on this assumption. If that happens, then we will have evidence against the null hypothesis.

2. From the data, we construct a test statistic whose value relates to the null hypothesis. Often the value of this statistic should be small if H_0 is true, so that a large value casts doubt on H_0.

3. Lots of different test statistics may relate to H_0. We choose one whose probability distribution is fully known if H_0 is true. For example: in Unit 7, we used test statistics that followed a normal distribution if H_0 was true; in Unit 8, test statistics followed a χ^2 distribution if H_0 was true; in Unit 10, most of the test statistics followed a t distribution if H_0 was true; while in the sign test in Unit 6, the test statistic follows a binomial distribution with $p = q = \frac{1}{2}$ if H_0 is true.

4. The possible values that the test statistic might have taken are divided into two sets:

   - Set A contains those values that are at least as unlikely as the value given by the sample data, if H_0 holds.

   - Set B contains values that are relatively likely to occur if H_0 is true. Specifically, it contains those values that are more likely to occur, if H_0 is true, than the actual value given by the sample data.

5. The actual value taken by the test statistic is in set A. We determine the probability of observing a value from that set. This probability is the p-value from the test. If it is small then either a very unusual event has happened, or H_0 is incorrect.

6. The p-value is interpreted as follows:

$p > 0.10$	Little evidence against H_0
$0.10 \geq p > 0.05$	Weak evidence against H_0
$0.05 \geq p > 0.01$	Moderate evidence against H_0
$0.01 \geq p > 0.001$	Strong evidence against H_0
$0.001 \geq p$	Very strong evidence against H_0

Unless we are using Minitab (or some other statistical software) we will seldom know the exact p-value. Instead the test statistic is compared with *critical values* given in an appropriate table (such as Table 28 in Subsection 4.4 of Unit 8 for χ^2 tests, or Table 2 in Subsection 3.3 of Unit 10 for t-tests – versions of both are in the Handbook). This determines the significance level at which H_0 can be rejected.

7. The conclusion from the hypothesis test is summarised in plain English. For example, the conclusion might be: *There is strong evidence that the new method is better than the old method.*

We next consider the hypothesis test of independence between the row and column variables of a contingency table, using the following example.

Example 3 *Coffee consumption*

A researcher wanted to examine whether a person's coffee consumption was associated with their age. She selected a random sample of 180 people and classified each person according to whether their age was under 35, 35–60 or at least 61, and whether their coffee consumption was low, medium or high. Results are given in Table 5. (The data are artificial.)

Table 5 Level of coffee consumption by age group

| | Coffee consumption | | | |
	Low	Medium	High	Total
Under 35	24	41	25	90
35–60	4	32	24	60
61 and over	8	17	5	30
Total	36	90	54	180

Coffee consumption by age group

The researcher was interested in whether there is an association between age and the level of coffee consumption, or whether these variables are independent. When examining these questions using the data in a contingency table, the null hypothesis is that the row and column variables are independent. This assumption of independence enables the Expected value in each cell to be calculated.

The alternative hypothesis is that row and column variables are not independent. Making the assumption 'row and column variables are not independent' would not enable us to calculate the Expected values in the cells, so that must not be chosen as the null hypothesis.

In this example the hypotheses are:

H_0: Age group and coffee consumption are independent.

H_1: Age group and coffee consumption are not independent.

For the hypothesis test, Expected values are needed. If the variables are independent and we treat the row totals and column totals as fixed, what values might you expect for the rest of Table 5? That is, suppose we knew the values in Table 6 (and nothing else), what would be reasonable estimates of other values in the table?

Table 6   Row and column totals

| | Coffee consumption | | | |
	Low	Medium	High	Total
Under 35				90
35–60				60
61 and over				30
Total	36	90	54	180

Well, half the people in the sample are aged under 35, so we would expect half of the people with a low level of coffee consumption to be under 35, half the people with medium coffee consumption to be under 35, and half the people with high coffee consumption to be under 35. Hence the Expected values for the top row of the table are $36/2 = 18$, $90/2 = 45$ and $54/2 = 27$.

Similarly, one-third of the people in the sample are aged 35–60, so we would expect one-third of the people with a low level of coffee consumption to be in that age group ($36/3 = 12$), one-third of the people with medium coffee consumption to be in that age group ($90/3 = 30$), and one-third of the people with high coffee consumption to be in that age group ($54/3 = 18$). For the '61 and over' group the Expected values are one-sixth of 36, 90 and 54 for the three levels of coffee consumption (i.e. 6, 15 and 9).

These values form the Expected table:

	Low	Medium	High	Total
Under 35	18	45	27	90
35–60	12	30	18	60
61 and over	6	15	9	30
Total	36	90	54	180

The general formula for calculating the Expected values is usually written as:

$$\text{Expected value} = \frac{\text{Row total} \times \text{Column total}}{\text{Overall total}}.$$

Thus, the Expected value for the first cell would usually be obtained from

$$\frac{90 \times 36}{180} = 18$$

and similarly for the other cells. (Check that the Expected values are all greater than or equal to 5, so that the χ^2 test is valid.)

Why might the data cast doubt on H_0? Well, the values in the Expected table, which were calculated under the assumption that H_0 is true, are not equal to the values observed in the sample, given in Table 5. The differences are the residuals. That is,

Residual = Observed − Expected.

The Residual for the first cell is $24 - 18 = 6$ and the following is the complete Residual table.

	Low	Medium	High
Under 35	6	−4	−2
35–60	−8	2	6
61 and over	2	2	−4

Now, even if row and column variables are independent (so that H_0 holds), the residuals would seldom all equal 0, because sample data is affected by random variation. The question is whether the residuals are so large that we should reject H_0. To answer this question, we must combine the information provided by the different residuals to form a test statistic. The distribution of this statistic must be fully known when H_0 is true. To this end, we calculate the χ^2 contribution of each cell and add these together. A cell's χ^2 contribution is

$$\frac{(\text{Residual})^2}{\text{Expected}}.$$

So the χ^2 contribution of the first cell is $6^2/18 = 2$.

The complete table of χ^2 contributions is:

	Low	Medium	High
Under 35	2	0.3556	0.1481
35–60	5.3333	0.1333	2
61 and over	0.6667	0.2667	1.7778

The χ^2 test statistic is the sum of the nine χ^2 contributions:

$$\chi^2 = 2 + 0.3556 + 0.1481 + 5.3333 + 0.1333 + 2 + 0.6667$$
$$+ 0.2667 + 1.7778$$
$$\simeq 12.682.$$

If H_0 is true, then the test statistic follows a χ^2 distribution. For an Observed table with r rows and c columns,

degrees of freedom $= (r - 1) \times (c - 1)$.

Here the Observed table is a 3×3 table, so its degrees of freedom are $(3 - 1) \times (3 - 1) = 4$. Hence we compare the test statistic (12.68) with a χ^2 distribution on 4 degrees of freedom. From Table 28 in Subsection 4.4 of Unit 8 (and in the Handbook), the 5% and 1% critical values are CV5 = 9.488 and CV1 = 13.277.

Since $12.682 > 9.488$, we reject H_0 at the 5% significance level but, as $12.682 < 13.277$, we do not reject H_0 at the 1% significance level.

We conclude that there is moderate evidence that the level of coffee consumption varies with age, but the evidence is not strong.

Examination of the χ^2 contributions shows that the biggest value is for the low level of coffee consumption in the 35–60 age range. The residual for this cell is negative. That is, the number of 35- to 60-year-olds having a low level of coffee consumption is smaller than expected under H_0. This is the main sample evidence of departure from independence.

Activity 19   *Alternative test statistic?*

To decide whether the Residuals are so large that we should reject H_0, we formed the test statistic

$$\sum \frac{(\text{Residual})^2}{\text{Expected}}.$$

Suggest a reason for not using the simpler quantity

$$\sum (\text{Residual})^2$$

as the test statistic.

Exercises on Section 4

Exercise 7   *Study of air pollution*

In a study of air pollution, a random sample of 100 households was selected in each of four localities. Each householder was asked if one or more members in the household were concerned by the level of air pollution. A summary of the responses is given in Table 7.

Table 7   Households with a concern about air pollution

Locality	One or more members concerned Yes	No	Total
A	25	75	100
B	16	84	100
C	12	88	100
D	30	70	100
Total	83	317	400

A hypothesis test is required of whether concern about air pollution varies with locality.

(a) Write down the null and alternative hypotheses.

(b) Obtain the Expected table.

(c) Hence obtain the Residual and χ^2 contributions tables.

(d) Calculate the χ^2 test statistic and note the appropriate critical values, CV5 and CV1 (using Table 28 in Subsection 4.4 of Unit 8 and in the Handbook).

(e) State your conclusions.

5 *z*-tests, *t*-tests and confidence intervals

Testing hypotheses about a population mean and forming a confidence interval for a population mean are common statistical tasks. So are testing hypotheses about the difference between the means of two populations and forming a confidence interval for that difference. These tasks are discussed in Subsection 5.2. Before that, in Subsection 5.1, underpinning results related to a normal distribution are reviewed.

5.1 The normal distribution

A normal distribution that has a mean $\mu = 5$ and a standard deviation $\sigma = 2$ is shown in Figure 5(a). The distribution is bell-shaped and, as it is symmetric, the median and mode also equal 5. Figure 5(b) shows the standard normal distribution, which has mean $\mu = 0$ and standard deviation $\sigma = 1$.

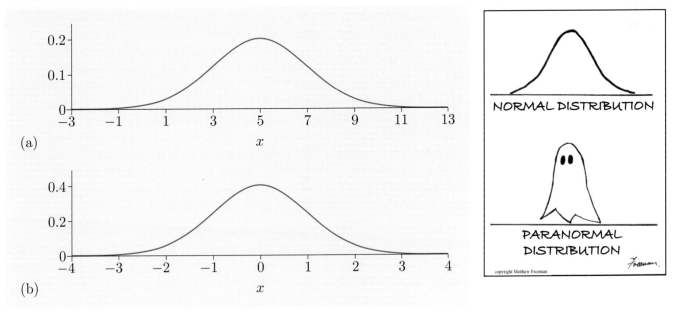

Figure 5 (a) A normal distribution with mean 5 and standard deviation 2; (b) a standard normal distribution.

Comparison of the two figures illustrates that all normal distributions have identical shapes. Consequently, we can transform from any normal distribution to the standard normal distribution.

> **Transforming a normal distribution to the standard normal distribution**
>
> If a variable x has a normal distribution with mean μ and standard deviation σ, then the variable
>
> $$z = \frac{x - \mu}{\sigma}$$
>
> has the standard normal distribution.

Activity 20   *Shell thicknesses*

The shell thickness, x, of eggs produced by a large flock of White Leghorn hens follows (approximately) a normal distribution with mean $\mu = 0.38\,\text{mm}$ and standard deviation $\sigma = 0.03\,\text{mm}$.

Calculate the value of z corresponding to each of the following values of x (in mm). In each case, interpret your answer by completing a sentence of the form 'So a shell thickness of *** mm is *** standard deviations *** than the mean thickness of *** mm.

(a) $x = 0.40$;   (b) $x = 0.30$.

White Leghorn hens

As noted in Activity 20, the thicknesses of eggshells of White Leghorn hens approximately follow a normal distribution. The heights of men in Scotland also approximately follow a normal distribution (as noted in Subsection 3.1 of Unit 7). So do the heights of 7-year-old boys, the cholesterol levels of young adults, the weight gains of calves on a standard diet and many other quantities. One reason that the normal distribution is important is because many natural quantities follow approximately a normal distribution. Indeed, the normal distribution is so ubiquitous that it is common to assume that a quantity follows a normal distribution unless there is reason to think otherwise. Thus, in the experiment where you grew mustard seedlings, you assumed that root length was normally distributed, both for seedlings grown in the light and those grown in the dark.

Of course, you should not assume that a quantity follows a normal distribution if the data suggest otherwise, or if the situation suggests that the distribution will not be normal. So, for instance, it would be unwise to assume that incomes in the general population follow a normal distribution, because we know, from Unit 3 (Subsection 1.4), that distributions of incomes are usually right-skew, with a few people earning far more than the median income.

You have also met another major reason for the importance of the normal distribution: the sampling distribution of a mean is approximately normal, regardless of whether or not the distribution of individual observations is normal. This result is part of the *central limit theorem*. The central limit theorem also specifies the mean and variance of the distribution of the mean.

> ### Approximate normality of the sampling distribution of the mean (central limit theorem)
>
> If n is large, no matter what shape the population distribution, the sampling distribution of the mean for samples of size n will be approximately normal. The mean will equal the population mean μ and the standard deviation will equal the standard error $\mathrm{SE} = \sigma/\sqrt{n}$.

Figure 6 reproduces Figure 2 from Unit 7 (Section 2). It shows the proportions of students obtaining each examination mark in MS221 in one presentation.

The distribution is clearly not bell-shaped, so it is far from normal.

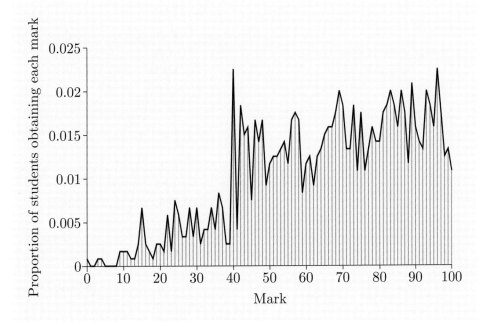

Figure 6   The distribution of MS221 exam marks

Suppose now that we took two students at random from the MS221 cohort and determined the mean of their two marks. The value of the mean depends on which two students we pick – repeatedly picking two students at random and calculating their mean mark will yield lots of different values. The distribution of the mean mark (from a sample of two students) is shown in Figure 7. The distribution is not bell-shaped, but is much closer to being bell-shaped than the distribution in Figure 6. If we take samples of 20 students (rather than just two) then the mean of their marks is normally distributed, approximately. That distribution is shown in Figure 8.

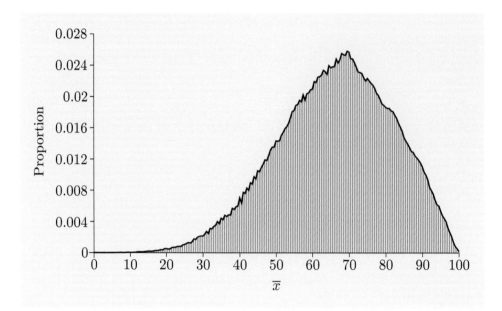

Figure 7   The distribution of the mean of 2 students' marks

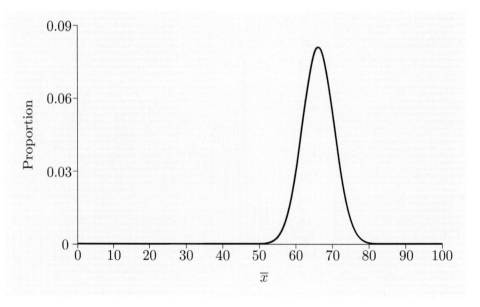

Figure 8   The distribution of the mean of 20 students' marks

Activity 21   *Distributions of sample means*

The distribution of the MS221 examination marks has mean $\mu = 66$ and standard deviation $\sigma = 22$.

(a) Give the mean and standard deviation of the sampling distribution of the mean for samples of size 5, and then for samples of size 15.

(b) Would the sampling distributions in (a) be approximately normal? Which would be closer to a normal distribution?

The Morane–Saulnier MS221 aircraft from 1928

5.2   Inference about the means of populations

This subsection contains new material, not previously covered in M140.

There are a number of different hypothesis tests for examining whether a population mean takes a specified value, or whether two populations have means that are equal; they have close similarities. We first consider how to choose the appropriate hypothesis test. A unified description of the tests is then given that highlights their similarities. A new hypothesis test is also introduced. Associated with each hypothesis test is a method of forming a confidence interval and these methods are described later in the section.

Which hypothesis test should be used?

M140 contains a number of different hypothesis tests for answering the following questions:

- Does the mean of a population take a specified value?
- Do the means of two populations have the same value?

For the first question, we have a single sample and would use one of the following tests:

- Test 1. One-sample z-test
- Test 2. One-sample t-test

For the second question, we have two samples of data, one from each of two populations. We would use one of the following tests:

- Test 3. Two-sample z-test
- Test 4. Matched-pairs t-test
- Test 5. Unpaired t-test for populations with a common variance
- Test 6. Unpaired t-test for populations with unequal variances

These tests make varied assumptions about observations following normal distributions and being random. Test 6 has not been covered in earlier units, but will be described later in this section. You will also learn in the Computer Book how to use Minitab to perform this test.

The flow chart in Figure 9 gives the steps to follow in order to decide which test should be used when there is just one population.

When there are two populations and we have a sample from each, one of the tests 3, 4, 5 or 6 would be used to test whether the population means are equal. The flow chart in Figure 10 gives the steps to follow in order to decide which of the tests to use (assuming one of these tests is suitable). The choice between test 5 or 6 depends upon whether 'yes' or 'no' is the response to the question 'Population variances equal?'. Using the rule of thumb given in Unit 10 (Subsection 3.3), we treat the population variances as equal if the sample variances differ by a factor of less than three.

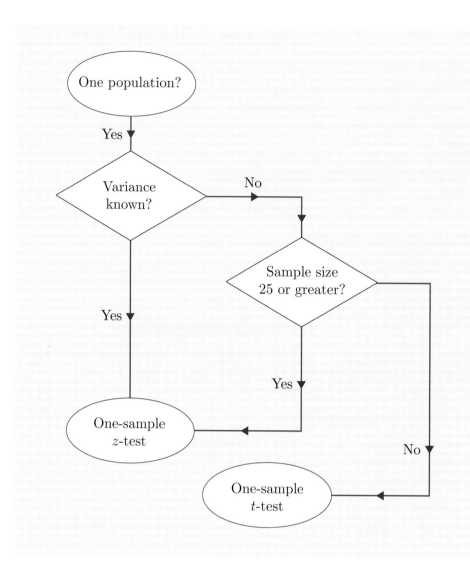

Figure 9   Flow chart for choosing a hypothesis test for inference about a population mean. (It is assumed that observations are random and that the population distribution is approximately normal if the sample size is small.)

Activity 22   *Choosing a one-sample test*

A sample is taken from a population in order to test the hypothesis that the population mean equals 15. What is the appropriate test for each of the following situations, assuming the population distribution is approximately normal?

(a) The sample size is 30 and the population variance is known.

(b) The sample size is 35 and the population variance is unknown.

(c) The sample size is 15 and the population variance is unknown.

(d) The sample size is 12 and the population variance is known.

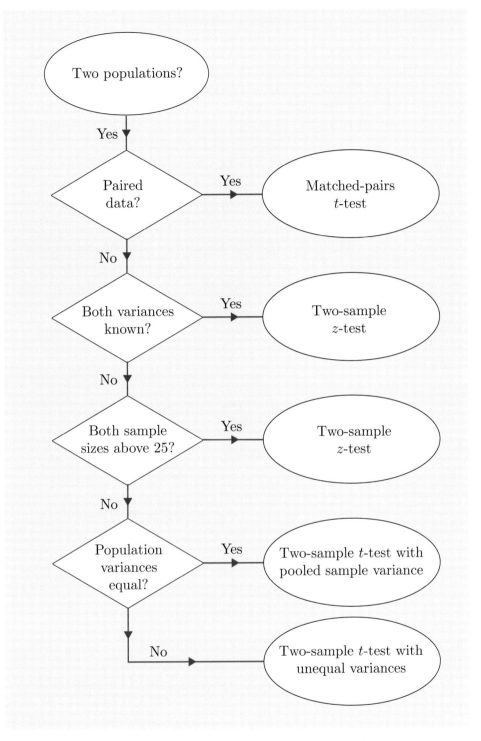

Figure 10   Flow chart for choosing a hypothesis test for inference about the difference between two population means. (Assumptions required for the selected test must also be satisfied.)

Activity 23   *Choosing a hypothesis test to compare two means*

Samples are taken from two populations in order to test the hypothesis that the population means are equal. What is the appropriate test for each of the following situations? (Assume population distributions are approximately normal, where necessary.) The sample sizes are n_1 and n_2, the population variances are σ_1^2 and σ_2^2, and the sample variances are s_1^2 and s_2^2.

(a) $n_1 = 30$, $n_2 = 50$; σ_1^2 and σ_2^2 are unknown; the data are not matched pairs; $s_1^2 = 12.1$ and $s_2^2 = 8.5$.

(b) $n_1 = 30$, $n_2 = 14$; σ_1^2 and σ_2^2 are unknown; the data are not matched pairs; $s_1^2 = 8.4$ and $s_2^2 = 9.6$.

(c) $n_1 = 12$, $n_2 = 12$; σ_1^2 and σ_2^2 are unknown; the data are matched pairs; $s_1^2 = 4.8$ and $s_2^2 = 7.3$.

(d) $n_1 = 10$, $n_2 = 10$; σ_1^2 and σ_2^2 are unknown; the data are not matched pairs; $s_1^2 = 12.1$ and $s_2^2 = 3.5$.

(e) $n_1 = 10$, $n_2 = 12$; σ_1^2 and σ_2^2 are known; the data are not matched pairs; $s_1^2 = 6.5$ and $s_2^2 = 5.9$.

You have now covered the material related to Screencast 3 for Unit 12 (see the M140 website).

Performing the hypothesis tests

After the appropriate test has been selected, the null and alternative hypotheses are specified. The (two-sided) hypotheses for all the tests are given in Table 8. For a one-sample test, the hypothesised value of the population mean (μ) is A. When there are two populations, μ_A and μ_B are the population means and $\mu_d = \mu_A - \mu_B$.

Table 8   Null and alternative hypotheses for the (two-sided) z- and t-tests

	H_0	H_1
One-sample tests	$\mu = A$	$\mu \neq A$
Matched-pairs tests	$\mu_d = 0$	$\mu_d \neq 0$
Other two-sample tests	$\mu_A - \mu_B = 0$	$\mu_A - \mu_B \neq 0$

After specifying H_0 and H_1, the test statistic must be calculated. Table 9 gives this statistic for all the tests.

- If there is only one sample, then the sample size, the sample mean and the standard deviation are n, $\overline{x}$ and s.

- If there are two samples forming matched pairs, then the sample mean and the standard deviation of the differences within a pair are $\overline{d}$ and s and the number of pairs is n.

- If there are two (unmatched) samples, then n_A and n_B denote the sample sizes, $\overline{x}_A$ and $\overline{x}_B$ are the sample means, and s_A and s_B are the sample standard deviations.

When two population variances are assumed to be equal, the pooled estimate of their common standard deviation is

$$s_\mathrm{p} = \sqrt{\frac{(n_A - 1)s_A^2 + (n_B - 1)s_B^2}{n_A + n_B - 2}}.$$

If the population standard deviation or population standard deviations are known, they will replace the corresponding sample values (this can only apply when the test statistic equals z).

Table 9 Estimated standard error (ESE) and test statistic for the z- and t-tests

Test	ESE	Test statistic
1. One-sample z-test	$\dfrac{s}{\sqrt{n}}$	$z = \dfrac{\overline{x} - A}{\mathrm{ESE}}$
2. One-sample t-test	$\dfrac{s}{\sqrt{n}}$	$t = \dfrac{\overline{x} - A}{\mathrm{ESE}}$
3. Two-sample z-test	$\sqrt{\dfrac{s_A^2}{n_A} + \dfrac{s_B^2}{n_B}}$	$z = \dfrac{\overline{x}_A - \overline{x}_B}{\mathrm{ESE}}$
4. Matched-pairs t-test	$\dfrac{s}{\sqrt{n}}$	$t = \dfrac{\overline{d}}{\mathrm{ESE}}$
5. Two-sample t-test with a common variance	$s_\mathrm{p}^2\sqrt{\dfrac{1}{n_A} + \dfrac{1}{n_B}}$	$t = \dfrac{\overline{x}_A - \overline{x}_B}{\mathrm{ESE}}$
6. Two-sample t-test with unequal variances	$\sqrt{\dfrac{s_A^2}{n_A} + \dfrac{s_B^2}{n_B}}$	$t = \dfrac{\overline{x}_A - \overline{x}_B}{\mathrm{ESE}}$

To examine the strength of evidence against H_0 that the sample data provide, the test statistic is compared to critical values.

- For tests 1 and 3, the test statistic follows a standard normal distribution, assuming H_0 holds. So the critical values for the two-sided test are 1.96 and -1.96 at the 5% significance level, and 2.58 and -2.58 at the 1% significance level. Hence, for example, the null hypothesis is rejected at the 5% significance level if the test statistic is greater than 1.96 or less than -1.96.

- For tests 2, 4 and 5, the test statistic follows a t distribution if H_0 holds. Critical values for the two-sided test at the 5% significance level are given in Table 2 in Subsection 3.3 of Unit 10 (and the Handbook). The number of degrees of freedom equals $n - 1$ for tests 2 and 4, and $n_A + n_B - 2$ for test 5. If the magnitude of the test statistic is greater than the critical value, then the null hypothesis is rejected at the 5% significance level.

- For test 6, the test statistic approximately follows a t distribution if H_0 holds. However, its degrees of freedom is given by a relatively complicated expression, outside the scope of M140.

> The result of the hypothesis test should be stated clearly and conclusions drawn that reflect the setting from which the data came. It is also good practice to state any assumptions that have been made. These will involve the randomness and independence of observations and, for samples of modest size, the assumption that variation in a population is adequately modelled by a normal distribution.

Test 6 is the 'new' hypothesis test that is appropriate when population variances appear to be unequal and the sample sizes are not both large. In activities in the Computer Book you will use Minitab to find p-values for this test.

Example 4   *Brinell hardness measurements*

In a Brinell hardness test, a hardened steel ball is pressed into the material being tested under a standard load. The diameter of the spherical indentation is then measured. A company is about to replace its current steel ball, Ball A, with a new steel ball, Ball B. Before doing so, it compares the measurements given by the two balls on eight pieces of material. Each piece of material was tested twice, once with each ball, giving the measurements in Table 10.

The company want to examine whether either ball gives, on average, higher measurements than the other.

Table 10   Diameter measurements from Brinell hardness tests

Sample	1	2	3	4	5	6	7	8
Ball A	63	44	62	51	32	53	46	64
Ball B	42	49	48	29	51	45	52	41

As a pair of measurements were made on each sample, the data are paired. Thus a paired t-test is appropriate (see the flow chart in Figure 10). We put $\mu_d = \mu_A - \mu_B$ where μ_A and μ_B are the population means for the two balls. The hypotheses are:

$$H_0:\ \mu_d = 0 \quad \text{and} \quad H_1:\ \mu_d \neq 0.$$

To obtain the test statistic, the difference (d) between A's reading and B's reading are determined for each sample.

Sample	1	2	3	4	5	6	7	8
Difference (d)	21	−5	14	22	−19	8	−6	23

Then $n = 8$,

$$\sum d = 21 - 5 + 14 + 22 - 19 + 8 - 6 + 23 = 58$$

and

$$\sum d^2 = 21^2 + (-5)^2 + 14^2 + 22^2 + (-19)^2 + 8^2 + (-6)^2 + 23^2 = 2136.$$

A Brinell hardness testing machine

Thus

$$\bar{d} = \frac{58}{8} = 7.25$$

and

$$s^2 = \frac{1}{n-1}\left(\sum d^2 - \frac{(\sum d)^2}{n}\right) = \frac{1}{7}\left(2136 - \frac{58^2}{8}\right)$$
$$\simeq 245.07.$$

These summary statistics give $s \simeq \sqrt{245.07} \simeq 15.655$,

$$\text{ESE} = \frac{s}{\sqrt{n}} \simeq \frac{15.655}{\sqrt{8}}$$
$$\simeq 5.5349$$

and

$$t = \frac{\bar{d}}{\text{ESE}} \simeq \frac{7.25}{5.5349}$$
$$\simeq 1.310.$$

The critical value for a *t*-test is obtained from Table 2 in Subsection 3.3 of Unit 10 (and the Handbook). The number of degrees of freedom is $n - 1 = 7$, so the critical value is 2.365. The value of t is 1.310, which is less than 2.365. Thus H_0 is not rejected at the 5% significance level.

The conclusion is that there is little evidence of one ball giving higher measurements, on average, than the other. This does not mean that the balls definitely do not differ systematically – a larger experiment might find evidence of a difference between them.

The assumptions underlying the test are that observations are random, each pair of measurements is independent of all other pairs, and the differences (d) are approximately normally distributed.

Activity 24   *Cholesterol reduction*

In a nutrition experiment, the effectiveness of two high-fibre diets at reducing serum cholesterol levels was examined. Fifty-seven men with high serum cholesterol were randomly allocated to receive an 'oat' diet or a 'bean' diet for 21 days. Table 11 summarises the fall in serum cholesterol levels (before diet − after diet). Test whether there is a difference between the diets in their effects on cholesterol levels. (The data are artificial.)

Table 11   Summary statistics for the fall in cholesterol (mg/dl) on two diets

	Sample size	Sample mean	Sample standard deviation
Oat	29	58.3	19.2
Bean	28	46.4	16.5

No good for this experiment: oats and beans together in these cookies

You have now covered the material related to Screencast 4 for Unit 12 (see the M140 website).

Constructing confidence intervals

The task of forming confidence intervals for a population mean was first addressed in Unit 9. Given a set of data, there are a range of likely values that the population mean might equal. A confidence interval gives a precisely defined range through consideration of hypothesis tests.

Let μ be the population and consider the hypotheses,

$$H_0: \mu = A \quad \text{and} \quad H_1: \mu \neq A.$$

Then H_0 will be rejected at the 5% significance level for some values of A but not for others.

> ### Confidence intervals
>
> A 95% confidence interval for μ includes all values of A for which we cannot reject H_0 at the 5% significance level.
>
> A 99% confidence interval for μ includes all values of A for which we cannot reject H_0 at the 1% significance level.

Thus a confidence interval contains the plausible values that μ might take. If you took a very large number of samples from a population, then from each sample you could calculate a 95% confidence interval for μ. Most of these intervals would contain the true value of μ, but some would not. The definition of a confidence intervals enables the following precise statements to be made.

> About 95% of the confidence intervals will contain the population mean. For the remaining 5%, about 2.5% will give intervals that are completely below the population mean and about 2.5% will give intervals completely above it.

So if you say that a 95% confidence interval includes the population mean, you will be right 95% of the time; you are 95% confident that your statement is correct.

At the same time, *after calculating a confidence interval*, it is wrong to say 'the probability is 0.95 that this confidence interval contains μ.' Once the confidence interval has been calculated, either it contains the value of μ or it does not. In the former case, the probability is 1 that the interval contains μ, while in the latter case, the probability is 0. (If we take lots of samples from a population, the confidence interval will keep changing but the population mean remains the same. Once the confidence interval has been determined, there is nothing left that is random. Therefore, it is only before gathering data that the probability is 0.95 that the *future* 95% confidence interval will contain μ.)

To show how a confidence interval can be obtained from a hypothesis test, consider the one-sample *t*-test of H_0: $\mu = A$ versus H_1: $\mu \neq A$. From Table 9, the test statistic is

$$t = \frac{\overline{x} - A}{\text{ESE}}.$$

If t_c is the critical value for the 5% significance level, then the hypothesis that A is the population mean is *not* rejected at the 5% level if

$$\frac{\overline{x} - A}{\text{ESE}} \leq t_c \quad \text{and} \quad -t_c \leq \frac{\overline{x} - A}{\text{ESE}}.$$

Thus, it is not rejected at the 5% level if

$$\overline{x} - A \leq t_c \times \text{ESE} \quad \text{and} \quad -t_c \times \text{ESE} \leq \overline{x} - A,$$

which is equivalent to

$$\overline{x} - t_c \times \text{ESE} \leq A \quad \text{and} \quad A \leq \overline{x} + t_c \times \text{ESE}.$$

Thus A is not rejected at the 5% significance level if it is in the interval

$$(\overline{x} - t_c \times \text{ESE}, \ \overline{x} + t_c \times \text{ESE}).$$

By definition, this interval is the 95% confidence interval for the population mean. It is an example of the following more general result.

Confidence intervals: they're everywhere!

> **Confidence interval for a mean or the difference between two means**
>
> The lower limit of the confidence interval is:
>
> > point estimate $-$ (z or t critical value) $\times$ ESE
>
> and the upper limit is:
>
> > point estimate $+$ (z or t critical value) $\times$ ESE,
>
> where ESE is the estimated standard error of the point estimate.

To apply this result requires a point estimate, a z or t critical value, and an ESE. The point estimate will be the sample mean when making inferences about one population mean, and it will be the difference between the two samples means when making inferences about the difference between two population means. Table 9 gives the ESE. Actually, it gives lots of ESEs. To decide which one is appropriate:

- If the interval is for a population mean, consider what hypothesis test you would use to test H_0: $\mu = A$. The ESE for that hypothesis test is the one that should be used to form the confidence interval.

- If the interval is for the difference between two population means, consider what hypothesis test you would use to test H_0: $\mu_A = \mu_B$. The ESE for that hypothesis test is the one that should be used to form the confidence interval.

The choice of hypothesis test also determines the z or t critical value that is used to form the confidence interval. If a z-test is the appropriate hypothesis test, then the z-value of 1.96 should be used for a 95% confidence interval and 2.58 for a 99% confidence interval. If a t-test is the appropriate hypothesis test, then t_c should be obtained from Table 2 in Subsection 3.3 of Unit 10 (and the Handbook); the degrees of freedom (as with the hypothesis tests) are $n - 1$ for the one-sample t-test and paired t-test, and $n_A + n_B - 2$ for the two-sample t-test with pooled sample variance.

Example 5 *Confidence interval from Brinell hardness measurements*

Example 4 concerned measurements from Brinell hardness tests using two hardened steel balls, Ball A and Ball B. A paired t-test was used to test whether the difference between the population means (μ_A and μ_B) was 0.

Suppose, now, that a 95% confidence interval for $\mu_A - \mu_B$ is required. Using the data in Example 4, the mean for Ball A is

$$\frac{63 + 44 + 62 + 51 + 32 + 53 + 46 + 64}{8} = 51.875$$

and the mean for Ball B is

$$\frac{42 + 49 + 48 + 29 + 51 + 45 + 52 + 41}{8} = 44.625.$$

Hence the point estimate is $51.875 - 44.625 = 7.25$. (This equals $\overline{d}$, of course, which was calculated in Example 4. The separate means for Ball A and Ball B did not have to be calculated and $\overline{d}$ could have been taken as the point estimate.)

From Example 4, ESE $\simeq 5.5349$. The degrees of freedom are $n - 1 = 7$ and, for 7 degrees of freedom, 2.365 is the critical value, t_c. The value of 2.365 could be obtained from Table 2 in Subsection 3.3 of Unit 10 (and the Handbook), but it has already been obtained in Example 4.

Hence the lower limit of the 95% confidence interval is

$$7.25 - 2.365 \times 5.5349 \simeq -5.8$$

and the upper limit is

$$7.25 + 2.365 \times 5.5349 \simeq 20.3,$$

so the 95% confidence interval for $\mu_A - \mu_B$ is $(-5.8, 20.3)$.

In the last example, notice that the 95% confidence interval contains the value 0 – so the hypothesis that the population means are equal would not be rejected at the 5% significance level. This was also the conclusion from the hypothesis test in Example 4, and it illustrates the following close connection between confidence intervals and hypothesis tests.

- If the 95% confidence interval does not include the value given by the null hypothesis, we reject the null hypothesis at the 5% significance level.

- If the 99% confidence interval does not include the value given by the null hypothesis, we reject the null hypothesis at the 1% significance level.

Activity 25 *Confidence intervals for cholesterol reduction*

Data from a nutrition experiment were summarised in Activity 24. The data related to the reduction in serum cholesterol level on two diets, an 'oat' diet (diet A) and a 'bean' diet (diet B). Let μ_A and μ_B denote the population mean reductions on the two diets.

(a) Construct a 95% confidence interval for $\mu_A - \mu_B$.

(b) Construct a 99% confidence interval for $\mu_A - \mu_B$.

(c) Which interval is shorter? Would that always be the shorter interval?

(d) Which of the confidence intervals contain the value 0? How does that relate to the results of the hypothesis test in Activity 24?

You have now covered the material needed for Subsection 12.2 of the Computer Book.

Exercises on Section 5

Exercise 8 *Which one-sample test?*

A sample is taken from a population in order to test the hypothesis that the population mean equals 50. What is the appropriate test for each of the following situations, assuming the population distribution is approximately normal?

(a) The sample size is 20 and the population variance is known.

(b) The sample size is 12 and the population variance is unknown.

(c) The sample size is 40 and the population variance is unknown.

(d) The sample size is 35 and the population variance is known.

Exercise 9   *Which test for comparing two means?*

Samples are taken from two populations in order to test the hypothesis that the population means are equal. What is the appropriate test for each of the following situations? (Assume population distributions are approximately normal, where necessary.) The sample sizes are n_1 and n_2, the population variances are σ_1^2 and σ_2^2, and the sample variances are s_1^2 and s_2^2.

(a) $n_1 = 8$, $n_2 = 18$; σ_1^2 and σ_2^2 are unknown; the data are not matched pairs; $s_1^2 = 23.8$ and $s_2^2 = 28.2$.

(b) $n_1 = 20$, $n_2 = 20$; σ_1^2 and σ_2^2 are unknown; the data are matched pairs; $s_1^2 = 1.3$ and $s_2^2 = 1.7$.

(c) $n_1 = 50$, $n_2 = 9$; σ_1^2 and σ_2^2 are unknown; the data are not matched pairs; $s_1^2 = 1.7$ and $s_2^2 = 9.1$.

(d) $n_1 = 30$, $n_2 = 30$; σ_1^2 and σ_2^2 are unknown; the data are not matched pairs; $s_1^2 = 11.3$ and $s_2^2 = 15.5$.

(e) $n_1 = 10$, $n_2 = 30$; σ_1^2 and σ_2^2 are unknown; the data are not matched pairs; $s_1^2 = 17.4$ and $s_2^2 = 10.6$.

6   Correlation and regression

Often, the reason for gathering data is to learn about the relationship between different variables. When only two variables are involved, much can be learned about their relationship by drawing a scatterplot of one variable against the other. In Subsection 6.1, we consider the information that a scatterplot can provide. In Subsection 6.2, correlation and regression are reviewed.

6.1   Scatterplots and relationships

Data are said to be linked when two or more variables are recorded for the same sampling units. Here, the focus is on the case where there are two variables, so that the linked data are paired data.

Scatterplots are a useful tool for examining the relationship between a pair of variables. They can address the following question/s.

Is there a relationship between the two variables? If so:

- Is the relationship positive or negative, or is it neither?

- Is the relationship strong or weak?

- Is the relationship linear?

Professor Hans Rosling (b. 1948)

Hans Rosling is a Swedish public health doctor, academic and statistician. He began his career in public health, spending some time in remote rural parts of Africa. Since 1997, he has been Professor of International Health at the Karolinska Institute, a world-renowned medical university in Stockholm.

More recently, Rosling has become famous for persuasively presenting data and ideas on health, international development and many other things. With his son and daughter-in-law he set up the Gapminder Foundation in 2005, to develop animated software for showing data and to use it to show global development trends.

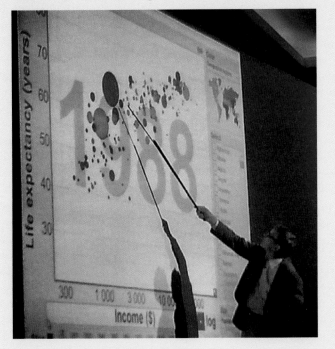

Professor Hans Rosling does great things with scatterplots!

Figure 11 plots, for ten towns, the percentage of households in owner-occupied housing against the percentage of employed residents working in manufacturing.

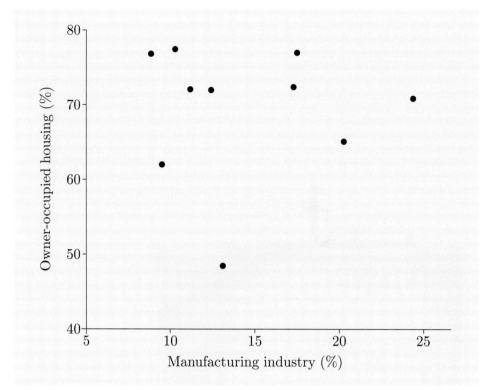

Figure 11   Percentage of employed residents working in manufacturing and percentage of households in owner-occupied houses

There appears to be no relationship between the variables: if in an eleventh town you knew the percentage of employed residents working in manufacturing, it would not give any indication of the likely percentage of households in that town who live in owner-occupied housing. Similarly, knowing the percentage of households in owner-occupied housing would give no indication of the percentage of employed residents who work in manufacturing.

> There is said to be no relationship between two variables when knowledge of one of them provides no information about the value of the other.

Figure 12 plots two variables that are related. The shaded area contains the points and it slopes upwards: as the percentage of unemployed men in a town increases, the percentage of households with no car also increases. Thus, if in an eleventh town the percentage of men unemployed were known, it would influence an estimate of the likely percentage of households in the town that had no car.

Figure 12   Percentage of males unemployed and percentage of households with no car in ten towns

The variables in Figure 12 are said to be *positively related* because an increase in one variable is associated with an increase in the other variable. Variables are said to be *negatively related* if an increase in one variable is associated with a decrease in the other variable. An example of negatively related variables is given in Figure 13.

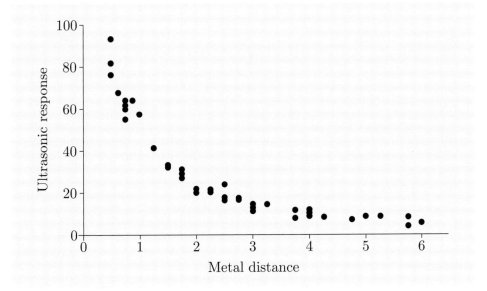

Figure 13   Data from an ultrasonic calibration study

Variables need not be positively or negatively related, even when there is clearly a relationship between them. This is illustrated in Figure 14, where y is large for values of x near 10 and values of x near 20, and smaller for values of x near 15.

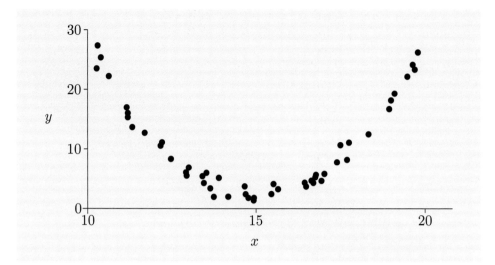

Figure 14 A scatterplot of some data

A relationship is said to be *strong* when all the points on a scatterplot lie close to a line.

A relationship is said to be *weak* when all the points only loosely follow a line.

The relationships in Figures 12, 13 and 14 are all strong. Figure 15 is an example of a weak (positive) relationship.

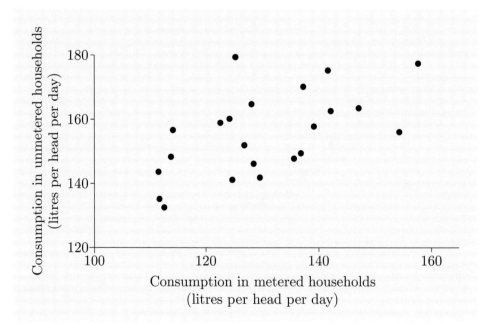

Figure 15 Average water consumption in metered and unmetered households

An important characteristic of a relationship is whether it is linear or non-linear. A relationship is said to be linear if it can be summarised reasonably well by a straight line. It is said to be non-linear if it can be summarised reasonably well by a curve but not by a straight line. Consequently, the relationships in Figures 13 and Figure 14 are non-linear, while Figure 12 shows a linear relationship. This is not typical though – linear relationships commonly occur in practice.

'I'll take it.'

Activity 26   *Identifying characteristics of relationships*

For each of the following six scatterplots, say whether there is a relationship between the variables. If there is one, classify it as (i) positive, negative or neither, (ii) weak or strong, and (iii) linear or non-linear.

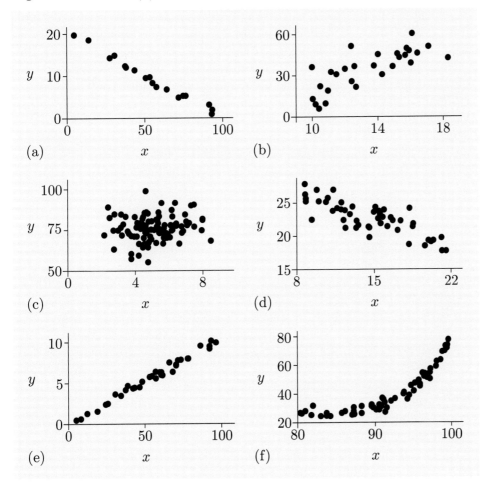

Figure 16   Six scatterplots showing different relationships

6.2   Linear relationships

> Correlation *measures* the strength of a linear relationship.
>
> Regression *describes* a linear relationship.

Correlation

The correlation coefficient has the following formula:

$$\text{Correlation} = \frac{\sum (x - \bar{x})(y - \bar{y})}{\sqrt{\sum (x - \bar{x})^2 \times \sum (y - \bar{y})^2}}.$$

The value of the correlation coefficient is always between -1 and $+1$. A value near $+1$ means there is a strong positive relationship between x and y and a value near -1 indicates a strong negative relationship between them. For example, the variables in Figure 12 (Subsection 6.1) show quite a strong positive relationship. Their correlation coefficient (calculated using the above formula and the data that gave the figure) is 0.91, which is reasonably close to 1. In contrast, the variables in Figure 15 have a relationship that is weak (and positive) with the correlation coefficient lower at $\simeq 0.57$. When there is little relationship between two variables, the correlation coefficient takes a value near 0. Thus in Figure 11, the two variables appear unrelated and the correlation coefficient is -0.01.

The correlation coefficient only reflects the degree to which a relationship is linear. In Figure 14, there is a very strong relationship but the relationship is non-linear – the correlation coefficient is 0.000 (correct to three decimal places). However, with many non-linear relationships, the relationship can *partly* be modelled by a straight line. For example, in Figure 13, the relationship is clearly non-linear, but a straight line with a negative slope would partly capture the negative relationship between the two variables. The correlation coefficient is -0.85, which is far from 0.

Activity 27   *Ordering correlation coefficients.*

Order the six scatterplots in Figure 16 (Subsection 6.1) according to the correlation between the variables in the plots. The scatterplot corresponding to the highest correlation coefficient should be first in the list, the one corresponding to the second highest correlation coefficient should be second in the list, and so on. Thus the one corresponding to the most negative correlation coefficient should be at the end of the list.

The following is the procedure for calculating the correlation coefficient.

Calculating the correlation coefficient

Given a batch of n linked data pairs, (x, y), the correlation coefficient (r) is obtained as follows:

1. Calculate $\sum x$, $\sum y$, $\sum x^2$, $\sum y^2$ and $\sum xy$.

2. Calculate
$$\sum (x - \bar{x})^2 = \sum x^2 - \frac{1}{n} \left(\sum x \right)^2,$$
$$\sum (y - \bar{y})^2 = \sum y^2 - \frac{1}{n} \left(\sum y \right)^2,$$
$$\sum (x - \bar{x})(y - \bar{y}) = \sum xy - \frac{1}{n} \left(\sum x \right) \left(\sum y \right).$$

3. Use the values from step 2 to calculate
$$r = \frac{\sum (x - \bar{x})(y - \bar{y})}{\sqrt{\sum (x - \bar{x})^2 \times \sum (y - \bar{y})^2}}.$$

Example 6   *Basal area and weight of trees*

During crop-thinning of a small forest of Sitka spruce, seven trees were felled and the cross-sectional area of each tree at its base (its *basal area*), x, and total dry weight, y, were measured. The following results were obtained.

Table 12   Basal area and dry weight of seven trees

x (m$^2 \times 100$)	2.24	1.06	0.79	1.78	1.22	0.54	1.40
y (kg)	79.1	33.9	19.2	54.8	51.0	12.0	46.7

To determine the correlation coefficient between x and y we first calculate:

$$\sum x = 2.24 + 1.06 + \ldots + 1.40 = 9.03$$

$$\sum y = 79.1 + 33.9 + \ldots + 46.7 = 296.7$$

$$\sum x^2 = 2.24^2 + 1.06^2 + \ldots + 1.40^2 = 13.6737$$

$$\sum y^2 = 79.1^2 + 33.9^2 + \ldots + 46.7^2 = 15\,703.59$$

$$\sum xy = 2.24 \times 79.1 + 1.06 \times 33.9 + \ldots + 1.40 \times 46.7 = 459.91.$$

The sample size is $n = 7$, so

$$\sum (x - \bar{x})^2 = \sum x^2 - \frac{(\sum x)^2}{n}$$
$$= 13.6737 - \frac{(9.03)^2}{7} = 2.025.$$

Sitka spruce

$$\sum (y - \bar{y})^2 = \sum y^2 - \frac{\left(\sum y \right)^2}{n}$$

$$= 15\,703.59 - \frac{(296.7)^2}{7} \simeq 3127.75.$$

$$\sum (x - \bar{x})(y - \bar{y}) = \sum xy - \frac{\left(\sum x \right)\left(\sum y \right)}{n}$$

$$= 459.91 - \frac{9.03 \times 296.7}{7} = 77.167.$$

Hence in this example,

$$\text{correlation} = \frac{\sum (x - \bar{x})(y - \bar{y})}{\sqrt{\sum (x - \bar{x})^2 \times \sum (y - \bar{y})^2}}$$

$$\simeq \frac{77.167}{\sqrt{2.025 \times 3127.75}} \simeq 0.97.$$

This correlation is close to 1, indicating a strong linear relationship between basal area and dry weight.

Regression

Data on Sitka spruce trees were given in Example 6. The dataset could be used to obtain an equation for estimating a tree's dry weight from the cross-sectional area at its base. The equation is potentially useful since, while a tree is growing, its basal area is much easier to measure than its weight. A suitable equation can be obtained through least squares linear regression, provided the relationship between the variables is linear.

In considering the correlation between two variables, it does not matter which variable is called x and which is called y – swapping them around would not change the value of the correlation coefficient. That is, in correlation the two variables have identical roles. In regression though, there is a response variable and an explanatory variable, and these have different roles.

I thought you wouldn't mind

The explanation...

> A *response* variable (usually denoted as y) is the variable that is being explained or whose value depends on the other variable. It is also the variable to be predicted if predictions are to be made.
>
> An *explanatory* variable (usually x) is the variable that is doing the explaining or is the variable on which the response variable depends.

Suppose now that the dry weight of a Sitka spruce is to be estimated from its basal area. Then the dry weight is y and the basal area is x. In Example 7, we will obtain the least squares regression line relating basal area to dry weight. The line is

$$y = -6.77 + 38.1x.$$

Given a tree's basal value, this equation gives its fitted value:

dry weight fitted value $= -6.77 + 38.1 \times$ basal area.

...and the response.

For example, the first tree in the dataset has a basal area of 2.24, so its fitted value is

$$-6.77 + 38.1 \times 2.24 \simeq 78.6.$$

If we did not know the tree's actual dry weight, then it would be estimated as 78.6.

The following table extends Table 12, from Example 6, to include the fitted values for the seven trees in the dataset.

Table 13 Basal areas, actual dry weights and fitted values of seven Sitka spruce

Basal area (x)	2.24	1.06	0.79	1.78	1.22	0.54	1.40
Actual dry weight (y)	79.1	33.9	19.2	54.8	51.0	12.0	46.7
Fitted value	78.6	33.6	23.3	61.0	39.7	13.8	46.6

Figure 17 is a scatterplot of these data and also shows the least squares regression line. The actual values of the data are marked by black dots. It can be seen that the regression line virtually passes through the third, fifth and seventh data points, and is close to the others. Hence the line fits the data well. (In Example 6, the correlation coefficient of 0.97 indicated a strong linear relationship between basal area and dry weight, so it could be anticipated that the line would fit the data well.)

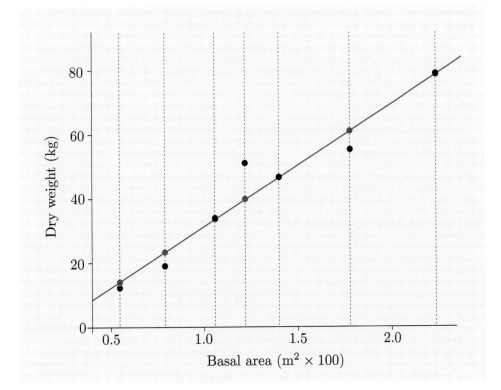

Figure 17 Plot of dry weight against basal area, with least squares regression line

> Residuals are defined as the differences between the fitted values and the data values:
>
> $$\text{Residual} = \text{Data} - \text{Fit}.$$

In Figure 17, the fitted values of the seven trees are shown as orange dots. From Table 13, their positions are $(2.24, 78.6)$, $(1.06, 33.6), \ldots, (1.40, 46.6)$. As the actual data values (the black dots) are at $(2.24, 79.1)$, $(1.06, 33.9), \ldots, (1.40, 46.7)$, the data points lie vertically above the fitted values, or vertically below them. Thus, residuals are the vertical distances from the data points to the line.

A regression line can serve various purposes, but to understand why it is constructed in the way that it is, think of the line as a way of predicting the response variable, y, when we know the value of the explanatory variable, x. Each residual is the inaccuracy in predicting a y-value in the dataset, given its corresponding x-value. Thus, the residuals indicate the usefulness of the line for making predictions. The aim in least squares regression is to minimise the sum of the squares of these residuals. Thus, in deciding how close a line is to the data points, the *perpendicular* distances from the data points to the line are not the quantities of interest – the focus is on the *vertical* distances from each data point to the line. The least squares regression is calculated as follows.

> **Calculation of the least squares regression line $y = a + bx$ for a set of n data points (x, y)**
>
> 1. Calculate $\sum x$, $\sum y$, $\sum (x - \overline{x})^2$ and $\sum (x - \overline{x})(y - \overline{y})$.
> 2. Calculate the means of x and y:
> $$\overline{x} = \frac{\sum x}{n} \quad \text{and} \quad \overline{y} = \frac{\sum y}{n}.$$
> 3. The slope b is given by
> $$b = \frac{\sum (x - \overline{x})(y - \overline{y})}{\sum (x - \overline{x})^2}.$$
> 4. The intercept a is given by
> $$a = \overline{y} - b\overline{x}.$$

For step 1 above, $\sum (x - \overline{x})^2$ and $\sum (x - \overline{x})(y - \overline{y})$ can be obtained from

$$\sum (x - \overline{x})^2 = \sum x^2 - \frac{\left(\sum x\right)^2}{n}$$

and

$$\sum (x - \overline{x})(y - \overline{y}) = \sum xy - \frac{\sum x \sum y}{n}.$$

However, if you have calculated the correlation coefficient, you will already have obtained these quantities as part of the procedure for its computation. (This reflects the close connection between correlation and regression.)

Example 7   *Regression line relating a tree's basal area and weight*

To determine the least squares regression line relating a Sitka spruce's basal area to its dry weight, the following quantities obtained in Example 6 will be used.

$$\sum x = 9.03, \quad \sum y = 296.7, \quad n = 7,$$

$$\sum (x - \overline{x})^2 = 2.025, \quad \sum (x - \overline{x})(y - \overline{y}) \simeq 77.167.$$

These give

$$\overline{x} = \frac{\sum x}{n} = \frac{9.03}{7} = 1.29 \quad \text{and} \quad \overline{y} = \frac{\sum y}{n} = \frac{296.7}{7} \simeq 42.386.$$

Hence, the slope is

$$b = \frac{\sum (x - \overline{x})(y - \overline{y})}{\sum (x - \overline{x})^2} = \frac{77.167}{2.025} \simeq 38.107,$$

and the intercept is

$$a = \overline{y} - b\overline{x} = 42.386 - 38.107 \times 1.29$$
$$\simeq 42.386 - 49.158 = -6.772.$$

These form the regression line:

$$y = -6.77 + 38.1x.$$

A regression line can be used to form estimates and make predictions. Standard terminology is to *estimate* a mean response and *predict* an individual response. The last example will be used to discuss the two cases.

Given a particular basal area, we might want to:

1.   Estimate the mean dry weight of Sitka spruce that have that basal area.

2.   Predict the dry weight of a single Sitka spruce tree that has that basal area.

In both cases, the estimate/prediction will be the point on the regression line that corresponds to the specified basal value, i.e. $-6.77 + 38.1x$, where x is the specified basal area. However, accuracy will not be the same in the two cases.

To elaborate, if the position of the regression line were known precisely, then the mean dry weight of Sitka spruce trees that have a particular basal area could be estimated with perfect accuracy. But there would still be uncertainty in predicting the dry weight of a single Sitka spruce tree from its basal area, because individual observations do not lie on the regression line – they vary around it.

More generally, if we took another sample of seven Sitka spruce, the regression line would not be identical to the one we have calculated. That is, the position of the regression line is affected by random variation. This random variation affects both the estimate of a mean response and the prediction of a single response. It is the only source of uncertainty that affects the estimated mean response, whereas individual variation also affects the accuracy with which a single response is predicted. Consequently, for any given x, there is greater uncertainty in predicting an individual response than in estimating a mean response.

Given a particular x, a confidence interval for the mean response can be determined using methods similar to those described in Subsection 5.2 (though the ESE is more complicated). Different values of x can be considered and the corresponding confidence interval determined for each. As x is varied, the confidence interval changes smoothly, getting narrower towards the mean of the x-values. This is illustrated in Figure 18, where long-dashed lines map end-points of the 95% confidence intervals for the mean dry weight as the basal area (x) changes.

An interval estimate for a prediction is referred to as a *prediction interval*. The dotted lines in Figure 18 map end-points of the 95% prediction intervals for an individual response. It can be seen that the prediction intervals are much wider than the confidence intervals – much of the uncertainty in predicting an individual value stems from the random variation of individual values about the regression line.

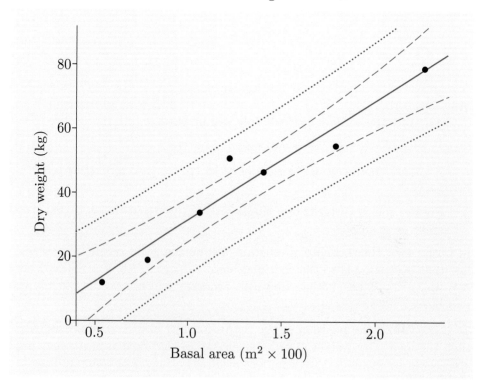

Figure 18   95% confidence intervals and 95% prediction intervals for dry weight as basal area varies

Figure 18 shows that the relationship between basal area and dry weight is approximately linear *when the basal area is between 0.5 and 2.3.* The data do not tell us whether the linear relationship extends outside that range. Hence, the regression line should not be used to make predictions (or estimate the mean response) for basal areas below 0.5 or above 2.3. More generally, making predictions outside the range of x-values in the original sample is termed **extrapolation** and should be avoided, as the validity of the predictions or prediction intervals would be unknown.

Exercises on Section 6

Exercise 10   *Checkout time*

The time taken (y seconds) to deal with a customer at a supermarket checkout consists of a basic part plus an amount that depends on the number of items bought. Observations of the time taken for each of 30 customers were recorded, together with the number of items (x) that the customer had bought. The following summarises the data:

$$\sum x = 620, \quad \sum y = 2776, \quad \sum xy = 79\,136$$
$$\sum x^2 = 19\,378, \quad \sum y^2 = 344\,742, \quad n = 30.$$

(a) Calculate the correlation coefficient between the time at the checkout and the number of purchases, based on this information.

(b) Does the correlation coefficient suggest that a least squares regression line would be a good way of representing the relationship between time at the checkout and number of purchases? What further information would you need in order to answer this question with more confidence?

Exercise 11   *Relating number of purchases to checkout time*

Using the data in Exercise 10, estimate the least squares regression line,

$$y = a + bx.$$

Interpret the slope and intercept of this line in the context of the time taken to serve a customer.

7 Computer work: binomial and t-test

In Subsection 3.2, you learned the general form of the binomial distribution. In this section, you will explore the shape of this distribution for different values of n and p. You will also use Minitab to perform an unpaired t-test to compare two population means when it is *not* assumed that the two population variances are equal. You should work through all of Chapter 12 of the Computer Book now, if you have not already done so.

Summary

In this unit, we have reviewed the main themes of M140: numerical and graphical summaries of data, the collection of data, probability, hypothesis testing, confidence intervals, correlation and regression. You may have seen more clearly the similarities and links between many of the concepts and methods that you have learned in the module. You will also have gained more practice at using many of these methods.

You have learned that the probabilities you calculated in Unit 6 for the sign test are probabilities from a binomial distribution in which $p = \frac{1}{2}$. You have learned how to calculate binomial probabilities for other values of p and to identify situations where the binomial distribution arises. You have also used Minitab to calculate binomial probabilities and explored the shape of the binomial distribution for different sample sizes and values of p.

There are a variety of situations in which z-tests and t-tests can be used to test whether a population mean has a particular value or if two population means are equal. You have learned how to choose the appropriate test for the different situations. You have also learned about a two-sample t-test that does not assume population variances are equal. You have learned to use Minitab to perform the test.

Learning outcomes

After working through this unit, you should be able to:

- interpret a growth chart
- combine different sampling methods in designing a survey
- identify situations where a binomial distribution applies
- calculate probabilities for a binomial distribution, both by hand and using Minitab
- choose an appropriate test for making inferences about a population mean
- choose an appropriate test for making inferences about the difference between two population means
- recognise the similarity of the test statistic for different forms of z-test and t-test
- describe the two-sample t-test for comparing two population means when the population variances are unequal and perform the test using Minitab.

Also, this unit has reviewed many learning objectives from the first 11 units of M140 – more than you might have thought. Working though the unit will have consolidated your ability to:

- find the mean and median of a batch of data
- find the upper and lower quartiles and the interquartile range of a batch of data
- calculate the variance and standard deviation of a batch of data
- prepare a five-figure summary of a batch of data
- draw and interpret the boxplot of a batch of data
- draw a stemplot of a batch of data
- use stemplots and boxplots to decide whether a batch of data is symmetric, left-skew or right-skew
- appreciate the priorities in summarising a batch of data
- find the weighted mean of a set of numbers with associated weights
- describe the major steps in producing the Retail Prices Index
- calculate a simple chained price index and explain what is meant by its base date
- describe quota sampling in general terms
- choose a simple random sample using random numbers and a labelled list of the target population
- choose a systematic random sample using random numbers and a labelled list of the target population
- describe the relative strengths and weaknesses of simple and systematic random sampling

- describe the principles involved in cluster sampling and stratified sampling
- choose a random sample for a stratified survey using random numbers and a labelled list of the target population
- choose a random sample for cluster sampling using random numbers and a labelled list of the target population
- distinguish between three kinds of experiments (exploratory, measurement and hypothesis testing)
- appreciate the need to randomise and reduce sources of bias when designing an experiment
- explain why placebos are used in clinical trials and the purpose of double-blind trials
- describe crossover, matched-pairs and group-comparative designs of clinical trials
- calculate probabilities based on random selection
- calculate joint and conditional probabilities
- state and use the relationship between joint and conditional probabilities
- express the independence of two events in terms of conditional probabilities
- state and use the general addition rule for probabilities
- count the number of ways that a specified combination can occur
- understand the concepts of a hypothesis test and the main steps in performing a hypothesis test
- carry out the χ^2 test for contingency tables, taking account of the size of Expected values
- interpret a χ^2 test in terms of the null and alternative hypotheses
- decide when to use the χ^2 test for contingency tables
- appreciate that we can think of all normal distributions in terms of the standard normal distribution
- apply the formula that transforms any variable x with a given normal distribution to the variable z with the standard normal distribution
- appreciate that, whatever the shape of the population distribution, for a large enough sample size the sampling distribution of the mean is nearly always approximately normal
- write down the mean and standard deviation of the sampling distribution of the mean for samples of size n, given the population mean, μ, and standard deviation, σ
- carry out a two-sample z-test to analyse the difference between means
- carry out a matched-pairs t-test
- examine whether it is reasonable to assume that two population variances are equal

- carry out a two-sample t-test when population variances are equal
- appreciate the relationship between hypothesis tests and confidence intervals
- calculate a confidence interval for a population mean
- interpret a confidence interval
- calculate a confidence interval for the difference between two population means
- explain what is meant by a relationship between two variables
- recognise positive and negative relationships from a scatterplot
- describe a relationship between two variables which is neither positive nor negative
- recognise strong and weak relationships from a scatterplot
- understand the concept of the correlation coefficient – in particular, how it relates to a relationship between two variables shown on a scatterplot
- calculate the correlation coefficient by hand
- understand the terms response variable and explanatory variable, and decide which is which in a given example
- calculate a least squares regression line for a batch of linked data by hand
- use a regression line to predict the value of the response variable, and know when it is appropriate to do this
- interpret a confidence interval for estimating the mean response using a least squares regression line
- interpret a prediction interval for individual predictions from a least squares regression line.

Take a bow for reaching the end of the last unit!

The module team

The following team worked on the production of M140 *Introducing statistics*.

Module team chairs

Paul Garthwaite and Karen Vines

Academic contributors

Paddy Farrington, Chris Jones, Kevin McConway, Heather Whitaker and Jane Williams

External assessor

Tony Lawrence (University of Warwick)

Critical readers

Alison Brand and Shirley John

Curriculum manager

Gloria Baldi

Media project manager

Stephen Clift

Learning media developer

Lucinda Simpson

Graphics media developer

Jon Owen

Interactive media developer

Callum Lester

Media developer, Sound & Vision

Michael Francis

Licensing & acquisitions assistant

Carol Houghton

With the assistance of

Andy Allum, Val Aspland, Joe Buchanunn, Jim Campbell, Matt Compton, Sian Contell, Martin Keeling, Barbara Langley-Poole, Tara Marshall, Sandy Nicholson, Angela Noufaily, Daphne Turner, Andrew Whitehead and Kaye Williams

M140 is based on a former Open University module, MDST242 *Statistics in Society*. Much of MDST242 is used in M140, so the module team that produced MDST242 (acknowledged elsewhere) have also made substantive input to M140.

Solutions to activities

Solution to Activity 1

(a) There are 10 data values. The fifth longest time between elections is 49 months and the sixth longest is also 49 months. As

$$\frac{49 + 49}{2} = 49,$$

the median is 49 months.

(b) Using the formula,

$$\bar{x} = \frac{44 + 7 + 55 + 49 + 48 + 58 + 61 + 49 + 47 + 60}{10}$$

$$= \frac{478}{10} = 47.8.$$

So the mean is 47.8 months.

(c) One period between general elections was only 7 months, much smaller than the other values. This small value pulls down the mean but has little effect on the median. For this reason, the mean is smaller than the median. However, the mean and median are quite close and both seem reasonably representative of the data. (Though you might argue that 7 months is an outlier, and so the median is preferable to the mean because it is not affected by the odd outlier.)

Solution to Activity 2

(a) There are 15 data values, so

$$\frac{n + 1}{4} = \frac{16}{4} = 4 \quad \text{and} \quad \frac{3(n + 1)}{4} = \frac{48}{4} = 12.$$

Hence the lower quartile is the 4th item and the upper quartile is the 12th item (4th from the top). Therefore $Q_1 = 57$ and $Q_3 = 65$. The interquartile range is the distance between them: $65 - 57 = 8$.

(b) Now there are 20 data values, so

$$\frac{n + 1}{4} = \frac{21}{4} = 5\frac{1}{4} \quad \text{and} \quad \frac{3(n + 1)}{4} = \frac{63}{4} = 15\frac{3}{4}.$$

Thus the lower quartile is one-quarter of the way from 17 to 19 and the upper quartile is three-quarters of the way from 23 to 24. Therefore $Q_1 = 17.5$, $Q_3 = 23.75$ and the interquartile range is $23.75 - 17.5 = 6.25 \simeq 6.3$.

Solution to Activity 3

The values of $\sum x^2$ and $\sum x$ must be determined. Don't write down each number you square; just use your calculator memory:

$$\sum x^2 = 20.5^2 + 21.6^2 + \cdots + 23.6^2 = 4112.92,$$

and

$$\sum x = 20.5 + 21.6 + \cdots + 23.6 = 192.0.$$

The sample size is $n = 9$ and so the variance equals

$$s^2 = \frac{1}{n-1}\left(\sum x^2 - \frac{(\sum x)^2}{n}\right) = \frac{1}{8}\left(4112.92 - \frac{192.0^2}{9}\right)$$

$$= \frac{1}{8}(4112.92 - 4096.0)$$

$$= 2.115.$$

The standard deviation equals

$$\sqrt{\text{variance}} = \sqrt{2.115} \simeq 1.45.$$

Solution to Activity 4

(a) Reading from the figure, 4.5 kg is the 2nd percentile at 10 weeks old, so 2% of boys weigh less than 4.5 kg at 10 weeks.

(b) 10 kg is the 75th percentile at 46 weeks old, so 25% of boys weigh more than 10 kg at 46 weeks.

(c) 6 kg is the 2nd percentile at 22 weeks old, and 7.5 kg is the 50th percentile. Hence the proportion of 22-week-old boys weighing between 6 kg and 7.5 kg is $50\% - 2\% = 48\%$.

Solution to Activity 5

(a) From the solution to Activity 2, $Q_1 = 57$ and $Q_3 = 65$.

There are 15 data values, so the middle value is the 8th. Therefore, $n = 15$ and $M = 63$.

The lowest and highest values are $E_L = 47$ and $E_U = 73$.

Hence the following is the five-figure summary of the data:

		63	
$n = 15$	57		65
	47		73

(b) This is the boxplot:

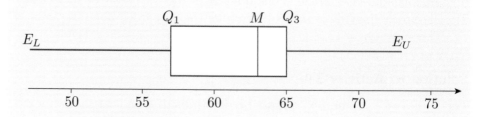

(c) The median (M) is much nearer the upper quartile (Q_3) than the lower quartile (Q_1) and the left-hand whisker is a little longer than the right-hand whisker. Hence the boxplot shows the data are left-skew and, from the position of M, the skewness is fairly marked.

Solution to Activity 6

(a) There is one particularly high value, 53.46 seconds, which is listed separately. The stretched stemplot looks like this:

```
        44 | 3 3
        44 | 5 5 6 7 8 9
        45 | 0 0 1 3 4
        45 | 6 8 8
        46 | 1 1 2
        46 | 6
        47 |
        47 | 5
        48 | 1
        48 | 9
       ─────────────────
        HI   534
```

$n = 24$ $44 \mid 3$ represents 44.3 seconds

(b) The stemplot shows that the data are clearly right-skew. There are a lot of values in the range 44–46.5 seconds, then a few values stretching out to 49 seconds, and then the value of 53.4 seconds.

Solution to Activity 7

For 'Food and catering',

$$rw = 1.013 \times 163 = 165.119.$$

Similar calculations for other groups yield the last column of the table.

Group	Price ratio for August 2013 relative to January 2013 (r)	2013 weights (w)	Price ratio × weight (rw)
Food and catering	1.013	163	165.119
Alcohol and tobacco	1.021	91	92.911
Housing and household expenditure	1.017	419	426.123
Personal expenditure	1.055	83	87.565
Travel and leisure	1.022	244	249.368

Then

$$\sum rw = 165.119 + 92.911 + \cdots + 249.368 = 1021.086$$

and

$$\sum w = 163 + 91 + \cdots 244 = 1000.$$

Thus the all-item price ratio is

$$\frac{\sum rw}{\sum w} = \frac{1021.086}{1000} \simeq 1.021.$$

Solution to Activity 8

(a) The numbers in each set are:

A	B	C	D	E	F
8	15	16	9	7	13

Dividing these by the population size of 68, the following gives the proportion of the population in each set:

A	B	C	D	E	F
0.118	0.221	0.235	0.132	0.103	0.191

(b) The labels selected are:

68, 42, 66, 14, 60, 63, 24, 06, 21, 52, 37, 19, 33, 55, 03, 11, 18.

The sample is shown in the following table:

Label	Initials	Set	Label	Initials	Set	Label	Initials	Set
03	A.P.D.	A	21	G.B.Y.	B	55	M.J.P.	E
06	J.L.	A	24	R.D.M.	C	60	M.A.T.	F
11	C.T.L.	B	33	D.J.S.	C	63	R.J.C.	F
14	J.S.R.	B	37	C.A.M.	C	66	E.D.	F
18	P.J.G.	B	42	A.L.	D	68	M.B.	F
19	W.W.S.	B	52	G.C.T.	E			

The numbers selected from each set are:

A	B	C	D	E	F
2	5	3	1	2	4

Dividing these by the sample size of 17, the following gives the proportion of the sample in each set:

A	B	C	D	E	F
0.118	0.294	0.176	0.059	0.118	0.235

Comparing these proportions with the proportions in solution (a), B and F are over-represented (and E is marginally over-represented), C and D are under-represented, while A is spot on.

(c) As we want to sample a quarter of the population, we will start at 1, 2, 3 or 4. The selected digit from row **10** is 3, so we start at label 03.

Every fourth label is in the sample:

03, 07, 11, 15, 19, 23, 27, 31, 35, 39, 43, 47, 51, 55, 59, 63, 67.

The sample is shown in the following table:

Label	Initials	Set	Label	Initials	Set	Label	Initials	Set
03	A.P.D.	A	27	T.P.H.	C	51	J.P.R.	E
07	J.D.H.	A	31	T.R.F.	C	55	M.J.P.	E
11	C.T.L.	B	35	D.L.	C	59	D.B.M.	F
15	S.L.	B	39	W.O.J.	C	63	R.J.C.	F
19	W.W.S.	B	43	L.R.P.	D	67	Y.S.H.	F
23	M.S.	B	47	Z.G.	D			

The numbers selected from each set are:

A	B	C	D	E	F
2	4	4	2	2	3

Dividing these by the sample size of 17, the following gives the proportion of the sample in each set:

A	B	C	D	E	F
0.118	0.235	0.235	0.118	0.118	0.176

The differences between these proportions and those in (a) are small. In fact, as each sample size must be a whole number they could not be closer. So the sample is a good representation of the population, as far as we can tell.

(d) The population is listed by set – first set A, then set B, ... Systematic sampling is picking every fourth person, so it is certain to take approximately a quarter of the people in each set. Hence it could be anticipated that the systematic sample would represent the population better than the simple random sample.

Solution to Activity 9

(a) There is no single correct answer to this question. One approach is to group parishes together so as to form a moderate number of strata – say about 10 strata. This is because there are too many parishes to treat each as an individual stratum. An alternative would be to treat the parishes as clusters and randomly sample 10 of them, say. (But forming clusters would not utilise knowledge about parishes regarding their geographic location, proportion of council houses, or age of houses in different areas.) Each stratum should consist of adjacent parishes that have a similar housing stock.

Houses within a stratum should be grouped by their council tax band and by whether or not they are privately owned. (Some council tax bands might be combined to reduce the number of strata.) Then streets within each of these strata should be treated as clusters and a random subset of them selected. It is essential to treat streets as clusters so as to reduce the travelling time of the interviewer.

A large number of houses should be selected (perhaps 50%) from each street, as only a small proportion will have any disabled people living in them. Most of the interviews will consequently be very fast, so walking between interviews should be minimised.

(b) The above procedure is likely to yield a sample that is better than a completely random sample at reflecting the characteristics of the unitary authority's housing stock. This should also hold for alternative sampling schemes that you may have proposed. Hence the procedure should reduce sampling variation compared with that of simple random sampling. The main benefit though, is that travelling time should be far less because only a modest number of streets (the clusters) will feature in the survey, so the survey should cost much less than with a simple random sample.

Solution to Activity 10

Statement G is true: in a double-blind trial, neither the patients nor the doctors know which patients have received the drug being tested and which the placebo, while an appropriate independent person does have this information. Consequently, statements A and D are false.

It has been shown that patients can genuinely respond to the process of being treated, even when the treatment contains no beneficial ingredient. Similarly, doctors can influence a patient's response in ways other than through the medication. Hence statement E is true, while B and C are false.

Patients must give informed consent before they are entered into a clinical trial. Thus they must always be told that they might be given just a placebo. Indeed, it would be unethical not to tell them that. Thus statement F is false.

Solution to Activity 11

(a) It is a group-comparative design because there are two groups, patients were allocated to the experimental group or control group at random and the design had no other features or additional complexity.

(b) The validity of the trial is questionable because any relevant gender differences would bias results. For example, if men tended to have more extreme arthritis symptoms than women, then the experimental treatment (taken by the women) would only seem poorer than the existing drug (taken by the men) if it was actually *much* worse than the existing drug.

(c) If the experiment is repeated, half the women should be allocated at random to the experimental group and half to the control group, using a simple random sample to choose which women were allocated to the experimental group. Similarly, half the men should be picked at random from the male patients and allocated to the experimental group and the other half of the men should be allocated to the control group. This meets the requirements of randomisation (so neither drug is deliberately favoured) and ensures the same gender ratio in the two groups. Essentially, this procedure treats women as one strata and men as a second strata – it is called *stratified randomisation*.

Solution to Activity 12

(a) There are 227 research fellows in the population of 794 academic statisticians. Hence, the probability that the selected person is a research fellow is

$$\frac{227}{794} \simeq 0.286.$$

(b) Among the 794 academic statisticians, there are 275 aged 30–39. Hence, the probability that the selected person is aged 30–39 is

$$\frac{275}{794} \simeq 0.346.$$

(c) Among the 794 academic statisticians, there are 82 research fellows aged 30–39. Hence, the probability that the selected person is a research fellow aged 30–39 is

$$\frac{82}{794} \simeq 0.103.$$

Solution to Activity 13

(a) The subpopulation of interest are the 211 people in Table 4 who are aged 40–49, of whom 70 are senior lecturers. Hence,

$$P(\text{senior lecturer}|\text{aged 40–49}) = \frac{70}{211} \simeq 0.332.$$

(b) Now the subpopulation of interest are the 156 people in Table 4 who are senior lecturers. Of these people, 70 are aged 40–49. Hence,

$$P(\text{aged 40–49}|\text{senior lecturer}) = \frac{70}{156} \simeq 0.449.$$

Solution to Activity 14

(a) There are 66 professors aged 50–59. As there are 794 academic statisticians,

$$P(\text{professor aged 50–59}) = \frac{66}{794} \simeq 0.083.$$

(b) There are 172 professors in total. Hence,

$$P(\text{professor}) = \frac{172}{794} \quad (\simeq 0.217).$$

(c) The subpopulation of interest are the 172 people in Table 4 who are professors, of whom 66 are aged 50–59. Hence,

$$P(\text{aged 50–59}|\text{professor}) = \frac{66}{172} \quad (\simeq 0.384).$$

(d) From (a),

$$P(A \text{ and } B) = P(\text{professor aged 50–59}) \simeq 0.083.$$

Also, from (b) and (c),

$$P(A) = P(\text{professor}) = \frac{172}{794}$$

and

$$P(B|A) = P(\text{aged 50–59}|\text{professor}) = \frac{66}{172}.$$

So

$$P(A) \times P(B|A) = \frac{172}{794} \times \frac{66}{172}$$

$$= \frac{66}{794}$$

$$\simeq 0.083 = P(A \text{ and } B).$$

(In decimals, $P(A) \times P(B) \simeq 0.217 \times 0.384 \simeq 0.083$.)

Solution to Activity 15

(a) From Table 4, there are 172 professors and $7 + 6 + 8 = 21$ so there are 21 academic statisticians aged at least 60 who are not professors. Hence, adding 172 to 21 gives a total of 193 UK academic statisticians who will be invited. If we simply added the number of professors (172) to the number of academic statisticians aged 60 or over (68), then we would double-count the 47 people who are both professors *and* aged 60 or over. Another way of obtaining the figure of 193 is from $172 + 68 - 47 = 193$.

(b) There are 47 UK academic statisticians who are both professors *and* aged 60 or over. So 47 people would be invited.

(c) From (a),

$$P(A \text{ or } B) = \frac{193}{794} \simeq 0.243$$

and from (b),

$$P(A \text{ and } B) = \frac{47}{794} \simeq 0.059.$$

(d) $$P(A) = \frac{172}{794} \simeq 0.217 \quad \text{and} \quad P(B) = \frac{68}{794} \simeq 0.086.$$

Hence,

$$P(A) + P(B) - P(A \text{ and } B) \simeq 0.217 + 0.086 - 0.059$$

$$= 0.244$$

$$\simeq P(A \text{ or } B).$$

Alternatively, to avoid having to deal with rounding you could put

$$P(A) + P(B) - P(A \text{ and } B) = \frac{172}{794} + \frac{68}{794} - \frac{47}{794}$$
$$= \frac{172 + 68 - 47}{794}$$
$$= \frac{193}{794}$$
$$= P(A \text{ or } B).$$

Solution to Activity 16

(a) The number of ways of choosing three pairs from six (order does not matter) is

$$^{6}C_3 = \frac{6 \times 5 \times 4}{3 \times 2 \times 1} = 20.$$

(b) The number of ways of choosing four pairs from nine is

$$^{9}C_4 = \frac{9 \times 8 \times 7 \times 6}{4 \times 3 \times 2 \times 1} = 126.$$

Solution to Activity 17

(a) $P(FSSSFS) = 0.4 \times 0.6 \times 0.6 \times 0.6 \times 0.4 \times 0.6$
$$= 0.6^4 \times 0.4^2$$
$$= 0.1296 \times 0.16$$
$$= 0.020\,736.$$

(b) The number of sequences of 6 days that give 4 successes is

$$^{6}C_4 = \frac{6 \times 5 \times 4 \times 3}{4 \times 3 \times 2 \times 1} = 15.$$

(c) $P(4 \text{ successful days in 6 days}) = {}^{6}C_4 \times 0.6^4 \times 0.4^2$
$$= 15 \times 0.020\,736$$
$$= 0.311\,04 \simeq 0.311.$$

(d) $P(5 \text{ successful days in 8 days}) = {}^{8}C_5 \times 0.6^5 \times 0.4^3$
$$= \frac{8 \times 7 \times 6 \times 5 \times 4}{5 \times 4 \times 3 \times 2 \times 1} \times 0.6^5 \times 0.4^3$$
$$= 56 \times 0.077\,76 \times 0.064 \simeq 0.279.$$

Solution to Activity 18

Define 'blood group O' as success, so that $p = P(S) = 0.44$ and $q = 1 - p = 0.56$. The number of trials (number of people) is $n = 7$ and we want $P(x = 2)$. Using the formula for the binomial distribution,

$$P(x = 2) = {}^7C_2 \times 0.44^2 \times 0.56^{(7-2)}$$
$$= {}^7C_2 \times 0.44^2 \times 0.56^5$$
$$\simeq \frac{7 \times 6}{2 \times 1} \times 0.1936 \times 0.055\,073$$
$$= 21 \times 0.010\,662$$
$$\simeq 0.224.$$

Solution to Activity 19

One reason for not using $\sum(\text{Residual})^2$ as the test statistic is that a residual's evidence against H_0 depends not only on the size of the Residual, but also on the size of the Expected value. To illustrate, suppose that a cell is expected to contain 3400 items but in fact contains 3420. The difference is relatively small – readily explained as random variation. On the other hand, if a cell is expected to contain 10 items but in fact contains 30, then the difference is large. Thus, although both cases give a $(\text{Residual})^2$ of $20^2 = 400$, only the latter provides strong evidence that the Expected value is wrong.

Another reason (which you will not be aware of) is that we do not know the probability distribution of $\sum(\text{Residual})^2$. As noted earlier (point 3 in the description of a hypothesis test), the probability distribution of a suitable test statistic must be fully known if H_0 is true.

Solution to Activity 20

(a) When $\mu = 0.38$ and $\sigma = 0.03$, the formula

$$z = \frac{x - \mu}{\sigma} \quad \text{gives} \quad z = \frac{x - 0.38}{0.03}.$$

When $x = 0.40$,

$$z = \frac{0.40 - 0.38}{0.03} = \frac{0.02}{0.03} \simeq 0.667.$$

So a shell thickness of $0.40\,\text{mm}$ is 0.667 standard deviations above the mean thickness of $0.38\,\text{mm}$.

(b) When $x = 0.30$,

$$z = \frac{0.30 - 0.38}{0.03} = \frac{-0.08}{0.03} \simeq -2.667.$$

So a shell thickness of $0.30\,\text{mm}$ is 2.667 standard deviations below the mean thickness of $0.38\,\text{mm}$.

Solution to Activity 21

(a) The sampling distribution of the mean mark for a sample of size 5 has mean 66 and standard deviation $\sigma/\sqrt{n} = 22/\sqrt{5} \simeq 9.83$.

The sampling distribution of the mean mark for a sample of size 15 also has mean 66, but its standard deviation is $22/\sqrt{15} \simeq 5.68$.

(b) The sample sizes of 5 and 15 are not large, so the distributions of the sample mean may differ a little from a normal distribution – more so with the smaller sample size of 5.

Solution to Activity 22

(a) The variance is known so, from the flow chart in Figure 9, use the z-test.

(b) The variance is unknown and the sample size is greater than 25 so, from Figure 9, use the z-test.

(c) The variance is unknown and the sample size is less than 25 so, from Figure 9, use the t-test.

(d) The variance is known so, from Figure 9, use the z-test.

Solution to Activity 23

(a) The data are not matched pairs, the population variances are unknown, and both sample sizes are above 25 so, from the flow chart in Figure 10, use the two-sample z-test.

(b) The data are not matched pairs, the population variances are unknown, one sample size is less than 25, but we can assume the population variances are equal ($9.6/8.4 \simeq 1.14 < 3$) so, from Figure 10, use the two-sample t-test with a pooled sample variance.

(c) The data are matched pairs so, from Figure 10, use the matched-pairs t-test.

(d) The data are not matched pairs, the population variances are unknown, one sample size is less than 25 (in fact, both are less than 25), and we cannot assume the population variances are equal ($12.1/3.5 \simeq 3.46 > 3$) so, from Figure 10, use the two-sample t-test with unequal variances.

(e) The data are not matched pairs and the population variances are known so, from the flow chart in Figure 10, use the two-sample z-test.

Solution to Activity 24

Let μ_A and μ_B denote the population mean reductions in cholesterol level on the oat and bean diets (diets A and B), respectively. Then

$$n_A = 29, \quad \bar{x}_A = 58.3, \quad s_A = 19.2,$$
$$n_B = 28, \quad \bar{x}_B = 46.4, \quad s_B = 16.5.$$

The data are not paired, the population variances are not known, and both sample sizes are above 25. From Figure 10, a two-sample z-test is appropriate.

The hypotheses are:

$$H_0: \mu_A = \mu_B \quad \text{and} \quad H_1: \mu_A \neq \mu_B.$$

We first calculate the value of ESE, the estimated standard error of $\bar{x}_A - \bar{x}_B$:

$$\text{ESE} = \sqrt{\frac{s_A^2}{n_A} + \frac{s_B^2}{n_B}} = \sqrt{\frac{19.2^2}{29} + \frac{16.5^2}{28}} \simeq 4.7366.$$

Hence the value of the test statistic is

$$z = \frac{\overline{x}_A - \overline{x}_B}{\text{ESE}} \simeq \frac{58.3 - 46.4}{4.7366} \simeq 2.512.$$

The critical values are ± 1.96 (at 5%) and ± 2.58 (at 1%). Since $1.96 < 2.512 < 2.58$, we can reject H_0 at the 5% significance level but not at the 1% significance level. There is moderate evidence that the two diets differ in the average reduction in serum cholesterol level that they yield. The reduction on the oat diet (diet A) appears to be greater.

The only assumptions needed for this hypothesis test are that observations are all random and independent. The sample sizes are quite large, so the central limit theorem implies that the distribution of $\overline{x}_A$ will be approximately normal, as will that of $\overline{x}_B$.

Solution to Activity 25

(a) The point estimate is $\overline{x}_A - \overline{x}_B = 58.3 - 46.4 = 11.9$. From the solution to Activity 24, ESE $\simeq 4.7366$. A two-sample z-test was used in Activity 24 so z-values will be the critical values.

For a 95% confidence interval, the z-value is 1.96. Hence the lower limit of the 95% confidence interval is

$$11.9 - 1.96 \times 4.7366 \simeq 2.62$$

and the upper limit is

$$11.9 + 1.96 \times 4.7366 \simeq 21.18.$$

Thus the 95% confidence interval for $\mu_A - \mu_B$ is $(2.62\,\text{mg/dl}, 21.18\,\text{mg/dl})$.

(b) For a 99% confidence interval, the z-value is 2.58. Hence the lower limit of the 99% confidence interval is

$$11.9 - 2.58 \times 4.7366 \simeq -0.32$$

and the upper limit is

$$11.9 + 2.58 \times 4.7366 \simeq 24.12.$$

Thus the 99% confidence interval for $\mu_A - \mu_B$ is $(-0.32\,\text{mg/dl}, 24.12\,\text{mg/dl})$.

(c) A 95% confidence interval is always shorter than the corresponding 99% interval, as in this example.

(d) The 99% confidence interval contains 0 while the 95% confidence interval does not contain 0. Hence the hypothesis H_0: $\mu_A - \mu_B = 0$ would not be rejected at the 1% significance level but it would be rejected at the 5% significance level. This was the result found in Activity 24.

Solution to Activity 26

In (a), the points all lie very close to a straight line sloping downwards, so there is a strong negative linear relationship between the two variables.

In (b), the points follow a general upward trend, but a smooth line could not be drawn through the points that lay close to many of them. Thus there is a weak positive relationship between the two variables – it may be linear, but that is not clear.

In (c), the scatterplot suggests no relationship between the two variables.

In (d), the points follow a clear downward trend, but most of them would be some way from a straight line drawn through them. Thus there is a negative relationship between the two variables that looks linear, but is not very strong.

In (e), the points all lie very close to a straight line sloping upwards, so there is a strong positive linear relationship between the two variables.

In (f), the points all lie very close to a line that increases from left to right, so there is a strong positive relationship between the two variables. However, the points clearly follow a curve (not a straight line) so the relationship is non-linear.

Solution to Activity 27

From the scatterplots:

- A strong positive linear relationship is shown in (e).
- A strong positive non-linear relationship is shown in (f).
- A weak positive relationship is shown in (b).
- No relationship is shown in (c).
- A weak negative relationship is shown in (d).
- A strong negative linear relationship is shown in (a).

From the figures it is not transparent whether (b) will give a higher correlation coefficient than (f), or vice versa. In fact, (f) has the higher correlation coefficient. The correct ordering is as follows. Correlation coefficients are also given. (You do not have the information to calculate the correlations.)

(e): 0.99,   (f): 0.88,   (b): 0.77,   (c): 0.13,   (d): −0.82,   (a): −0.99.

Solutions to exercises

Solution to Exercise 1

(a) We start in row **36** of the random number table.

For the first stratum, we want six numbers between 01 and 23:

18, 17, 19, 08, 01, 16.

Rearranged in order, the labels are:

01, 08, 16, 17, 18, 19.

For the second stratum, we want six numbers between 24 and 48. Starting in the random number table at the point where we left off, we get:

31, 42, 25, 37, 35, 44.

Rearranged in order, the labels are:

25, 31, 35, 37, 42, 44.

For the third stratum, we want five numbers between 49 and 68. Continuing from where we left off in the random number table, we get:

61, 55, 64, 68, 56.

Rearranged in order, the labels are:

55, 56, 61, 64, 68.

(b) The first two single digits between 1 and 6 in row **95** are 4 and 6, which correspond to set D and set F.

Set D is of size 9, so we select $9/3 = 3$ people from set D. Set F is of size 13 and $13/3$ rounds up to 5, so we select five people from set F.

Starting in row **72**, for set D we want three random number pairs between 40 and 48:

42, 48, 46.

Continuing on, for set F we want five numbers between 56 and 68:

61, 59, 68, 65, 60.

Hence, the following are the people in the subsamples (rearranged in the order of their labels):

- from set D: A.L., A.T. and Y.H.
- from set F: D.B.M., M.A.T., A.N.D., G.K.S. and M.B.

Solution to Exercise 2

(a) Age-bands should be formed (perhaps under 25, 25–34, 35–44, 45–54, 55 or over), and job grades should be grouped together (perhaps forming five or six groups) so that similar grades are in the same group.

Employees should be listed so that those who share the same age-band and grade-group are listed consecutively. Each age-band/grade-group combination is a stratum.

A sample of 500 from 6000 means that a 12th of the workforce is to be included in the sample. Generate a random number between 1 and 12 (either using a computer or random number tables). Pick out every 12th person from the list, starting with the person given by the random number. This gives a systematic sample and the proportion of people chosen from each stratum will be approximately the same for each stratum.

(b) Non-sampling errors could arise from refusal to answer, employee absence, out-of-date data, incorrect (or incorrectly transcribed) data, etc.

Solution to Exercise 3

(a) For a crossover design, a random half of the women should take the new treatment for four weeks. They should then switch to the old treatment. The difference of each patient's symptoms under the two treatments should be recorded. The other half of the women should start on the old treatment for four weeks and then switch to the new treatment. The difference in response between new and old treatments is again the quantity of interest. The same should be done with the men. This design means that order of treatment should not bias results, and gender-bias is also controlled. A reasonable time on each treatment should elapse before symptoms are measured, so that they reflect the current treatment.

(b) For a matched-pairs design, pairs of patients are required. The patients within a pair should be similar with respect to gender, age and severity of illness. Then one person in the pair would be picked at random and allocated to the experimental treatment and the other person in the pair would receive the control treatment. The difference in their symptoms would be the data analysed.

(c) Finding matched pairs is hard, while a crossover trial is straightforward to run because arthritis is a chronic condition. Hence the crossover design is more suitable than a matched-pairs design. When they are suitable, crossover designs are better than group-comparative designs because they remove much of the variation between individuals as each individual is compared with himself or herself. Hence a group-comparative design would not be better.

Solution to Exercise 4

(a) Define events A and B as follows.

> A: a randomly picked academic statistician is aged 40–49.
>
> B: a randomly picked academic statistician is a lecturer.

Then

$$P(A) = \frac{211}{794} \simeq 0.266 \quad \text{and} \quad P(A|B) = \frac{59}{239} \simeq 0.247.$$

As $P(A)$ does not equal $P(A|B)$, events A and B are not independent.

(b) As

$$P(B) = \frac{239}{794} \simeq 0.301 \quad \text{and} \quad P(A|B) \simeq 0.247,$$

then

$$P(A \text{ and } B) \simeq 0.301 \times 0.247 \simeq 0.074.$$

(c) Using the answers from (a) and (b),

$$P(A \text{ or } B) = P(A) + P(B) - P(A \text{ and } B)$$
$$\simeq 0.266 + 0.301 - 0.074 = 0.493.$$

Solution to Exercise 5

(a) The number of successes follows a binomial distribution. As $p = 0.2$, $q = 1 - p = 0.8$.

Here $n = 4$, so

$$P(x = 1) = {}^4C_1 \times 0.2^1 \times 0.8^{(4-1)}$$
$$= \frac{4}{1} \times 0.2 \times 0.8^3 = 0.4096 \simeq 0.410.$$

(b) Now $n = 5$, so

$$P(x = 2) = {}^5C_2 \times 0.2^2 \times 0.8^{(5-2)}$$
$$= \frac{5 \times 4}{2 \times 1} \times 0.2^2 \times 0.8^3 = 0.2048 \simeq 0.205.$$

(c) Now $n = 7$, so

$$P(x = 0) = {}^7C_0 \times 0.2^0 \times 0.8^{(7-0)}$$
$$= 0.8^7 \simeq 0.210,$$

as ${}^7C_0 = 1$ and $0.2^0 = 1$.

Solution to Exercise 6

(a) It must be assumed that whether one person feels better is independent of whether other people feel better. Then probabilities come from a binomial distribution with $n = 6$, $p = 0.6$ and $q = 1 - p = 0.4$.

$$P(x = 2) = {}^6C_2 \times 0.6^2 \times 0.4^4$$
$$= \frac{6 \times 5}{2 \times 1} \times 0.36 \times 0.0256$$
$$= 0.138\,24.$$

(b) Using the same assumptions as in (a),

$$P(x = 1) = {}^6C_1 \times 0.6^1 \times 0.4^5$$
$$= \frac{6}{1} \times 0.6 \times 0.010\,24$$
$$\simeq 0.036\,86$$

and

$$P(x = 0) = {}^6C_0 \times 0.6^0 \times 0.4^6$$
$$= 0.4^6 \simeq 0.004\,10.$$

Thus $P(2 \text{ or fewer people feeling better})$ is

$$P(x = 2) + P(x = 1) + P(x = 0) \simeq 0.138\,24 + 0.036\,86 + 0.004\,10$$
$$\simeq 0.179.$$

Solution to Exercise 7

(a) The hypotheses are as follows:

H_0: locality and concern about air pollution are independent.

H_1: locality and concern about air pollution are not independent.

(b) Copy marginal totals from the Observed table to the Expected table.

Then the Expected value for the first cell is:

$$\frac{\text{Row total} \times \text{Column total}}{\text{Overall total}} = \frac{100 \times 83}{400}$$
$$= 20.75.$$

The other values are obtained in the same manner, leading to the following Expected table:

Locality	Yes	No	Total
A	20.75	79.25	100
B	20.75	79.25	100
C	20.75	79.25	100
D	20.75	79.25	100
Total	83	317	400

As a check on your calculations, the Expected values within the table must add to the marginal totals (apart from unimportant rounding errors).

(c) The Residual table is found by subtracting the terms of the Expected table from those of the Observed table. For the first cell, we have

$$25 - 20.75 = 4.25.$$

The Residual table is

Locality	Yes	No
A	4.25	−4.25
B	−4.75	4.75
C	−8.75	8.75
D	9.25	−9.25

The χ^2 contribution of the first cell is

$$\frac{(\text{Residual})^2}{\text{Expected}} = \frac{4.25^2}{20.75}$$

$$\simeq 0.8705.$$

The complete table of χ^2 contributions is:

Locality	Yes	No
A	0.8705	0.2279
B	1.0873	0.2847
C	3.6898	0.9661
D	4.1235	1.0797

(d) The χ^2 test statistic is the sum of the eight χ^2 contributions:

$$\chi^2 = 0.8705 + 0.2279 + 1.0873 + 0.2847 + 3.6898$$
$$+ 0.9661 + 4.1235 + 1.0797$$
$$\simeq 12.330.$$

The Observed table is a 4×2 table, so its degrees of freedom are $(4 - 1) \times (2 - 1) = 3$. Hence CV5 = 7.815 and CV1 = 11.345.

(e) Since $12.330 > 11.345$, we reject the null hypothesis at the 1% significance level. Thus there is strong evidence that concern in a household about air pollution varies with locality.

Solution to Exercise 8

(a) The variance is known so, from the flow chart in Figure 9 (Subsection 5.2), use the z-test.

(b) The variance is unknown and the sample size is less than 25 so, from Figure 9, use the t-test.

(c) The variance is unknown and the sample size is greater than 25 so, from Figure 9, use the z-test.

(d) The variance is known so, from Figure 9, use the z-test.

Solution to Exercise 9

(a) The data are not matched pairs, the population variances are unknown, one sample size is less than 25 (in fact, both are less than 25), but we can assume the population variances are equal $(28.2/23.8 \simeq 1.18 < 3)$ so, from the flow chart in Figure 10, use the two-sample t-test with a pooled sample variance.

(b) The data are matched pairs so, from Figure 10, use the matched-pairs t-test.

(c) The data are not matched pairs, the population variances are unknown, one sample size is less than 25, and we cannot assume the population variances are equal $(9.1/1.7 \simeq 5.35 > 3)$ so, from Figure 10, use the two-sample t-test with unequal variances.

(d) The data are not matched pairs, the population variances are unknown, and both sample sizes are above 25 so, from Figure 10, use the two-sample z-test.

(e) The data are not matched-pairs, the population variances are unknown, one sample size is less than 25, and we can assume the population variances are equal $(17.4/10.6 \simeq 1.64 < 3)$ so, from Figure 10, use the two-sample t-test with a pooled sample variance.

Solution to Exercise 10

(a) The data give:

$$\sum(x - \bar{x})^2 = \sum x^2 - \frac{(\sum x)^2}{n}$$
$$\simeq 19\,378 - \frac{(620)^2}{30} \simeq 6564.7.$$

$$\sum(y - \bar{y})^2 = \sum y^2 - \frac{(\sum y)^2}{n}$$
$$= 344\,742 - \frac{(2776)^2}{30} \simeq 87\,869.5.$$

$$\sum(x - \bar{x})(y - \bar{y}) = \sum xy - \frac{(\sum x)(\sum y)}{n}$$
$$= 79\,136 - \frac{620 \times 2776}{30} \simeq 21\,765.3.$$

Hence,

$$\text{correlation} = \frac{\sum(x - \bar{x})(y - \bar{y})}{\sqrt{\sum(x - \bar{x})^2 \times \sum(y - \bar{y})^2}}$$
$$\simeq \frac{21\,765.3}{\sqrt{6564.7 \times 87\,869.5}} \simeq 0.91.$$

(b) The correlation coefficient is quite large, so a straight line should be useful for capturing the relationship between time at the checkout and number of purchases. However, the relationship might be non-linear, in which case there would be better ways of capturing the relationship.

The data on each individual customer is needed, so that a scatterplot of y against x could be drawn. That would enable the relationship between the variables to be seen much more clearly – the question of whether a straight-line relationship is appropriate could then be answered with greater confidence.

Solution to Exercise 11

From Exercise 10,

$$\sum x = 620, \quad \sum y = 2776, \quad \text{and} \quad n = 30.$$

So

$$\overline{x} = \frac{\sum x}{n} = \frac{620}{30} \simeq 20.667$$

and

$$\overline{y} = \frac{\sum y}{n} = \frac{2776}{30} \simeq 92.533.$$

Also, from the solution to Exercise 10,

$$\sum (x - \overline{x})^2 \simeq 6564.7 \quad \text{and} \quad \sum (x - \overline{x})(y - \overline{y}) \simeq 21\,765.3.$$

Hence, the slope is

$$b = \frac{\sum (x - \overline{x})(y - \overline{y})}{\sum (x - \overline{x})^2} \simeq \frac{21\,765.3}{6564.7} \simeq 3.3155,$$

and the intercept is

$$a = \overline{y} - b\overline{x} = 92.533 - 3.3155 \times 20.667$$
$$= 92.533 - 68.521 \simeq 24.012.$$

These give the regression line:

$$y = 24.0 + 3.32x.$$

The intercept of 24.0 implies the basic part of serving a customer (taking money and giving change, etc.) takes 24.0 seconds, on average. The slope of 3.32 means that each item takes 3.32 seconds to process, on average.

Acknowledgements

Grateful acknowledgement is made to the following sources:

Figure 2: Reproduced with permission of the Royal College of Paediatrics and child health.

Introduction, photo © Ratina Thongteeka/Dreamstime.com

Subsection 1.1 photo: Courtesy of Waveney District Council

Subsection 1.2 cartoon: http://xkcd.com/833/. This file is licensed under the Creative Commons Attribution-Non-commercial Licence http://creativecommons.org/licenses/by-nc/3.0/

Subsection 1.3 photo: Courtesy Flotrack.org

Subsection 2.1 cartoon: www.causeweb.org

Subsection 2.1 photo (cluster sampling): Howard Stanbury / http://www.flickr.com/photos/27195496@N00/2725957867. This file is licensed under the Creative Commons Attribution-Non-commercial-ShareAlike Licence http://creativecommons.org/licenses/by-nc-sa/3.0/

Subsection 2.2 photo, taken from: http://rogueestate.com/2009/11/09/the-curried-bacon-experiment/

Subsection 2.2 cartoon, taken from: http://stats.stackexchange.com/questions/423/what-is-your-favorite-data-analysis-cartoon

Subsection 3.1 photo, used with permission of the Statistical Laboratory, University of Cambridge

Subsection 3.1 cartoon, www.causeweb.org

Section 4 photo (left-hand image) © Konradbak/Dreamstime.com

Section 4 photo (right-hand image): With kind permission of https://multimedia.actiononhearingloss.org.uk/

Subsection 5.1 cartoon, www.causeweb.org

Subsection 5.1 photo, United States Department of Agriculture / http://en.wikipedia.org/wiki/File:Poultry_Classes_Blog_photo_-_Flickr_-_USDAgov.jpg. This file is licensed under the Creative Commons Attribution Licence http://creativecommons.org/licenses/by/3.0/

Subsection 5.2 photo (Brinell hardness testing machine), taken from: www.mltest.com/images/stories/shb-3000c.jpg

Subsection 5.2 photo (cookies), taken from: www.fitsugar.com/Healthy-Oatmeal-Cookie-Recipe-Using-Beans-22665129

Subsection 5.2 figure (confidence intervals guide), taken from: http://excelmasterseries.com

Subsection 6.1 photo (Hans Rosling): With permission of Hans Rosling

Subsection 6.1 cartoon, www.cartoonstock.com

Subsection 6.2 photo (Sitka spruce): Wsiegmund. This file is licensed under the Creative Commons Attribution-Share Alike Licence http://creativecommons.org/licenses/by-sa/3.0/

Exercises on Section 6, photo: Veleta. This file is licensed under the Creative Commons Attribution-Share Alike Licence http://creativecommons.org/licenses/by-sa/3.0/

Learning outcomes, photo: Ethan Prater. This file is licensed under the Creative Commons Attribution Licence http://creativecommons.org/licenses/by/3.0/

Every effort has been made to contact copyright holders. If any have been inadvertently overlooked the publishers will be pleased to make the necessary arrangements at the first opportunity.

Index